KS3 MATHS

David Rayner

Elmwood Press

© David Rayner
First published 2000 by
Elmwood Press
80 Attimore Road
Welwyn Garden City
Herts. AL8 6LP
Tel. 01707 333232

Reprinted 2003, 2005

British Library Cataloguing in Publication Data

Rayner, David

  1. Mathematics—1961–
  I. Title

  ISBN 1 902 214 072

Numerical answers are published in a separate book

Typeset and illustrated by Tech-Set, Gateshead, Tyne and Wear
Printed and bound in Great Britain

CONTENTS

PREFACE

KS3 Maths is written for pupils in year 9 and contains all the material in the revised National Curriculum. Most classrooms contain children with a range of abilities in mathematics. This book is written to cater for this situation.

The author believes that children learn mathematics most effectively by *doing* mathematics. Many youngsters who find mathematics difficult derive much more pleasure and enjoyment from the subject when they are doing questions which help them build up their confidence. Pupils feel a greater sense of satisfaction when they work in a systematic way and when they can appreciate the purpose and the power of the mathematics they are studying.

The author, who is an experienced teacher, emphasises a thorough grounding in the fundamentals of number when working in the lower secondary classroom. In particular the recommendations of the National centre for Numeracy lie behind the approach adopted to mental arithmetic and calculations performed without calculators.

There is no set path through the book and it is anticipated that most teachers will prefer to take sections in the order of their own choice. No text book will have the 'right' amount of material for every class and the author believes that it is better to have too much material rather than too little. Consequently teachers should judge for themselves which sections or exercises can be studied later. On a practical note, the author recommends the use of exercise books consisting of 7 mm squares.

Opportunities for work towards the 'Using and Applying Mathematics' attainment target appears throughout the book. Many activities, investigations, games and puzzles are included to provide a healthy variety of learning experiences. The author is aware of the difficulties of teaching on 'Friday afternoons' or on the last few days of term, when both pupils and teachers are tired, and suitable activities are included.

David Rayner

Part 1

1.1 Powers and roots

Indices

- Indices are used as a convenient way of writing products. The most common index used is 2.

  $3 \times 3 = 3^2$ [three squared]

  $7 \times 7 = 7^2$ [seven squared]

- To work out $3 \cdot 5^2$ on a calculator press $\boxed{3 \cdot 5}$ $\boxed{x^2}$.

  The answer is $12 \cdot 25$.

- $2 \times 2 \times 2 \times 2 = 2^4$ [2 to the power 4]

  $7 \times 7 \times 7 \times 7 \times 7 = 7^5$ [7 to the power 5]

- To work out 2^5 on a calculator press $\boxed{2}$ $\boxed{x^y}$ $\boxed{5}$ $\boxed{=}$

  The answer is 32.

Exercise 1

1. Work out without a calculator

    (a) 3^2 (b) 5^2 (c) 1^2 (d) 10^2 (e) 2^2

2. Use the $\boxed{x^2}$ button to work out:

    (a) 6^2 (b) 12^2 (c) 20^2 (d) 15^2 (e) 18^2

3. Use the $\boxed{x^2}$ button to work out:

    (a) $1 \cdot 4^2$ (b) $3 \cdot 1^2$ (c) $0 \cdot 8^2$ (d) $5 \cdot 4^2$ (e) 100^2

    (f) 31^2 (g) $7 \cdot 5^2$ (h) 200^2 (i) $0 \cdot 2^2$ (j) $1 \cdot 25^2$

4. Find the areas of these squares

    (a)

        8 cm

    (b)

        2.4 cm

    (c)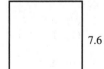

        7.6 cm

5. Write in index form

    (a) $2 \times 2 \times 2$ (b) $4 \times 4 \times 4 \times 4 \times 4$ (c) $3 \times 3 \times 3 \times 3 \times 3 \times 3 \times 3$

    (d) 9×9 (e) $10 \times 10 \times 10$ (f) $1 \times 1 \times 1 \times 1 \times 1 \times 1 \times 1 \times 1$

6. Write in index form
  (a) $4 \cdot 5 \times 4 \cdot 5$ (b) $1 \cdot 4 \times 1 \cdot 4 \times 1 \cdot 4$ (c) $a \times a \times a \times a \times a$
  (d) $p \times p \times p$ (e) $n \times n \times n \times n$ (f) $5 \times 5 \times 3 \times 3 \times 3$

7. Use the $\boxed{x^y}$ button to work out

  (a) 7^3 (b) 2^7 (c) 3^5 (d) 4^3 (e) 10^4
  (f) 3^6 (g) $1 \cdot 4^3$ (h) $0 \cdot 1^2$ (i) 3×4^2 (j) $2^3 \times 5^2$

8. Each side of a square field is $110 \, \text{m}$ long. Work out the area of the field.

9. Here is a piece of centimetre graph paper. Work out the area of each 'tiny' square.

10. Solve these equations
  (a) $x^2 = 9$ (b) $x^2 = 100$ (c) $x^3 = 8$
  (d) $x^3 = 1000$ (e) $x^6 = 1$ (f) $x^6 = 64$

11. Use a calculator to work out $0 \cdot 9^n$ for $n = 2, 3, 4, 5, 6, 7, 8, 10, 20$
  Copy and complete the following sentence:
  'As n becomes larger and larger, $0 \cdot 9^n$ gets _____.'

12. Solve these equations
  (a) $2^x = 8$ (b) $10^x = 100$ (c) $3^x = 81$

13.* The graph shows the curve $y = 3^x$.

  Use the graph to give an estimate for the value of x which satisfies the equation $3^x = 15$.

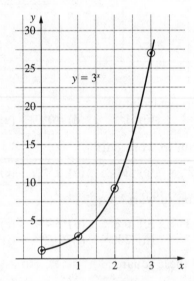

14. Write the answers using indices.
  (a) $3^2 \times 3^3$ (b) $5^3 \times 5^4$ (c) $a^2 \times a^7$ (d) $10^2 \times 10^4$
  (a) $4^3 \div 4^2$ (b) $6^5 \div 6^3$ (c) $10^3 \div 10^1$ (d) $x^7 \div x^2$

15. Copy and complete these two sentences
  (a) When we multiply two numbers in index form we $\boxed{}$ the indices.
  (a) When we divide two numbers in index form we $\boxed{}$ the indices.

Square roots

- A square has an area of 289 cm².
  How long is a side of the square?
  In other words, what number *multiplied* by *itself* makes 289?
  The answer is the *square root* of 289.

  On a calculator press $\boxed{289}$ $\boxed{\sqrt{}}$.

  The side of the square is 17 cm. [Check $17 \times 17 = 289$]

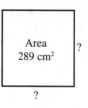

- Most numbers do not have an exact square root.
  Here is a square of area 286 cm².
  To find the length of a side of the square work out $\sqrt{286}$.

  On a calculator press $\boxed{286}$ $\boxed{\sqrt{}}$.

  The calculator shows 16·911535.
  To one decimal place, the side of the square is 16·9 cm.

Exercise 2

1. Work out without a calculator:

   (a) $\sqrt{25}$ (b) $\sqrt{49}$ (c) $\sqrt{100}$ (d) $\sqrt{1}$ (e) $\sqrt{81}$

2. Find the sides of these squares

   (a) Area = 16 cm²   (b) Area = 9 cm²   (c) Area = 121 cm²

3. Use a calculator to find the following, correct to 1 d.p.

   (a) $\sqrt{20}$ (b) $\sqrt{15}$ (c) $\sqrt{8\cdot3}$ (d) $\sqrt{516}$ (e) $\sqrt{1273}$
   (f) $\sqrt{0\cdot74}$ (g) $\sqrt{0}$ (h) $\sqrt{0\cdot038}$ (i) $\sqrt{58^2}$ (j) $\sqrt{17^2}$

4. A square tile has an area of 50 cm². Find the length of each side of the tile correct to the nearest mm.

5. A square table has an area of 15 000 cm². Find the length of each side of the table correct to the nearest cm.

6. A square field has an area of 8 hectares. How long is each side of the field, correct to the nearest m?
[1 hectare = 10 000 m²]

7. Each small square on a 'mini' chess board has an area of 12 cm²
Find L, correct to the nearest mm.

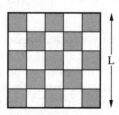

8. The area of square A is equal to the sum of the areas of squares B, C and D.
   Find the length x, correct to 1 d.p.

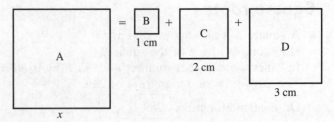

9. We know that $2^3 = 8$ ['two cubed equals 8'].

   Now $\sqrt[3]{8} = 2$. The *cube root* of 8 equals 2.
   The symbol $\sqrt[3]{}$ means 'the cube root of '.
   Find the following
   (a) $\sqrt[3]{27}$ (b) $\sqrt[3]{125}$ (c) $\sqrt[3]{1000}$ (d) $\sqrt[3]{1}$

10. A cube has a volume of $64 \, cm^3$.
    Find the length of the side of the cube.

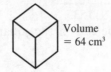

Volume
= 64 cm³

1.2 Number patterns

Prime numbers

A *prime* number is divisible by only two different numbers: by itself and by one. The first six prime numbers are 2, 3, 5, 7, 11, 13. Note that one is *not* a prime number.

Exercise 1

1. Draw a number square like the one shown.
   (a) Cross out in pencil the number 1.
   (b) Cross out in pencil all the even numbers, but leave the number 2.
   (c) Draw a red circle around all the numbers divisible by 3, but leave the number 3.
   (d) Cross out in pencil all the numbers divisible by 5, but leave the number 5.
   (e) Draw a green circle around all the numbers divisible by 7, but leave the number 7.
   (f) Cross out in red all the numbers divisible by 11, but leave the number 11.

   You should be able to see several patterns in the table.

   (g) The numbers divisible by 3 form diagonals across the table.
   (h) The numbers divisible by 11 form one diagonal across the table.
   (i) The numbers divisible by 7 form a pattern which is not so obvious. Can you describe it?

1	2	3	4	5	6	7	8	9	10
11	12	13	14	15	16	17	18	19	20
21	22	23	24	25	26	27	28	29	30
31	32	33	34	35	36	37	38	39	40
41	42	43	44	45	46	47	48	49	50
51	52	53	54	55	56	57	58	59	60
61	62	63	64	65	66	67	68	69	70
71	72	73	74	75	76	77	78	79	80
81	82	83	84	85	86	87	88	89	90
91	92	93	94	95	96	97	98	99	100

The numbers which have been left blank are all the prime numbers between 1 and 100. You have drawn a square for finding prime numbers known as the 'sieve of Eratosthenes'. Eratosthenes was a famous Greek mathematician working over 2000 years ago.

2. How many prime numbers are there between 1 and 100?

3. Write down two prime numbers which add up to another prime number.

4. How many of the prime numbers are even?

5. How many of the prime numbers are odd?

6. Find three prime numbers which add up to another prime number.

7. (Harder) Use a calculator to find which of the following are prime numbers.

(a) 103   (b) 145   (c) 151   (d) 188
(e) 143   (f) 108   (g) 221   (h) 293
(i) 493   (j) 323   (k) 1999   (l) 2639

Factors

- The number 12 can be written as two numbers multiplied together in three different ways

$$\boxed{1 \times 12} \qquad \boxed{2 \times 6} \qquad \boxed{3 \times 4}$$

The numbers 1, 12, 2, 6, 3, 4 are all the *factors* of 12.

- $\boxed{1 \times 8} = 8 \qquad \boxed{2 \times 4} = 8$

The factors of 8 are 1, 2, 4, 8.

Exercise 2

Write down all the factors of the following numbers
1. 6   **2.** 4   **3.** 10   **4.** 7   **5.** 15
6. 18   **7.** 24   **8.** 21   **9.** 36   **10.** 40
11. 32   **12.** 31   **13.** 60   **14.** 63   **15.** 85

16. Factors of a number which are also prime numbers are called prime factors. We can find these prime factors using a 'factor tree'

(a) Here is a factor tree for 60   (b) Here is a factor tree for 24

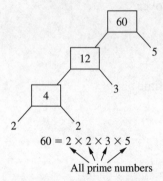

$$60 = 2 \times 2 \times 3 \times 5$$

All prime numbers

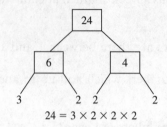

$$24 = 3 \times 2 \times 2 \times 2$$

(c) Draw a factor tree for 36.

In Questions **17** to **28** draw a factor tree for each number.

17. 28	**18.** 32	**19.** 34	**20.** 81
21. 84	**22.** 216	**23.** 294	**24.** 200
25. 1500	**26.** 2464	**27.** 4620	**28.** 98 175

29. The number 345 has 3 and 5 as factors.
Write another three-digit number which has 3 and 5 as factors.

30. The number 432 has 2 and 9 as factors.
Write another three-digit number which has 2 and 9 as factors.

31.* Which number less than 100 has the most prime factors?

32.* Which number less than 1000 has the most *different* prime factors? (You cannot repeat a factor.)

Multiples

The *multiples* of 5 divide by 5 with no remainder.
The first four multiples of 5 are 5, 10, 15, 20.
The first four multiples of 6 are 6, 12, 18, 24.

Exercise 3

Write down the first four multiples of:

1. 3   **2.** 4   **3.** 2   **4.** 7   **5.** 10

Write down the first six multiples of:

6. 5   **7.** 8   **8.** 9   **9.** 11   **10.** 20

11. Find which numbers the following sets are multiples of
(a) 8, 12, 20, 28
(b) 25, 30, 55, 60
(c) 14, 21, 35, 70

L.C.M. and H.C.F.

(a) The first few multiples of 4 are   4, 8, 16, (20), 24, 28 ...

The first few multiples of 5 are   5, 10, 15, (20), 25, 30, 35 ...

The *Lowest Common Multiple* (L.C.M.) of 4 and 5 is 20. It is the lowest number which is in both lists.

(b) The factors of 12 are   1, 2, 3, (4), 6, 12

The factors of 20 are 1, 2, (4), 5, 10, 20

The *Highest Common Factor* (H.C.F.) of 12 and 20 is 4. It is the highest number which is in both lists.

Exercise 4

1. (a) Write down the first four multiples of 2.
   (b) Write down the first four multiples of 5.
   (c) Write down the L.C.M. of 2 and 5.

2. (a) Write down the first four multiples of 4.
   (b) Write down the first four multiples of 12.
   (c) Write down the L.C.M. of 4 and 12.

3. Find the L.C.M. of
   (a) 6 and 9   (b) 8 and 12   (c) 14 and 35
   (d) 2, 4 and 6   (e) 3, 5 and 10   (e) 4, 7 and 9

4. The table shows the factors and common factors of 24 and 36.

number	factors	common factors
24	1, 2, 3, 4, 6, 8, 12, 24	1, 2, 3, 4, 6, 12
36	1, 2, 3, 4, 6, 9, 12, 18, 36	

Write down the H.C.F. of 24 and 36.

5. Find the H.C.F. of
   (a) 12 and 18   (b) 22 and 55   (c) 45 and 72
   (d) 12, 18 and 20   (e) 36, 60 and 72   (f) 20, 40 and 50

6. Don't confuse you L.C.M.'s with your H.C.F.'s!
   (a) Find the H.C.F. of 12 and 30.
   (b) Find the L.C.M of 8 and 20.
   (c) Write down two numbers whose H.C.F. is 11.
   (d) Write down two numbers whose L.C.M. is 10.

7. Given that $1386 = 2 \times 3 \times 3 \times 7 \times 11$ and $858 = 2 \times 3 \times 11 \times 13$, find the highest common factor of 1386 and 858. [i.e. The highest number that goes into 1386 and 858].

8. If $1170 = 2 \times 3 \times 3 \times 5 \times 13$ and $10725 = 3 \times 5 \times 5 \times 11 \times 13$, find the highest common factor of 1170 and 10725.

Satisfied numbers

The number 4 is an even number *and* a square number. It *satisfies* both categories.

1. Copy the grid below and use a pencil for your answers (so that you can rub out mistakes.)
   Write the numbers from 1 to 9, one in each box, so that all the numbers satisfy the conditions for both the row and the column.

	Number between 5 and 9	Square number	Prime number
Factor of 6	6	?	?
Even number	?	?	?
Odd number	?	?	?

2. Copy the grid and write the numbers from 1 to 9, one in each box.

	Prime number	Multiple of 3	Factor of 16
Number greater than 5			
Odd number			
Even number			

3. This one is more difficult. Write the numbers from 1 to 16, one in each box.

	Prime number	Odd number	Multiple of two	Even number
Numbers less than 7				
Factor of 36				
Numbers less than 12				
Numbers between 11–17				

4. Design a grid with categories of your own and ask a friend to solve it.

1.3 Negative numbers

- If the weather is very cold and the temperature is 3 degrees below zero, it is written $-3°$.

- If a golfer is 5 under par for his round, the scoreboard will show -5.

- On a bank statement if someone is £55 overdrawn [or 'in the red'] it would appear as $-£55$.

  These above are examples of the use of negative numbers.

- An easy way to begin calculations with negative numbers is to think about changes in temperature:
  (a) Suppose the temperature is $-2°$ and it rises by $7°$.
      The new temperature is $5°$.
      We can write $-2 + 7 = 5$.
  (b) Suppose the temperature is $-3°$ and it falls by $6°$.
      The new temperature is $-9°$.
      We can write $-3 - 6 = -9$.

Exercise 1

In Questions **1** to **12** move up or down the thermometer to find the new temperature.

1. The temperature is $+8°$ and it falls by $3°$.

2. The temperature is $+4°$ and it falls by $5°$.

3. The temperature is $+2°$ and it falls by $6°$.

4. The temperature is $-1°$ and it falls by $6°$.

5. The temperature is $-5°$ and it rises by $1°$.

6. The temperature is $-8°$ and it rises by $4°$.

7. The temperature is $-3°$ and it rises by $7°$.

8. The temperature is $+4°$ and it rises by $8°$.

9. The temperature is $+9°$ and it falls by $14°$.

10. The temperature is $-13°$ and it rises by $13°$.

11. The temperature is $-6°$ and it falls by $5°$.

12. The temperature is $-25°$ and it rises by $10°$.

In Questions **13** to **22** state whether the temperature has risen or fallen and by how many degrees.

13. It was $-5°$ and it is now $-8°$.
    14. It was $5°$ and it is now $-1°$.

15. It was $9°$ and it is now $-1°$.
    16. It was $-2°$ and it is now $-7°$.

17. It was $-11°$ and it is now $-4°$.
    18. It was $-8°$ and it is now $3°$.

19. It was $-15°$ and it is now $0°$.
    20. It was $-7°$ and it is now $-2°$.

21. It was $-3°$ and it is now $-83°$.
    22. It was $4°$ and it is now $-11°$.

23. Copy each sequence and fill in the missing numbers.

(a) 9,   6,   3,   ☐,   ☐

(b) ☐, -1,   3,   7,   11

(c) ☐,   ☐, -10, -5,   0

24. A diver is below the surface of the water at $-15\,\text{m}$. He dives down by $6\,\text{m}$, then rises $4\,\text{m}$. Where is he now?

Adding and subtracting

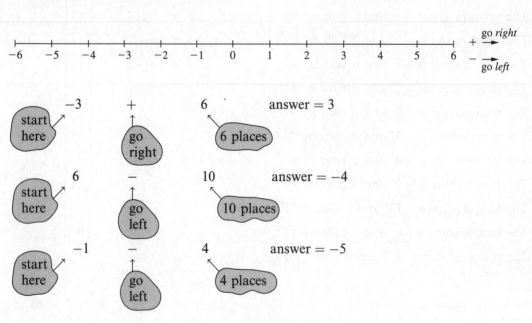

For adding and subtracting with negative numbers a number line is very useful.

Exercise 2

1. Use a number line to work out

2. Use a number line to work out

3. Use a number line to work out
   (a) $3 - 6$ (b) $-2 + 4$ (c) $-3 - 2$
   (d) $-6 + 9$ (e) $5 - 8$ (f) $-8 + 2$
   (g) $5 - 10$ (h) $-8 + 3$ (i) $-3 - 4$
   (j) $-3 + 7$ (k) $-10 + 10$ (l) $8 - 12$

4. Work out
   (a) $-7 + 4$ (b) $6 - 11$ (c) $-3 - 3$
   (d) $8 - 20$ (e) $-4 + 8$ (f) $9 - 2$
   (g) $-8 - 3$ (h) $-12 + 5$ (i) $-2 + 2$
   (j) $4 - 10$ (k) $-6 + 1$ (l) $-6 - 5$

5. Now work out these
   (a) $-5 + 5$ (b) $6 - 9$ (c) $-4 - 1$
   (d) $8 - 7$ (e) $-2 + 2$ (f) $-6 - 2$
   (g) $2 - 10$ (h) $-5 + 6$ (i) $8 - 13$
   (j) $-50 + 10$ (k) $-4 - 14$ (l) $20 - 100$

6. Work out the missing number.
   (a) $8 - ? = 6$ (b) $3 - ? = -1$ (c) $-8 + ? = -3$
   (d) $-2 - ? = -7$ (e) $? - 7 = -3$ (f) $? + 4 = -4$
   (g) $? + 8 = 3$ (h) $8 - ? = -4$ (i) $-5 - ? = -12$

Two signs together

The calculation $8 - (+3)$ can be read as
 '8 take away positive 3'.

Similarly $6 - (-4)$ can be read as
 '6 take away negative 4'.

In the sequence of subtractions on
the right the numbers in column A
go down by one each time.
The numbers in column B
increase by one each time.

$$
\begin{array}{ccc}
A & & B \\
\downarrow & & \downarrow \\
8 - (+3) &=& 5 \\
8 - (+2) &=& 6 \\
8 - (+1) &=& 7 \\
8 - (0) &=& 8
\end{array}
$$

Continuing the sequence downwards:

$$
\begin{array}{ccc}
8 - (-1) &=& 9 \\
8 - (-2) &=& 10 \\
8 - (-3) &=& 11
\end{array}
$$

We see that $8 - (-3)$ becomes $8 + 3$.

This always applies when subtracting negative numbers. It is possible to replace *two* signs next to each other by *one* sign as follows:

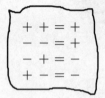

$$+ + = +$$
$$- - = +$$
$$- + = -$$
$$+ - = -$$

Remember: 'same signs: +'
              'different signs: −'

When two adjacent signs have been replaced by one sign in this way, the calculation is completed using the number line as before.

Work out the following

(a) $-7 + (-4)$
     $= -7 - 4$
     $= -11$

(b) $8 + (-14)$
     $= 8 - 14$
     $= -6$

(c) $5 - (+9)$
     $= 5 - 9$
     $= -4$

(d) $6 - (-2) + (-8)$
     $= 6 + 2 - 8$
     $= 0$

Exercise 3

1. Work out
  (a) $6 + (-4)$
  (d) $-3 + (+2)$
  (g) $7 - (+10)$
  (j) $-8 + (-2)$

  (b) $5 - (+7)$
  (e) $-3 + (-6)$
  (h) $8 - (-2)$
  (k) $-6 - (-6)$

  (c) $8 - (-4)$
  (f) $-9 + (-1)$
  (i) $10 - (-3)$
  (l) $-7 + (-2)$

2. Work out
  (a) $-3 - (-2)$
  (d) $8 + (-11)$
  (g) $-6 - (-2)$
  (j) $5 + (-9)$

  (b) $7 + (-8)$
  (e) $-4 - (-4)$
  (h) $9 + (-9)$
  (k) $-3 - (-8)$

  (c) $-6 + (-2)$
  (f) $7 - (+10)$
  (i) $-3 - (+4)$
  (l) $4 + (-8)$

3. Now do these
  (a) $8 + (-6)$
  (d) $-9 - (-3)$
  (g) $12 + (-9)$
  (j) $-17 - (+4)$

  (b) $-7 - (+3)$
  (e) $11 + (-20)$
  (h) $3 - (+8)$
  (k) $-5 - (-5)$

  (c) $16 - (-2)$
  (f) $-17 - (-3)$
  (i) $100 + (-99)$
  (l) $6 - (+11)$

4. Work out the missing number.
  (a) $7 + (?) = -2$
  (d) $? + (-8) = -10$
  (g) $3 - (?) = 6$

  (b) $5 - (?) = 8$
  (e) $9 + (?) = -20$
  (h) $7 - (?) = 0$

  (c) $? - (-2) = 10$
  (f) $7 - (?) = 12$
  (i) $12 + (?) = -100$

5. Work out

(a) $6 + (-8)$ (b) $-9 - (-6)$ (c) $-8 - (+6)$

(d) $4 - (-4)$ (e) $0 + (-5)$ (f) $3 - (-2) + (-8)$

(g) $-2 + (-1) - (-4)$ (h) $6 + (-10) - (+2)$ (i) $4 + (-7) - (-4)$

Multiplying and dividing

- In the sequence of multiplications shown, the numbers in column A go down by one each time.
  The numbers in column B go down by five each time

$$
\begin{array}{c}
A \quad\ B \\
\downarrow \quad\ \downarrow \\
5 \times \ 3 = \ 15 \\
5 \times \ 2 = \ 10 \\
5 \times \ 1 = \ 5 \\
5 \times \ 0 = \ 0
\end{array}
$$

Continuing the sequence:
We see that:

$$
\begin{array}{c}
5 \times -1 = \ -5 \\
5 \times -2 = -10 \\
5 \times -3 = -15
\end{array}
$$

> 'When a positive number is multiplied by a negative number the answer is negative'.

- In this sequence the numbers in column C go down by one each time.
  The numbers in column D *increase* by 3 each time.

$$
\begin{array}{c}
C \quad\ D \\
\downarrow \quad\ \downarrow \\
-3 \times \ 3 = -9 \\
-3 \times \ 2 = -6 \\
-3 \times \ 1 = -3 \\
-3 \times \ 0 = \ 0
\end{array}
$$

Continuing the sequence:

$$
\begin{array}{c}
-3 \times -1 = \ 3 \\
-3 \times -2 = \ 6 \\
-3 \times -3 = \ 9
\end{array}
$$

We see that:

> 'When two negative numbers are multiplied together the answer is positive.'

Summary of rules.

(a) When two numbers with the *same* sign are multiplied together, the answer is *positive*.

(b) When two numbers with *different* signs are multiplied together, the answer is *negative*.

(c) For division the rules are the same as for multiplication.

Examples: $-3 \times (-7) = 21$ $5 \times (-3) = -15$ $-12 \div 3 = -4$

                $20 \div (-2) = -10$ $-10 \div (-20) = \frac{1}{2}$ $-1 \times (-2) \times (-3) = -6$

Exercise 4

Work out

1. $5 \times (-2)$ **2.** -2×4 **3.** $7 \times (-2)$ **4.** $-3 \times (-2)$

5. $-3 \times (-1)$ **6.** $-4 \times (-1)$ **7.** -5×2 **8.** $5 \times (-1)$

9. -4×2 **10.** $-3 \times (-3)$ **11.** $6 \times (-3)$ **12.** $-8 \times (-1)$

13. $12 \div (-2)$ **14.** $-8 \div (-1)$ **15.** $6 \div (-2)$ **16.** $-10 \div (-2)$

17. $-20 \div (-1)$ **18.** $12 \div (-3)$ **19.** $-3 \div (-1)$ **20.** $9 \div (-3)$

21. Work out

  (a) $-7 \times (-2)$ (b) -3×6 (c) $8 \div (-8)$

  (d) $10 \times (-3)$ (e) $-2 \times (-2)$ (f) $-12 \div 3$

  (g) $-5 \times (-4)$ (h) -1×23 (i) $-2 \times (-2)^2$

  (j) $0 \times (-7)$ (k) $(-3)^2$ (l) $-3 \times (-2) \times (-3)$

22. Find the missing numbers

  (a) $-4 \times ? = 12$ (b) $3 \times ? = -12$ (c) $-8 \div -4 = ?$

  (d) $5 \times ? = -5$ (e) $? \times (-3) = 9$ (f) $12 \div ? = -6$

  (g) $? \div (-3) = 9$ (h) $? \div 5 = -4$ (i) $-2 \times ? = 1$

  (j) $0 \cdot 1 \times ? = -1$ (k) $(-3)^2 \times (?) = -9$ (l) $(?)^3 = -1$

Review exercise

This exercise has questions involving addition, subtraction, multiplication and division.

1. Work out

  (a) $-7 + 13$ (b) $-5 - (-4)$ (c) -7×4

  (d) $-12 \div (-12)$ (e) $-6 + (-3)$ (f) $-11\frac{1}{2} + 10$

  (g) $-8 - 5$ (h) $12 - 60$ (i) $3 \times (-3)$

  (j) $(-2)^2$ (k) $5 - (-5)$ (l) $6 \div (-12)$

2. Find the missing numbers

  (a) $5 \times ? = -50$ (b) $-2 \div ? = 1$ (c) $5 - (?) = 12$

  (d) $? + (-7) = -9$ (e) $10 - ? = -3$ (f) $? \div (-3) = -1$

  (g) $-7 - 7 = ?$ (h) $? \times (-10) = 5$ (i) $-4 - (?) = -9$

  (j) $-3 \times ? = 0$ (k) $8 - ? = -8$ (l) $(?)^3 = -8$

3. Work out

  (a) $-3 + (-2)$ (b) $-8 \div 8$ (c) $5 + (-7)$

  (d) $-2 \times \left(-\frac{1}{2}\right)$ (e) $8 \div (-8)$ (f) $-7 - (-2)$

  (g) $-12 \div (-2)$ (h) $(-3)^3$ (i) $6 + (-6 \cdot 5)$

  (j) $(-8 + 2)^2$ (k) $(-2)^2 \times (-3)$ (l) $(-3 - (-2))^2$

4. Copy and complete the *multiplication* square shown.

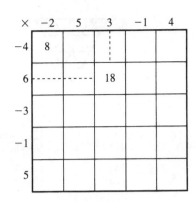

1.4 Fractions

Equivalent fractions

- In the diagram, $\frac{3}{6}$ of the shape is shaded. If you look at it a different way you can see that $\frac{1}{2}$ of the shape is shaded.

  The two fractions $\frac{3}{6}$ and $\frac{1}{2}$ are the same.
  We say they are equivalent.
  We normally use the simpler fraction which in this case is $\frac{1}{2}$.

- In this diagram, $\frac{4}{12}$ of the shape is shaded.
  A simpler fraction, which is the same as $\frac{4}{12}$, is $\frac{1}{3}$.
  You can *cancel* $\frac{4}{12}$ by dividing 4 and 12 by 4.

  So $\dfrac{\cancel{4}^{1}}{\cancel{12}_{3}} = \dfrac{1}{3}$.

Exercise 1

In Questions **1** to **9** write down the fraction shaded. If possible write the fraction in a simpler form.

1.

2.

3.

4.

5.

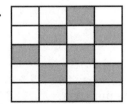

6.

7.   **8.**   **9.**

In Questions **10** to **25** fill in the missing numbers

10. $\dfrac{4}{8} = \dfrac{\square}{2}$ **11.** $\dfrac{6}{8} = \dfrac{\square}{4}$ **12.** $\dfrac{8}{12} = \dfrac{\square}{3}$ **13.** $\dfrac{2}{10} = \dfrac{\square}{5}$

14. $\dfrac{9}{12} = \dfrac{3}{\square}$ **15.** $\dfrac{15}{30} = \dfrac{1}{\square}$ **16.** $\dfrac{3}{9} = \dfrac{1}{\square}$ **17.** $\dfrac{9}{15} = \dfrac{\square}{5}$

19. $\dfrac{3}{7} = \dfrac{\square}{14}$ **20.** $\dfrac{3}{5} = \dfrac{\square}{10}$ **21.** $\dfrac{1}{4} = \dfrac{\square}{8}$ **22.** $\dfrac{3}{10} = \dfrac{\square}{30}$

23. $\dfrac{9}{24} = \dfrac{\square}{8}$ **24.** $\dfrac{5}{7} = \dfrac{25}{\square}$ **25.** $\dfrac{16}{24} = \dfrac{2}{\square}$

In Questions **26** to **33** find the odd one out.

26. (a) 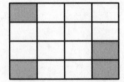 (b)   (c)

27. (a) 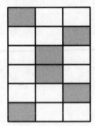 (b)   (c)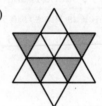

28. $\dfrac{2}{3}, \dfrac{4}{9}, \dfrac{4}{6}$ **29.** $\dfrac{1}{5}, \dfrac{3}{15}, \dfrac{3}{10}$ **30.** $\dfrac{3}{4}, \dfrac{8}{12}, \dfrac{6}{9}$

31. $\dfrac{2}{5}, \dfrac{6}{15}, \dfrac{4}{10}$ **32.** $\dfrac{5}{8}, \dfrac{6}{10}, \dfrac{12}{20}$ **33.** $\dfrac{3}{8}, \dfrac{5}{12}, \dfrac{6}{16}$

Fraction of a number

- The dungeon of a castle contained 135 prisoners of whom $\frac{4}{5}$ were innocent of any crime.
  How many innocent prisoners were there?

- We need to work out $\frac{4}{5}$ of 135.
  $\frac{1}{5}$ of 135 = 135 ÷ 5
  $\qquad = 27$
  So $\frac{4}{5}$ of 135 = 27 × 4
  $\qquad\qquad = 108$

There were 108 innocent prisoners in the dungeon.

Exercise 2

Work out

1. $\frac{2}{5}$ of 100

2. $\frac{3}{4}$ of 40

3. $\frac{2}{3}$ of 15

4. $\frac{5}{6}$ of 24

5. $\frac{3}{5}$ of 260

6. $\frac{3}{4}$ of 92

7. $\frac{5}{8}$ of £496

8. $\frac{2}{7}$ of £3500

9. $\frac{4}{5}$ of 80 kg

10. The petrol tank of a car holds 60 litres. How much petrol is in the tank when it is $\frac{4}{5}$ full?

11. In six years Alan Shearer scored 198 goals and $\frac{2}{9}$ of these were headers. How many headers did he score?

12. Susie's new jeans are 96 cm long when she buys them. After washing they shrink to $\frac{7}{8}$ of their previous length. What is the new length of the jeans?

13. In a spelling test full marks were 48. How many marks did Belize get if he got $\frac{5}{6}$ of full marks?

14. What fraction of £1 is 27 p?
What fraction of 1 m is 97 cm?
What fraction of 1 kg is 250 g?
What fraction of 1 km is 1 m?
What fraction of one year is one day?
What fraction of one year is December?

15. On each bounce a ball rises to $\frac{3}{4}$ of its previous height. How high will a ball bounce if it is dropped from a height of 2 metres?

16. In a sale spiders, which normally cost £12, were sold at '$\frac{2}{5}$ off'. How much did the spiders cost in the sale?

Work out

17. $\frac{5}{7}$ of £175

18. $\frac{2}{9}$ of $378

19. $\frac{5}{6}$ of 204 kg

20. $\frac{1}{8}$ of 12 hours

21. $\frac{3}{8}$ of 12 hours

22. $\frac{3}{4}$ of £4·20

23. $\frac{1}{10}$ of £55

24. $\frac{2}{3}$ of 1275 m

25. $\frac{5}{8}$ of £4976

Fractions of fractions

- The grey shaded strip is $\frac{1}{5}$ of the rectangle

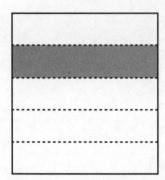

The black section is $\frac{1}{4}$ of $\frac{1}{5}$ of the rectangle.

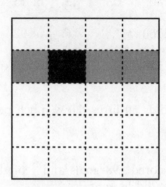

The rectangle on the right is divided into 20 equal parts so the black section is $\frac{1}{20}$ of the rectangle.

So $\frac{1}{4}$ of $\frac{1}{5}$ of the rectangle $= \frac{1}{20}$ of the rectangle

Notice that $\frac{1}{4} \times \frac{1}{5} = \frac{1}{20}$.

The word 'of' can be replaced by a multiplication.

- Look at these multiplications

(a) $\dfrac{2}{3} \times \dfrac{1}{5} = \dfrac{2}{15}$

(b) $\dfrac{3}{7} \times \dfrac{1}{4} = \dfrac{3}{28}$

(c) $\dfrac{1}{2} \times \dfrac{5}{6} = \dfrac{5}{12}$

(d) $\dfrac{3}{4} \times \dfrac{1}{6} = \dfrac{\cancel{3}^{1}}{\cancel{24}_{8}} = \dfrac{1}{8}$

(e) $\dfrac{6}{7} \times \dfrac{2}{3} = \dfrac{\cancel{12}^{4}}{\cancel{21}_{7}} = \dfrac{4}{7}$

> To multiply fractions: multiply the numerators, multiply the denominators and then cancel down if necessary

Exercise 3

All fractions should be given in their simplest form.

1. What fractions are these?

    (a) $\frac{1}{4}$ of $\frac{1}{3}$ (b) $\frac{1}{5}$ of $\frac{3}{5}$ (c) $\frac{2}{3}$ of $\frac{3}{4}$ (d) $\frac{3}{5}$ of $\frac{1}{4}$

2. Work out

    (a) $\frac{2}{5} \times \frac{3}{5}$ (b) $\frac{3}{7} \times \frac{1}{4}$ (c) $\frac{3}{8} \times \frac{2}{5}$ (d) $\frac{3}{4} \times \frac{1}{6}$

    (e) $\frac{5}{8} \times \frac{1}{2}$ (f) $\frac{5}{6} \times \frac{3}{4}$ (g) $\frac{2}{7} \times \frac{3}{4}$ (h) $\frac{1}{8} \times \frac{3}{5}$

    (i) $\frac{2}{9} \times \frac{3}{5}$ (j) $\frac{3}{11} \times \frac{1}{2}$ (k) $\frac{4}{9} \times \frac{3}{4}$ (l) $\frac{5}{12} \times \frac{8}{10}$

3. The diagram shows a square of side 1 m divided into four rectangles A, B, C and D.
Find the areas of A, B, C and D in m².

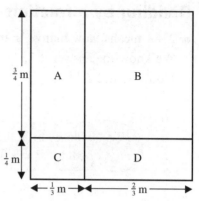

4. Nicki says that $0\cdot3 \times 0\cdot3 = 0\cdot9$
Write $0\cdot3$ as a fraction.
Multiply the fraction by itself and write the answer as a decimal.
Was Nicki's answer correct?

5. Draw a copy of the rectangle.
(a) Shade in $\frac{1}{3}$ of the squares.
(b) Draw crosses in $\frac{1}{5}$ of the unshaded squares.
(c) How many squares are neither shaded nor have crosses in them?

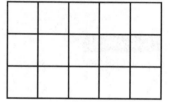

6. In an episode of 'Baywatch' there were 60 actors. $\frac{3}{4}$ of them were women and $\frac{3}{5}$ of the women were in swimsuits. How many women were in swimsuits?

7. We can multiply mixed fractions by changing them to improper fractions ('top heavy fractions')
For example: $2\frac{1}{2} \times \frac{3}{4} = \frac{5}{2} \times \frac{3}{4} = \frac{15}{8} = 1\frac{7}{8}$

Work out   (a) $3\frac{1}{2} \times \frac{2}{3}$ (b) $1\frac{3}{4} \times \frac{1}{5}$

8. Work out
(a) $2\frac{1}{2} \times \frac{1}{4}$ (b) $2\frac{1}{2} \times \frac{1}{6}$ (c) $3\frac{1}{2} \times \frac{3}{10}$ (d) $1\frac{1}{2} \times \frac{2}{3}$
(e) $3\frac{1}{4} \times \frac{1}{10}$ (f) $\frac{3}{5} \times 4\frac{1}{4}$ (g) $2\frac{1}{2} \times 1\frac{1}{2}$ (h) $3\frac{1}{2} \times 3\frac{1}{2}$

9. An centipede is born with 60 legs. It loses $\frac{1}{5}$ of its legs falling downstairs and a further $\frac{1}{3}$ of the remainder following an argument with a blackbird. How many legs has it left?

Dividing by a fraction

- $2 \div \frac{1}{4}$ means 'how many $\frac{1}{4}$'s are there in 2?

  We know the answer is 8.

  Notice that $2 \div \frac{1}{4} = \frac{2}{1} \times \frac{4}{1}$

  $\qquad\qquad\qquad = 8$

> To divide by a fraction, turn the fraction you are dividing by upside down and then multiply.

Examples

(a) $\frac{3}{5} \div \frac{1}{4} = \frac{3}{5} \times \frac{4}{1}$

$\qquad\quad = \frac{12}{5}$

$\qquad\quad = 2\frac{2}{5}$

(b) $\frac{5}{6} \div \frac{3}{4} = \frac{5}{6} \times \frac{4}{3}$

$\qquad\quad = \frac{20}{18} = \frac{10}{9}$

$\qquad\quad = 1\frac{1}{9}$

Exercise 4

1. $\frac{1}{2} \div \frac{1}{4}$
2. $\frac{1}{3} \div \frac{1}{2}$
3. $\frac{3}{4} \div \frac{1}{3}$
4. $\frac{2}{3} \div \frac{1}{2}$

5. $\frac{1}{5} \div \frac{1}{2}$
6. $\frac{1}{2} \div \frac{1}{5}$
7. $\frac{3}{4} \div \frac{4}{5}$
8. $\frac{1}{2} \div \frac{1}{6}$

9. $\frac{5}{6} \div \frac{1}{3}$
10. $\frac{2}{5} \div \frac{2}{3}$
11. $\frac{5}{7} \div \frac{9}{10}$
12. $\frac{5}{12} \div \frac{1}{8}$

13. $\frac{3}{7} \div \frac{3}{5}$
14. $\frac{9}{14} \div \frac{6}{7}$
15. $\frac{11}{15} \div \frac{1}{10}$
16. $\frac{4}{3} \div \frac{8}{1}$

17. $\frac{2}{5} \div \frac{2}{1}$
18. $\frac{5}{7} \div \frac{6}{1}$
19. $\frac{4}{9} \div 6$
20. $\frac{5}{11} \div 3$

In Questions **21** to **28** you must decide whether to multiply or divide.

21. A wine glass holds $\frac{1}{7}$ of a litre of wine. How many times can the glass be filled from a bottle which contains 2 litres of wine?

22. How many pieces of wood, each $5\frac{1}{2}$ cm long, can be cut from a plank 132 cm long?

23. An unfortunate motorist has to fill a five litre petrol can using a mug which takes only $\frac{5}{8}$ of a litre each time. How many times does he have to use a mug?

24. A sum of £20 is divided between several people so that each receives $\frac{2}{5}$ of a pound.
    How many people receive a share?

25. A sheet of paper is $\frac{1}{10}$ mm thick. How thick is a pad containing 360 sheets of paper?

26. Five people share a prize of £11·20. How much does each person receive?

27. In a sale a book is reduced to $\frac{2}{5}$ of its original price. What is the sale price if it originally cost £2·25?

28. Which is the greater: $\frac{5}{6}$ of £7·86 or $\frac{5}{8}$ of £10·24?

Adding and taking away

- Fractions can be added when they have the same denominator (bottom number).

- Here are some easy ones.

  $\frac{1}{5} + \frac{2}{5} = \frac{3}{5}, \quad \frac{2}{7} + \frac{3}{7} = \frac{5}{7}, \quad \frac{1}{10} + \frac{5}{10} = \frac{6}{10}$

- In these questions one of the fractions has to be changed to an equivalent fraction

  (a) $\frac{1}{2} + \frac{1}{4}$ (b) $\frac{1}{6} + \frac{1}{3}$ (c) $\frac{5}{8} - \frac{1}{4}$

  $ = \frac{2}{4} + \frac{1}{4}$ $ = \frac{1}{6} + \frac{2}{6}$ $ = \frac{5}{8} - \frac{2}{8}$

  $ = \frac{3}{4}$ $ = \frac{3}{6}$ $ = \frac{3}{8}$

Exercise 5

Work out

1. $\frac{1}{7} + \frac{2}{7}$ **2.** $\frac{1}{6} + \frac{4}{6}$ **3.** $\frac{5}{8} + \frac{1}{8}$

4. $\frac{2}{9} + \frac{3}{9}$ **5.** $\frac{3}{10} + \frac{4}{10}$ **6.** $\frac{3}{11} + \frac{2}{11}$

Draw fraction charts, using squared paper, and use them with the remaining questions

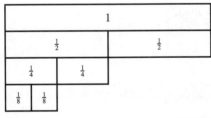 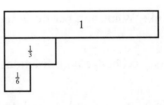

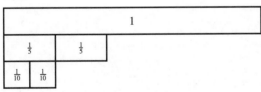

In Questions **7 to 15** fill in the missing numbers.

7. $\frac{1}{2} = \frac{}{8}$ **8.** $\frac{2}{3} = \frac{}{6}$ **9.** $\frac{3}{5} = \frac{}{10}$

10. $\frac{3}{4} = \frac{}{8}$ **11.** $\frac{4}{5} = \frac{}{10}$ **12.** $\frac{1}{3} = \frac{}{6}$

13. $\frac{1}{2} = \frac{}{10}$ **14.** $\frac{1}{4} = \frac{2}{}$ **15.** $\frac{8}{10} = \frac{}{5}$

Work out

16. $\frac{1}{4} + \frac{1}{2}$ **17.** $\frac{1}{6} + \frac{2}{3}$ **18.** $\frac{3}{8} + \frac{1}{2}$

19. $\frac{3}{8} + \frac{1}{4}$ **20.** $\frac{4}{5} + \frac{1}{10}$ **21.** $\frac{2}{5} + \frac{3}{10}$

22. $\frac{7}{8} - \frac{1}{2}$ **23.** $\frac{2}{3} - \frac{1}{6}$ **24.** $\frac{1}{2} - \frac{1}{8}$

25. $\frac{3}{5} - \frac{1}{10}$ **26.** $\frac{3}{4} - \frac{3}{8}$ **27.** $\frac{5}{6} - \frac{1}{3}$

28. $\frac{1}{5} + \frac{1}{10}$ **29.** $\frac{1}{8} + \frac{1}{16}$ **30.** $\frac{1}{10} + \frac{1}{20}$

31. Joe gave $\frac{1}{8}$ of his sweets to his brother and $\frac{1}{4}$ of his sweets to his sister. What fraction did he give away altogether?

32. Kate gave $\frac{1}{10}$ of her toys to a friend and $\frac{1}{5}$ of her toys to her sister. What fraction of her toys does she still have?

33. In her will a woman leaves $\frac{1}{2}$ of her money to her son, $\frac{1}{4}$ to her daughter, $\frac{1}{8}$ to her dog, $\frac{1}{16}$ to her cat, $\frac{1}{32}$ to her canary and the rest is divided equally between her three goldfish.

What fraction does each goldfish receive?

34. In an election, everyone voted for either A, B or C. If A got $\frac{1}{4}$ of the votes and B got $\frac{3}{8}$ of the votes, what fraction of the votes did C get?

Harder questions

- To work out $\frac{1}{2} + \frac{1}{5}$ we have to change *both* fractions so that they have the same denominator (bottom number).

  So $\frac{1}{2} + \frac{1}{5}$

  $= \frac{5}{10} + \frac{2}{10}$ (Think: 'What number do 2 and 5 go into?')

  $= \frac{7}{10}$

- To work out $\frac{3}{4} - \frac{1}{6}$ we have to change *both* fractions

  So $\frac{3}{4} - \frac{1}{6}$

  $= \frac{9}{12} - \frac{2}{12}$ (Think: 'What number do 4 and 6 go into?')

  $= \frac{7}{12}$

Exercise 6

1. Copy and complete these calculations

   (a) $\frac{1}{2} + \frac{2}{5}$ (b) $\frac{3}{5} - \frac{1}{2}$ (c) $\frac{1}{2} - \frac{1}{5}$

      $= \frac{5}{10} + \frac{4}{10}$ $= \frac{\square}{10} - \frac{\square}{10}$ $= \frac{\square}{10} - \frac{\square}{10}$

      $=$ $=$ $=$

2. Copy and complete these calculations

(a) $\dfrac{1}{3} + \dfrac{2}{5}$ (b) $\dfrac{1}{2} + \dfrac{1}{7}$ (c) $\dfrac{2}{5} + \dfrac{1}{4}$

$= \dfrac{\square}{15} + \dfrac{6}{15}$ $= \dfrac{\square}{14} + \dfrac{\square}{14}$ $= \dfrac{8}{20} + \dfrac{\square}{20}$

$=$ $=$ $=$

3. Work out

(a) $\frac{1}{3} + \frac{1}{7}$

     Think: What do 3 and 7
            go into?

(b) $\frac{1}{5} + \frac{1}{6}$

     Think: What do 5 and 6
            go into?

4. Work out

(a) $\frac{1}{2} + \frac{1}{3}$ (b) $\frac{2}{3} - \frac{1}{2}$ (c) $\frac{2}{3} + \frac{1}{4}$

(d) $\frac{1}{6} + \frac{1}{4}$ (e) $\frac{1}{3} + \frac{1}{4}$ (f) $\frac{3}{4} - \frac{1}{3}$

5. Work out

(a) $\frac{1}{3} + \frac{1}{5}$ (b) $\frac{2}{5} + \frac{2}{3}$ (c) $\frac{1}{4} + \frac{1}{5}$

(d) $\frac{4}{5} - \frac{1}{2}$ (e) $\frac{2}{3} - \frac{1}{4}$ (f) $\frac{2}{3} - \frac{1}{5}$

1.5 Proportion

(a) If 11 litres of petrol costs £5·72, find the cost of 27 litres.

The cost of petrol is *directly* proportional to the quantity bought.

     11 litres costs £5·72
$\therefore$ 1 litre costs £5·72 ÷ 11 = £0·52
$\therefore$ 27 litres costs £0·52 × 27
                 = £14·04

(b) A farmer has enough hay to feed 5 horses for 6 days. How long would the hay last for 3 horses?

The length of time for which the horses can be fed is *inversely* proportional to the number of horses to be fed.

     5 horses can be fed for 6 days
$\therefore$ 1 horse can be fed for 30 days
$\therefore$ 3 horses can be fed for 10 days.

In the first example above it was helpful to work out the cost of *one* litre of petrol.

In the second example we found the time for which *one* horse could be fed.

To do these questions you need to think logically.

- If five men can paint a tower in 10 days, how long would it take one man?

- If 33 books cost £280·50, how much will one book cost?

Exercise 1

The first 7 questions involve *direct* proportion. The last 7 questions involve *inverse* proportion

1. If 5 hammers cost £20, find the cost of 7.

2. Magazines cost £16 for 8. Find the cost of 3 magazines.

3. Find the cost of 2 cakes if 7 cakes cost £10·50.

4. A machine fills 1000 bottles in 5 minutes. How many bottles will it fill in 2 minutes?

5. A train travels 100 km in 20 minutes. How long will it take to travel 50 km?

6. 11 discs cost £13·20. Find the cost of 4 discs.

7. Fishing line costs £1·40 for 50 m. Find the cost of 300 m.

8. If 12 men can build a house in 6 days, how long will it take 6 men?

9. Six women can dig a hole in 4 hours. How long would it take 2 women to dig the same hole?

10. A farmer has enough hay to feed 20 horses for 3 days. How long would the hay last for 60 horses?

11. Twelve people can clean an office building in 3 hours. How long would it take 4 people?

12. Usually it takes 12 hours for 8 men to do a job. How many men are needed to do the same job in 4 hours?

13. Five teachers can mark 60 exam papers in 4 hours. How long would it take one teacher to mark all 60 papers?

14. 10 ladybirds eat 400 greenflies in 3 hours.
    Copy and complete the following:
    (a) 20 ladybirds eat * greenflies in 3 hours.
    (b) 20 ladybirds eat * greenflies in 9 hours.
    (c) 10 ladybirds eat 200 greenflies in * hours.
    (d) * ladybirds eat 4000 greenflies in 3 hours.

Exercise 2

1. If 7 packets of coffee cost £8·54, find the cost of 3 packets.

2. Find the cost of 8 bottles of wine, given that 5 bottles cost £11·90.

3. If 7 cartons of milk hold 14 litres, find how much milk there is in 6 cartons.

4. On an army exercise, 5 soldiers took 6 hours to dig a trench. How long would it have taken 3 soldiers to dig an identical trench?

5. A party of 10 people exploring a desert took enough water to last 5 days. How long would the water have lasted if there had been only 5 people in the party?

6. A worker takes 8 minutes to make 2 circuit boards. How long would it take to make 7 circuit boards?

7. On a rose bush there are enough greenfly to last 9 ladybirds 4 hours. How long would the greenfly last if there were only 6 ladybirds.

8. The total weight of 8 tiles is 1720 g. How much do 17 tiles weigh?

9. A machine can fill 3000 bottles in 15 minutes. How many bottles will it fill in 2 minutes?

10. A train travels 40 km in 120 minutes. How long will it take to travel 55 km at the same speed?

11. If 4 grapefruit can be bought for £2·96, how many can be bought for £8·14?

12. £15 can be exchanged for 126 francs. How many francs can be exchanged for £37·50?

13. Usually it takes 10 hours for 4 men to build a wall. How many men are needed to build the same wall in 8 hours?

14. A car travels 280 km on 35 litres of petrol. How much petrol is needed for a journey of 440 km?

15. 10 bags of corn will feed 60 hens for 3 days. Copy and complete the following:
    (a) 30 bags of corn will feed * hens for 3 days.
    (b) 10 bags of corn will feed 20 hens for * days.
    (c) 10 bags of corn will feed * hens for 18 days.
    (d) 30 bags of corn will feed 90 hens for * days.

16. 4 machines produce 5000 batteries in 10 hours. How many batteries would 6 machines produce in 10 hours?

17. Newtonian spiders can spin webbs in straight lines.
    If 15 spiders can spin a webb of length 1 metre in 30 minutes, how long will it take 6 spiders to spin a webb of the same length?

18.* In the army all holes are dug 4 feet deep. It takes 8 soldiers 36 minutes to dig a hole 18 feet long by 10 feet wide. How long will it take 5 soldiers to dig a hole 36 feet by 10 feet?

19.* It takes b beavers n hours to build a dam. How long will it take half the beavers to build the same size dam?

1.6 Estimating

- In some situations an estimate of a quantity is more helpful than the actual number. For example we may know that on January 1st 1996 the population of France is 61 278 514 and the population of Greece is 9 815 972. For purposes of comparison we could use 60 million for France and 10 million for Greece so that the population of France is *about* six times that of Greece.

- Find an estimate for the area of a circular pond of radius 10·8 m.
  We know that area = $\pi \times$ (radius)^2.
  The value of π is about 3 and the radius is about 10 m.
  So area $\approx 3 \times 10^2$
  The area of the pond is about 300 m^2.

- Estimate, correct to one significant figure

  (a) $\dfrac{58 \cdot 2 \times 28 \cdot 4}{18 \cdot 27} \approx \dfrac{6\cancel{0} \times 30}{2\cancel{0}} \approx 90$

  (b) $\dfrac{42 \cdot 3 + 56 \cdot 1}{2 \cdot 14} \approx \dfrac{40 + 60}{2} \approx 50$

  (c) 48% of £22 615 $\approx \dfrac{50}{1\cancel{0}\cancel{0}} \times 20\,0\cancel{0}\cancel{0} \approx$ £10 000

Exercise 1

Do not use a calculator. Decide, by estimating, which of the three answers is closest to the exact value. Write the letter A, B or C for each part.

	Calculation	A	B	C
1.	98.4×11.1	100	90	1000
2.	6.83×9.74	30	70	700
3.	18.9×21.8	200	400	4000
4.	5.1×9.23	4.9	99	49
5.	1.01×80.6	8	80	0.8
6.	6.8×11.4	80	44	600
7.	18.9×21	40	4000	400
8.	2.2×96	22	200	440
9.	972×21.4	10 000	2000	20 000
10.	$24\,723 \times 10.37$	2.5 million	250 000	25 000
11.	$208.4 \div 18.9$	0.1	2	20
12.	$83.75 \div 1.18$	82	8.2	120
13.	$55.14 \div 99.6$	0.2	0.5	2
14.	$1211 \div 986.4$	1.2	12	0.8
15.	$38.4 \div 0.96$	0.4	4	38
16.	207×2.16	4400	208	410
17.	73.4×97.4	70 000	700	7000
18.	1200×0.89	120	1200	360
19.	3.2×4.2	8.2	13.4	83.4
20.	4.01×960	3800	380	940
21.	$\dfrac{4.2 + 98.71}{1.95}$	5	50	80
22.	$\dfrac{84.3 - 2.72}{41.7}$	1.2	2.1	5.6
23.	$\dfrac{1.85 \times 61.4}{30.6}$	0.4	4	20
24.	9.8% of 122.7	12	120	1.2
25.	51% of 2613	560	130	1300
26.	$4.12 + 594.6$	5	600	2400
27.	$201.8 - 0.113$	0.7	50	200
28.	$0.0714 + 92.4$	90	0.4	900
29.	$\sqrt{25.13} \times 6.03$	15	30	150
30.	$22.2 \times \sqrt{97.6}$	2000	20	200

Exercise 2

1. Steve buys 52 cinema tickets at £4·95 each. Estimate the total cost.

2. One hundred and four people share the cost of hiring a coach. Roughly how much does each person pay if the total cost was £3118?

3. The total weight of 18 people in a lift was 1224 kg. Work out the approximate average (mean) weight of the people.

4. A Grand Prix racing car goes around each lap in about 1 minute 52·6 seconds. Roughly how many minutes will the car take to go 72 laps?

5. Tracy buys five articles at £1·99 each and 28 items at 21p each. Roughly how much does she spend altogether?

6. A pile of 19 sheets of card is 62 mm thick. Roughly how thick is each sheet of card?

7. A wedding cake weighing 9·2 kg is cut up and shared between 107 guests. About how much cake, in grams, does each person get?

8. The monthly rental for a video is £9·25. About how much is paid in rent over four years?

9. The total weight of 95 000 marbles is 308 kg. Roughly how many grams does each marble weigh?

In Questions 10 and 11 there are nine calculations and nine answers. Write down each calculation and choose the correct answer from the list given.

10. (a) 1·8 × 10·4   (b) 9·8 × 9·1   (c) 7·9 × 8·1
    (d) 76·2 × 1·9   (e) 3·8 × 8·2   (f) 8·15 × 5·92
    (g) 36·96 ÷ 4   (h) 9·6 ÷ 5   (i) 0·11 + 3·97
    Answers: 63·99, 18·72, 31·16, 4·08, 1·92, 9·24, 144·78, 89·18, 48·248.

11. (a) 5·89 × 10   (b) 1·02 ÷ 10   (c) 101·4 ÷ 5
    (d) 7·2 × 1·9   (e) 4·3 × 6·8   (f) 3·57 ÷ 3
    (g) 7·76 ÷ 2   (h) 10% of 350   (i) 43·56 ÷ 6
    Answers: 13·68, 7·26, 29·24, 3·88, 1·19, 20·28, 58·9, 0·102, 35·0.

12. In the numbers below the decimal point has been left out. Write
out each line and put the decimal point in the right place.
(a) length of a football pitch   9572 m
(b) width of this book   1831 cm
(c) height of the classroom door   205 m
(d) weight of a box of Corn Flakes   5000 g
(e) area of a postcard   1450 cm^2
(f) price of 1000 four finger Kit Kats   £22000

Multiplying and dividing by numbers between 0 and 1

When you multiply by a number greater than 1, you make it bigger   E.g. $5 \cdot 7 \times 1 \cdot 2 > 5 \cdot 7$

When you multiply by a number less than 1, you make it smaller   E.g. $5 \cdot 7 \times 0 \cdot 8 < 5 \cdot 7$

When you divide by a number greater than 1, you make it smaller   E.g. $5 \cdot 7 \div 1 \cdot 2 < 5 \cdot 7$

When you divide by a number less than 1, you make it bigger   E.g. $5 \cdot 7 \div 0 \cdot 8 > 5 \cdot 7$

Look at these calculations and decide whether the symbol in the box should be '>' or
'<'.

$8 \cdot 5 \times 1 \cdot 18$ ☐ $8 \cdot 5$, $19 \cdot 4 \div 0 \cdot 3$ ☐ $19 \cdot 4$, $211 \div 1 \cdot 4$ ☐ 211

Exercise 3

1. Write down each statement with either '>' or '<' in the box.

(a) $4 \cdot 2 \times 0 \cdot 93$ ☐ $4 \cdot 2$ (b) $18 \cdot 6 \times 1 \cdot 75$ ☐ $18 \cdot 6$

(c) $67 \div 0 \cdot 74$ ☐ 67 (d) $5 \cdot 9 \times 0 \cdot 811$ ☐ $5 \cdot 9$

2. Write down each statement and next to it write 'true' or 'false'.
(a) $3 \cdot 58 \times 1 \cdot 3 > 3 \cdot 58$ (b) $19 \times 0 \cdot 92 > 19$ (c) $5 \cdot 5 \times 1 \cdot 04 > 5 \cdot 5$
(d) $9 \cdot 2 \div 1 \cdot 5 < 9 \cdot 2$ (e) $11 \cdot 2 \div 0 \cdot 87 > 11 \cdot 2$ (f) $67 \div 1 \cdot 34 < 67$
(g) $59 \times 0 \cdot 89 < 59$ (h) $10 \cdot 42 \times 0 \cdot 73 < 10 \cdot 42$ (i) $17 \div 0 \cdot 99 > 17$
(j) $0 \cdot 2^2 > 0 \cdot 2$ (k) $161 \div 0 \cdot 41 > 161$ (l) $(0 \cdot 85)^2 < 0 \cdot 85$

In Questions **3** to **13** give your answer correct to one significant
figure. Do *not* use a calculator.

3. A doctor is paid a salary of £49 450 per year. Work out a rough
estimate for her weekly pay.

4. Estimate the mean weight of articles with the following weights:
4·9 kg,   0·21 kg,   0·72 kg,   25·1 kg,   0·11 kg.

5. In 1996 Helen's pay was £19 380 per year. In 1997 she receives a
pay increase of 19·2%. Estimate the increase in Helen's pay.

6. Two people on a bike travel at an average speed of 98·7 km/h from 08.10 until 12.17. Roughly how far do they go?

7. Estimate the area of a circular pond of radius 7·1 m.

8. A lorry can carry a maximum load of 30 tonnes. A copy of Elmwood's Almanac weighs 475 g. The manager of the delivery firm estimates that each lorry can take about 6000 copies of the book. Is this a reasonable estimate? If not suggest a better estimate. [1 tonne = 1000 kg]

9. In the grounds of his palace, the Sultan of Brunei has a circular pond with a circumference of 61·5 m. Estimate the diameter of the pond in metres.

10. Estimate the mean weight, in kg, of two wrestlers weighing 131 kg and 72·4 kg respectively.

11. Give an estimate for each of the following calculations.

(a) $\dfrac{1\cdot97 \times 19\cdot6}{5\cdot14}$ (b) $\dfrac{2848\cdot7 - 1\cdot94}{0\cdot32 + 39\cdot83}$ (c) 52% of 0·394 kg

(d) $\dfrac{3\cdot15 + 30\cdot63}{0\cdot104}$ (e) $\frac{7}{15}$ of £3918.25   (f) $\dfrac{207\cdot5 + 4\cdot21 + 0\cdot63}{109\cdot4 + 293\cdot2}$

(g) $\dfrac{5\cdot13 \times 18\cdot777}{0\cdot952}$ (h) $\pi \times 9\cdot73^2$ (i) 12% of £2057

12. Decide whether or not the following are reasonable estimates. Write 'yes' or 'no' for each part.
(a) The total weight of thirty 14 year-olds = 1500 kg.
(b) The time taken by an international athlete to run 1 mile = 240 s.
(c) The total weight of 10 £1 coins = 1 kg.
(d) The top speed of your maths teacher's car = 150 km/h.
(e) The height of a four storey office building = 80 m.

13. The population of the Earth is about 6 billion. Estimate how many people share the same birthday as you.

Estimating game

- This is a game for two players. On squared paper draw an answer grid with the numbers shown.

Answer grid

198	1089	99	100	360	18
180	450	22	440	155	1980
1240	200	45	62	100	550
40	620	495	279	800	55
2000	80	220	10	891	250
4950	1550	1000	3960	3069	341

- The players now take turns to choose two numbers from the question grid below and multiply them on a calculator.

Question grid

2	5	9
11	20	31
40	50	99

The number obtained is crossed out on the answer grid using the player's own colour.

- The game continues until all the numbers in the answer grid have been crossed out. The object is to get four answers in a line (horizontally, vertically or diagonally). The winner is the player with most lines of four.

- A line of *five* counts as *two* lines of four.
  A line of *six* counts as *three* lines of four.

1.7 Sequences

Sequences are very important in mathematics. Scientists carrying out research will often try to find patterns or rules to describe the results they obtain from experiments.
Codewriters and codebreakers can use complicated sequences to work out new codes for transmitting secret information.
When answering questions on sequences try to keep an 'open' mind so that you can find rules by 'trial and error'.

Exercise 1

1. The numbers in boxes make a sequence. Find the next number.

(a) | 9 | 7 | 5 | 3 | □ |

(b) | 4 | 9 | 14 | 19 | □ |

(c) | 2 | 9 | 16 | 23 | □ |

(d) | 2 | 3 | 5 | 8 | 12 | □ |

In Questions **2** to **17** write down the sequence and find the next number.

2. 21, 17, 13, 9,

3. 60, 54, 48, 42,

4. 1, 2, 4, 8, 16,

5. $\frac{1}{2}$, 1, $1\frac{1}{2}$, 2,

6. 3, $4\frac{1}{2}$, 6, $7\frac{1}{2}$

7. 60, 59, 57, 54, 50,

8. 5, 7, 10, 14,

9. 3, 30, 300, 3000,

10. 1·7, 1·9, 2·1, 2·3,

11. 1, 3, 9, 27,

12. 8, 4, 0, −4, −8,

13. 7, 5, 3, 1, −1,

14. 1, 2, 4, 7, 11

15. −2, −1, 0, 1,

16. 200, 100, 50, 25,

17. 11, 10, 8, 5, 1,

18. Write down the sequence and find the missing number.

(a) | 3 | 6 | 12 | 24 | □ |

(b) | 4 | □ | 10 | 13 | 16 |

(c) | 32 | 16 | 8 | 4 | □ |

(d) | □ | 6 | 3 | 0 | −3 |

The next four questions are more difficult. Find the next number

19. 1, 2, 6, 24, 120,

20. 12, 11, 13, 10, 14,

21. 27, 9, 3, 1,

22. 3, 10, 19, 30,

23. Look at this sequence

$$3^2 = 9$$
$$33^2 = 1089$$
$$333^2 = 110\,889$$
$$3333^2 = 11\,108\,889$$

Write down the value of $33\,333^2$ and the value of $33\,333\,333^2$.

Exercise 2

1. Here is the start of a sequence of rectangles

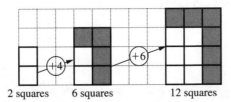

2 squares   6 squares   12 squares

(a) Draw the next rectangle in the sequence and count the squares.
(b) The number of squares in the rectangles makes a number pattern. Copy and complete the boxes and circles below.

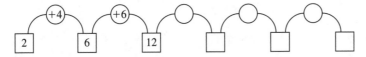

2. Here is the start of a sequence of shapes. Each new diagram is made by adding squares around the outside of the last shape.

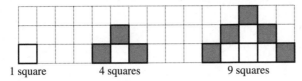

1 square   4 squares   9 squares

(a) Draw and shade in the next shape in the sequence and count the squares in the shape.
(b) The total number of squares in the shapes makes a number pattern. Copy and complete the boxes and circles below.

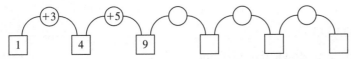

3. In the sequence of squares the number of matches is shown.

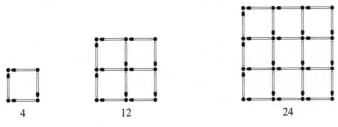

4   12   24

(a) Draw the next square in the sequence and write down the number of matches in the square.
(b) Copy and complete the number pattern below.

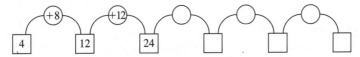

4. The rule for the number sequences below is

'double and add 1'

Find the missing numbers

(a) $2 \rightarrow 5 \rightarrow 11 \rightarrow 23 \rightarrow \boxed{}$

(b) $\boxed{} \rightarrow 7 \rightarrow 15 \rightarrow 31$

(c) $\boxed{} \rightarrow 51 \rightarrow \boxed{} \rightarrow \boxed{}$

5. The rule for the number sequences below is

'multiply by 3 and take away 2'

Find the missing numbers

(a) $2 \rightarrow 4 \rightarrow 10 \rightarrow \boxed{}$

(b) $\boxed{} \rightarrow 7 \rightarrow 19 \rightarrow 55$

(c) $1 \rightarrow \boxed{} \rightarrow \boxed{} \rightarrow \boxed{}$

6. Copy this pattern and write down the next three lines. Do not use a calculator!

$1 \times 999 = 999$
$2 \times 999 = 1998$
$3 \times 999 = 2997$
$4 \times 999 = 3996$

7. (a) Copy this pattern and write down the next two lines

$3 \times 5 = 15$
$33 \times 5 = 165$
$333 \times 5 = 1665$
$3333 \times 5 = 16\,665$

(b) Copy and complete $333\,333\,333 \times 5 =$

8. (a) Copy this pattern and write down the next line.

$1 \times 9 = 9$
$21 \times 9 = 189$
$321 \times 9 = 2889$
$4321 \times 9 = 38\,889$
$54\,321 \times 9 = 488\,889$

(b) Complete this line $87\,654\,321 \times 9 =$

9. (a) Copy this pattern and write down the next line.

$1 + 9 \times 0 = 1$
$2 + 9 \times 1 = 11$
$3 + 9 \times 12 = 111$
$4 + 9 \times 123 = 1111$

(b) Find the missing numbers

$\boxed{} + 9 \times \boxed{} = 1111111$

10. (a) Copy this pattern and write down the next line

$3 \times 4 = 3 + 3 \times 3$
$4 \times 5 = 4 + 4 \times 4$
$5 \times 6 = 5 + 5 \times 5$

(b) Copy and complete

$10 \times 11 =$
$11 \times 12 =$

11.* The odd numbers can be added in groups to give an interesting sequence

1		$=$	$1 =$	1^3	$(1 \times 1 \times 1)$
	$3 + 5$	$=$	$8 =$	2^3	$(2 \times 2 \times 2)$
	$7 + 9 + 11$	$=$	$27 =$	3^3	$(3 \times 3 \times 3)$

The numbers 1, 8, 27 are called *cube* numbers. Another cube number is 5^3 (we say '5 cubed')

$5^3 = 5 \times 5 \times 5 = 125$

Write down the next three rows of the sequence to see if the sum of each row always gives a cube number.

12.* A famous sequence in mathematics is Pascal's triangle.

(a) Look carefully at how the triangle is made.
Write down the next row. It starts: 1 7 ...
(b) Look at the diagonal marked A.
Predict the next three numbers in the sequence
1, 3, 6, 10, 15, ...
(c) Work out the *sum* of the numbers in each row of Pascal's triangle. What do you notice?
(d) Without writing down all the numbers, work out the sum of the numbers in the 10th row of the triangle.

```
            1
          1   1
        1   2   1
      1   3   3   1
    1   4   6   4   1
  1   5  10  10   5   1
1   6  15  20  15   6   1
```

13.* (a) Look at the pattern below and then continue it for a further three rows.

$2^2 + 2 + 3 = 9$
$3^2 + 3 + 4 = 16$
$4^2 + 4 + 5 = 25$
$\vdots \quad \vdots \quad \vdots \quad \vdots$

(b) Write down the line which starts
$12^2 + \ldots$
(c) Write down the line which starts
$20^2 + \ldots$
(d) Write down the line which starts $x^2 + \ldots$

Differences in sequences

Different numbers of lines are drawn below and the maximum
number of crossovers for each is shown.

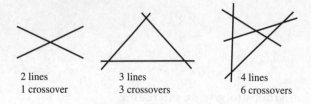

| 2 lines | 3 lines | 4 lines |
| 1 crossover | 3 crossovers | 6 crossovers |

lines	crossovers
2	1
3	3
4	6
5	10

One method for predicting further results is to look at the *differences*
between the numbers in the 'crossovers' column.

lines	crossovers	differences
2	1	
		2
3	3	
		3
4	6	
		4
5	10	
		⑤
6	⑮	

predictions

The differences form an easy pattern so that we can predict that
there will be 15 crossovers when 6 lines are drawn.

- Consider the sequence below.
  2, 10, 30, 68, 130

- The first, second and third differences are shown
  below.

	First difference	Second difference	Third difference
2			
	8		
10		12	
	20		6
30		18	
	38		6
68		24	
	62		⑥
130		㉚	
	㊲		
㉒㉒			

An obvious pattern is seen so that the numbers
circled can be predicted.

Exercise 3

2. Here is a sequence of matchstick squares

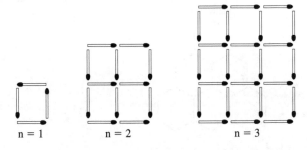

n = 1   n = 2   n = 3

Shape number, n	No. of matches	Difference
1	4	
2	12	8
3	24	12
4	40	16
5	?	

Use the differences to predict the number of matches in shape number 5.

2. Below is a sequence of rectangles where each new diagram is obtained by drawing around the outside of the previous diagram, leaving a space of 1 unit.

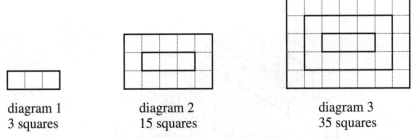

diagram 1   diagram 2   diagram 3
3 squares   15 squares   35 squares

(a) Draw diagram 4 and count the number of squares it contains. Enter the number in a table and use differences to *predict* the number of squares in diagram 5.

diagram	squares	differences
1	3	
2	15	12
3	35	20
4		

(b) Now draw diagram 5 to check if your prediction was correct.

3. Below are the first three members of a sequence of patterns of hexagons made with sticks.

diagram 1   diagram 2   diagram 3

6 sticks

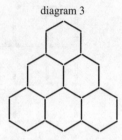

Draw diagram 4 and count the number of sticks it contains. Write your results in a table and then predict the number of sticks needed to make diagram 6.

4. Below are three sequences. Use differences to predict the next two numbers in each sequence.

(a)	(b)	(c)
1	3	11
6	6	14
13	13	22
22	24	35
33	39	53
?	?	?
?	?	?

5. The numbers 1, 2, 3, ... 96 are written in a spiral which starts in the centre.

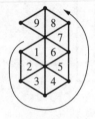

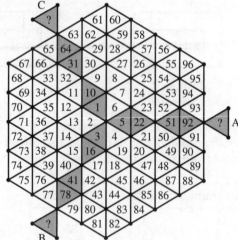

There are, in fact, many sequences in the pattern.
(a) In the row marked A, the numbers are
    5   22   51   92.
    Predict the next number in this sequence.
(b) Predict the next number in the rows marked B and C.

Part 2

2.1 Arithmetic without a calculator

(a) $56 + 711 + 8$

```
   5 6
 7 1 1
+    8
-----
 7 7 5
   1
```

(b) $383 - 57$

```
   7 1
 3 8 3
-   5 7
-----
 3 2 6
```

(c) 214×7

```
   2 1 4
 ×     7
-------
 1 4 9 8
     2
```

(d) $5 \cdot 6 + 12 \cdot 32$

```
   5 · 6 0   ← add zero
+ 1 2 · 3 2
---------
 1 7 · 9 2
```

[Line up the decimal points]

(e) $5 \cdot 26 \times 10$

$= 52 \cdot 6$

Move the decimal point one place to the right

(f) $28 \cdot 1 \div 100$

$= 0 \cdot 281$

Move the decimal point two places to the left.

(g)
```
     2 4
 × 0 · 3   ← one figure after
 -------     the decimal point
   7 · 2
     1     ← one figure after
             the decimal point
```

(h) $79 \cdot 2 \div 6$

```
      1 3 · 2
 6) 7 ⁷9 ·¹2
```

(i) $17 - 5 \cdot 4$

```
     6   1
 1 7̸ · 0̸
 -  5 · 4
 -------
 1 1 · 6
```

Exercise 1

Work out, without a calculator

1. $847 + 325$

2. $7140 + 396$

3. $294 - 157$

4. $6293 - 1734$

5. 35×4

6. 73×6

7. 214×8

8. 315×7

9. 23×100

10. 315×10

11. 17×1000

12. $5 \cdot 62 \times 10$

13. $59 \div 10$

14. $647 \div 100$

15. $8 \cdot 3 \div 10$

16. $219 \div 1000$

17. 43×20

18. 26×300

19. 124×200

20. $5184 + 2787$

21. $5615 - 3916$

22. $284 + 19 + 564$

23. 316×5

24. $56\,000 \div 20$

25. $19 \cdot 2 - 5 \cdot 8$

26. $11 + 5 \cdot 2$

27. 173×8

28. $868 \div 7$

29. $98 \cdot 7 \div 7$

30. $0 \cdot 38 - 0 \cdot 252$

31. $73 \cdot 2 \div 100$

32. $5 \cdot 1 \times 100$

33. $42 + 0.72 + 5.3$	**34.** $5.48 \div 4$	**35.** $2900 - 1573$	**36.** 0.95×9
37. $14\,490 \div 6$	**38.** $4000 - 264$	**39.** 5.24×0.5	**40.** $8.52 \div 4$
41. 52×0.04	**42.** $234 + 23.4$	**43.** $0.612 \div 6$	**44.** 5.2×2000
45. $0.0924 \div 4$	**46.** $0.72 - 0.065$	**47.** 73×0.3	**48.** $5.7 \div 100$

Multiplying decimal numbers

- 5×0.3 is the same as $5 \times \frac{3}{10}$. Work out $(5 \times 3) \div 10 = 15 \div 10 = 1.5$

  4.2×0.2 is the same as $4.2 \times \frac{2}{10}$. Work out $(4.2 \times 2) \div 10 = 8.4 \div 10 = 0.84$

  21.4×0.05 is the same as $21.4 \times \frac{5}{100}$. Work out $(21.4 \times 5) \div 100 = 1907 \div 100 = 19.07$

- Quick method: When we multiply two decimal numbers together, the answer has the same number of figures to the right of the decimal point as the total number of figures to the right of the decimal point in the question.

  (a) 0.3×0.4
  $(3 \times 4 = 12)$
  So $0.3 \times 0.4 = 0.12$

  (b) 0.7×0.05
  $(7 \times 5 = 35)$
  So $0.7 \times 0.05 = 0.035$

  (c) 8.4×0.2
  $(84 \times 2 = 168)$
  So $8.4 \times 0.2 = 1.68$

  (d) 200×0.04
  $(200 \times 4 = 800)$
  So $200 \times 0.04 = 8.00$

Exercise 2

1. 0.4×0.2	**2.** 0.6×0.3	**3.** 0.8×0.2	**4.** 0.4×0.03
5. 0.7×3	**6.** 0.7×0.02	**7.** 0.9×0.5	**8.** 6×0.04
9. 0.04×0.05	**10.** 0.7×0.7	**11.** 8×0.1	**12.** 14×0.3
13. 15×0.03	**14.** 0.4×0.04	**15.** 0.001×0.6	**16.** 33×0.02
17. 1.2×0.3	**18.** 3.2×0.2	**19.** 1.4×0.4	**20.** 2.1×0.5
21. 3.61×0.3	**22.** 2.1×0.6	**23.** 0.31×0.7	**24.** 0.42×0.02
25. 0.33×0.02	**26.** 3.24×0.1	**27.** 8.11×0.07	**28.** 16.2×0.8
29. 5.06×0.05	**30.** 30.9×0.3	**31.** 0.2^2	**32.** 0.4^2

Dividing by a decimal

- In the sequence of divisions shown, the numbers in column A go down by a factor of 10 each time.
  The answers in column B *increase* by a factor of 10 each time.

$$A \qquad B$$
$$\downarrow \qquad \downarrow$$
$$56 \div 100 = 0 \cdot 56$$
$$56 \div \ 10 = 5 \cdot 6$$
$$56 \div \ \ 1 = 56$$

  Continuing the sequence:

$$56 \div \ 0 \cdot 1 = 560$$
$$56 \div 0 \cdot 01 = 5600$$

- We see that: dividing by 0·1 is the same as multiplying by 10,
  dividing by 0·01 is the same as multiplying by 100.

  This is not surprising because $0 \cdot 1 = \frac{1}{10}$ and $0 \cdot 01 = \frac{1}{100}$.

- How many $\frac{1}{10}$s are there in 1?   Answer: 10

  How many $\frac{1}{10}$s are there in 7?   Answer: 70

  How many $\frac{1}{10}$s are there in 5·2?   Answer: 52

  How many $\frac{1}{100}$s are there in 1?   Answer: 100

  How many $\frac{1}{100}$s are there in 13?   Answer: 1300

- This is how we divide by a decimal number.

$$\frac{5 \cdot 62}{0 \cdot 2}$$

  Move the decimal point one place to the right in *both* numbers.
  We want to divide by a whole number.
  We have in effect multiplied both numbers by 10.
  Since *both* numbers are multiplied by 10 the answer is not changed.

$$\frac{56 \cdot 2}{2}$$

  Is obtained.

$$\frac{28 \cdot 1}{2) \, 56 \cdot 2}$$

  Do the division as normal.
  Answer = 28·1

- Here are three more examples.

(a) $\dfrac{0 \cdot 368}{0 \cdot 4}$ Move the points one place

$$\frac{3 \cdot 68}{4}$$

$$\frac{0 \cdot 92}{4) \, 3 \cdot 68}$$

(b) $\dfrac{0 \cdot 915}{0 \cdot 03}$ Move the points two places

$$\frac{91 \cdot 5}{3}$$

$$\frac{30 \cdot 5}{3) \, 91 \cdot 5}$$

(c) $\dfrac{1 \cdot 272}{0 \cdot 006}$ Move the points three places

$$\frac{1272}{6}$$

$$\frac{2 \, 1 \, 2}{6) \, 1 \, 2 \, 7^1 2}$$

Exercise 3

Work out, without a calculator

1. $1.46 \div 0.2$
2. $2.52 \div 0.4$
3. $0.942 \div 0.3$
4. $0.712 \div 0.2$

5. $0.375 \div 0.5$
6. $0.522 \div 0.6$
7. $6.54 \div 0.2$
8. $1.944 \div 0.6$

9. $0.1368 \div 0.04$
10. $0.228 \div 0.04$
11. $0.498 \div 0.06$
12. $5.04 \div 0.7$

13. $3.744 \div 0.09$
14. $0.1685 \div 0.005$
15. $0.2846 \div 0.2$
16. $0.0585 \div 0.09$

17. $0.0257 \div 0.005$
18. $1.872 \div 0.08$
19. $0.268 \div 0.4$
20. $0.39 \div 0.006$

21. $0.42 \div 0.03$
22. $7.041 \div 0.01$
23. $0.1638 \div 0.001$
24. $15.33 \div 0.07$

25. $0.993 \div 0.3$
26. $1.05 \div 0.6$
27. $8.4 \div 0.02$
28. $7.52 \div 0.4$

29. $4.006 \div 0.002$
30. $17.4 \div 0.2$
31. $54 \div 0.3$
32. $32 \div 0.4$

Speed tests

These questions can be done in two ways:
(a) Read out by the teacher with books closed.
(b) With books open.

In either case *only the answer* is written down. Be as quick as possible!

Test 1	Test 2	Test 3	Test 4
1. $7 + 4$	**1.** $8 + 5$	**1.** $40 - 19$	**1.** $20 - 7$
2. 5×7	**2.** 6×5	**2.** $8 + 7$	**2.** $11 + 17$
3. $12 \div 3$	**3.** $20 \div 2$	**3.** $24 \div 8$	**3.** 6×4
4. $20 - 8$	**4.** $35 - 6$	**4.** $24 \div 8$	**4.** $40 \div 10$
5. 6×4	**5.** 7×4	**5.** $15 - 2$	**5.** $21 + 9$
6. $12 + 13$	**6.** $8 + 25$	**6.** $50 + 60$	**6.** $60 - 11$
7. $20 \div 4$	**7.** $100 - 75$	**7.** $80 - 7$	**7.** 5×5
8. 3×7	**8.** 8×5	**8.** 9×3	**8.** $49 \div 7$
9. $9 + 8$	**9.** $64 - 14$	**9.** $20 - 4$	**9.** $25 - 9$
10. $11 - 2$	**10.** $11 + 18$	**10.** $9 + 9$	**10.** $8 + 18$
11. $16 \div 8$	**11.** $25 \div 5$	**11.** $30 \div 3$	**11.** 7×5
12. 10×3	**12.** 9×4	**12.** 11×7	**12.** $40 - 3$
13. $21 + 11$	**13.** $14 + 17$	**13.** $50 - 15$	**13.** $81 \div 9$
14. $30 - 16$	**14.** $20 - 7$	**14.** $9 + 19$	**14.** 7×6
15. 8×8	**15.** 7×5	**15.** $30 \div 5$	**15.** $55 + 45$

Know your tables

You will (hopefully) know your multiplication tables up to 12×12. Here is a test square to check both the speed and accuracy of your memory. You should try to make a copy of the square with all 100 answers correct in about ten minutes.

Two numbers have been put in to show how the square works.

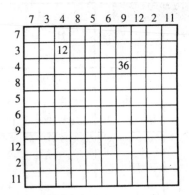

Hidden words

(a) Start in the top left box.
(b) Work out the answer to the calculation in the box.
(c) Find the answer in the top corner of another box.
(d) Write down the letter in that box.
(e) Repeat steps (b), (c) and (d) until you arrive back at the top left box. What is the message.

1.

6·4	66	274	985	12
	L	N	E	S
5×15	$2^3 + 3^3$	20% of 50	15×100	$756 \div 9$
422	75	1·68	10	2·4
N	S	R	C	I
10^3	$150 - 67$	8×22	$8·7 \div 10$	$37 + 385$
3·85	176	0·87	1000	83
U	E	H	F	O
$0·16 \times 10$	$421 - 147$	$5 + 1·4$	$8·4 \div 5$	$385 \div 7$
55	1500	1·6	35	84
L	I	N	I	S
$1000 - 15$	$\frac{2}{3}$ of 99	$0·4 \times 6$	25% of 48	$5·32 - 1·47$

2.

612	0·8	0·77	0·2	0·62
	T	W	V	T
$1·8 + 8·2$	5% of 400	$2^3 \times 6$	5×69	20% of 65
32	10	13	18	250
C	B	R	E	U
$50\,000 \div 200$	$\frac{2}{5}$ of 450	$0·6 \times 2·6$	80% of 80	$0·9^2 - 0·1^2$
1·56	0·6	180	0·15	64
E	R	E	S	S
$\frac{3}{8}$ of 48	$\frac{1}{2}$ of 0·3	$(0·2)^2$	$6·4 \div 0·2$	$806 - 194$
0·04	0·27	20	48	345
A	O	D	N	E
10% of 2	$770 \div 1000$	$0·3 - 0·03$	$3·1 \times 0·2$	$4·2 \div 7$

3.

45 $\frac{1}{2} + \frac{1}{4}$	4 H 2^4	371 C $10 \div 1000$	21 A $5 \div 8$	0·51 S $21 - 5 \times 4$
896 M $1^2 + 2^2 + 3^3$	0·06 E $51 \div 100$	0·05 L 1% of 250	0·01 E $5 \times (5 - 2)^2$	34 Y $5 \cdot 1 \times 100$
0·625 T $\frac{2}{3} \times \frac{1}{5}$	1 O $6000 \div 20$	$\frac{3}{4}$ M $4 + 5 \times 6$	$\frac{3}{8}$ S $0 \cdot 3 \times 0 \cdot 2$	32 I 53×7
510 C $\frac{3}{5}$ of 35	16 A $\frac{1}{2} - \frac{1}{8}$	2·5 Y $8 + 888$	300 N $\frac{1}{4} - 0 \cdot 2$	$\frac{2}{15}$ C $20 \div (12 - 7)$

2.2 Fractions, decimals and percentages

● **Fractions** – these are used to show parts of any whole.

In sharing a pizza between 3 people we use thirds $\left(\frac{1}{3}\right)$,

between 5 we use fifths $\left(\frac{1}{5}\right)$ ...

● **Decimals** – these are the most popular fractions on earth!

Think of all the currencies which use hundredths $\left(\frac{1}{100}\right)$ of whole units: pounds and pence, dollars and cents, francs and centimes. The list goes on and on. Decimals use units, tenths $\left(\frac{1}{10}\right)$, hundredths $\left(\frac{1}{100}\right)$, thousandths $\left(\frac{1}{1000}\right)$, ... and

● **Percentages** – these are a link between fractions and decimals. We work out what size and fraction would be if it were given as a number of hundredths. Each hundredth is called 1 per cent (1%).

Changing fractions to decimals

(a) We can think of the fraction $\frac{3}{5}$ as $3 \div 5$. When we perform the division, we obtain the decimal which is equivalent to $\frac{3}{5}$.

$$\frac{0 \cdot 6}{5)3 \cdot {}^3 0}$$ Answer: $\frac{3}{5} = 0 \cdot 6$

(b) $\frac{5}{8}$ can be thought of as $5 \div 8$.

$$\frac{0 \cdot 6\ 2\ 5}{8)5 \cdot {}^5 0 {}^2 0 {}^4 0}$$ Answer: $\frac{5}{8} = 0 \cdot 625$

Exercise 1

Without using a calculator, change the following fractions to decimals. Afterwards use your calculator to check your answer.

1. $\frac{2}{5}$ 2. $\frac{1}{4}$ 3. $\frac{3}{8}$ 4. $\frac{1}{5}$ 5. $\frac{9}{10}$

6. $\frac{3}{4}$ 7. $\frac{3}{5}$ 8. $\frac{4}{8}$ 9. $\frac{3}{10}$ 10. $\frac{7}{8}$

Change these mixed numbers to decimals.

11. $1\frac{2}{5}$ 12. $4\frac{3}{4}$ 13. $3\frac{1}{2}$ 14. $1\frac{7}{8}$ 15. $5\frac{1}{100}$

Write in order of size, smallest first. Use a calculator.

16. $\frac{7}{8}$, $0 \cdot 85$ $\frac{9}{10}$ 17. $\frac{13}{20}$, $0 \cdot 645$, $\frac{31}{50}$

18. $\frac{3}{4}$, $0 \cdot 715$, $\frac{29}{40}$ 19. $\frac{3}{16}$, $0 \cdot 18$, $\frac{1}{5}$

20. When these numbers are written in order, smallest first, which one is in the middle? (Give your answer as a decimal).

$\frac{3}{5}$, $0 \cdot 06$, $\frac{63}{100}$, $0 \cdot 654$, $\frac{13}{20}$

$\frac{3}{5}$ is $3 \div 5$

so $\frac{3}{5} = 0 \cdot 6$

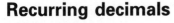

Recurring decimals

Some fractions give rise to decimals which repeat themselves forever. We call these recurring decimals, and use the notation below to save us from writing out the number until our ink runs out!

(a) $0 \cdot 555 \ldots$ We write $0 \cdot \dot{5}$

(b) $0 \cdot 434343 \ldots$ We write $0 \cdot \dot{4}\dot{3}$

(c) $0 \cdot 5265265 \ldots$ We write $0 \cdot \dot{5}2\dot{6}$
We only put the dot above the digits at the start and the end of the repeating pattern.

(a) Change $\frac{1}{3}$ to a decimal.

$$3\overline{)1 \cdot {}^1 0 {}^1 0 {}^1 0 {}^1 0 {}^1 0 \ldots}$$
$$0 \cdot 3\ 3\ 3\ 3\ 3 \ldots$$

The calculation is never going to end.

We write $\frac{1}{3} = 0 \cdot \dot{3}$. We say 'nought point three recurring'.

(b) Change $\frac{3}{11}$ to a decimal.

$$11\overline{)3 \cdot {}^3 0 {}^8 0 {}^3 0 {}^8 0 {}^3 0 {}^8 0 \ldots}$$
$$0 \cdot 2\ 7\ 2\ 7\ 2\ 7 \ldots$$

This time a *pair* of figures recurs.

We write $\frac{3}{11} = 0 \cdot \dot{2}\dot{7}$

(c) Change $\frac{1}{7}$ to a decimal.

$$7\overline{)1 \cdot {}^1 0 {}^3 0 {}^2 0 {}^6 0 {}^4 0 {}^5 0 {}^1 0 {}^3 0 0 \ldots}$$
$$0 \cdot 1\ 4\ 2\ 8\ 5\ 7\ 1\ 42 \ldots$$

The sequence '142857' recurs.

We write $\frac{1}{7} = 0 \cdot \dot{1}4285\dot{7}$

Exercise 2

Change the following fractions to decimals

1. $\frac{2}{3}$ 2. $\frac{2}{9}$ 3. $\frac{7}{9}$ 4. $\frac{1}{6}$ 5. $\frac{5}{12}$

6. $\frac{1}{30}$ 7. $\frac{7}{30}$ 8. $\frac{4}{15}$ 9. $\frac{2}{11}$ 10. $\frac{5}{11}$

11. (a) Work out each of the following as a decimal: $\frac{1}{7}, \frac{2}{7}, \frac{3}{7}, \frac{4}{7}, \frac{5}{7}, \frac{6}{7}$.
    (b) What do you notice about the answers?

12.* (a) Write out the 13 times table up to and including 9×13.
     (b) Use division to change the following fractions to decimals.

       (i) $\frac{1}{13}$ (ii) $\frac{4}{13}$ (iii) $\frac{9}{13}$.

     (c) Write down what you notice about the answers.

Changing decimals to fractions

This process usually has 2 parts:
(a) Finding the single fraction which is equivalent to the given decimal.
(b) Converting this fraction to its simplest form (if necessary).

Units	$\frac{1}{10}$'s	$\frac{1}{100}$'s	$\frac{1}{1000}$'s	Fraction	Simplest form
0	·1	7		$\frac{17}{100}$	$\frac{17}{100}$ (same)
0	·2			$\frac{2}{10}$	$\frac{2}{10} = \frac{1}{5}$
0	·0	0	4	$\frac{4}{1000}$	$\frac{4}{1000} = \frac{1}{250}$
0	·5	2	3	$\frac{523}{1000}$	$\frac{523}{1000}$ (same)
2	·8			$2 + \frac{8}{10}$	$2\frac{4}{5}$

Exercise 3

Change the following decimals to fractions in their most simple form.

1. 0·4   **2.** 0·7   **3.** 0·03   **4.** 0·05   **5.** 0·007

6. 0·006   **7.** 0·08   **8.** 0·12   **9.** 0·38   **10.** 0·015

11. 0·25   **12.** 0·45   **13.** 0·37   **14.** 0·025   **15.** 0·125

16. 0·99   **17.** 0·58   **18.** 0·625   **19.** 4·5   **20.** 3·6

Changing to a percentage

> To change a fraction or a decimal to a percentage, multiply by 100

(a) To change $\frac{2}{5}$ to a percentage, multiply by 100.

$$\frac{2}{5} \times \frac{100}{1} = \frac{200}{5}$$
$$= 40\%$$

(b) To change $\frac{1}{8}$ to a percentage, multiply by 100.

$$\frac{1}{8} \times \frac{100}{1} = \frac{100}{8}$$
$$= 12\frac{1}{2}\%$$

(c) To change $\frac{3}{7}$ to a percentage, multiply by 100.

$$\frac{3}{7} \times \frac{100}{1} = \frac{300}{7}$$
$$= 42 \cdot 857\ldots\%$$
$$= 43\%, \text{ to the nearest whole number.}$$

(d) To change 0·37 to a percentage, multiply by 100.

$$0 \cdot 37 \times 100 = 37\%$$

Exercise 4

Change these fractions to percentages.

1. $\frac{1}{2}$ **2.** $\frac{3}{4}$ **3.** $\frac{2}{5}$ **4.** $\frac{7}{10}$ **5.** $\frac{13}{20}$

6. $\frac{1}{8}$ **7.** $\frac{5}{8}$ **8.** $\frac{1}{4}$ **9.** $\frac{7}{20}$ **10.** $\frac{71}{100}$

11. Here are some examination results. Change them to percentages.
   (a) $\frac{14}{25}$ (b) $\frac{33}{40}$ (c) $\frac{42}{60}$ (d) $\frac{66}{120}$

12. Class 8P and class 8W were each set a maths test. The average mark for 8P was $\frac{25}{40}$ and the average mark for 8W was $\frac{15}{25}$. Which class had the higher average percentage result?

13. Change these decimals to percentages.
   (a) 0·32   (b) 0·14   (c) 0·03   (d) 0·815   (e) 1·4

14. Change these fractions to percentages, rounding to the nearest whole number.
   (a) $\frac{5}{6}$ (b) $\frac{7}{12}$ (c) $\frac{4}{9}$ (d) $\frac{6}{11}$ (e) $\frac{2}{3}$

2.3 Ratio and map scales

Look at this plant.

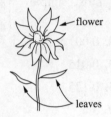

As a RATIO we say 'flowers to leaves'.
flowers : leaves
=   1 : 2

Exercise 1 The Snodget.

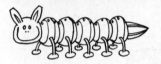

SIDE VIEW

The Snodget is a strange creature. It is born with no middle, and no feet!

Every 7 days it grows a middle section, and 2 feet.

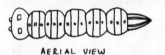

AERIAL VIEW

Important Snodget ratios,
A. Spots : Stripes   B. Age in days : Number of sections
    = 3 : 2   = 7 : 1

The Snodget above is 35 days old.

1. How many **stripes** has a Snodget with:
   (a) 6 spots?
   (b) 9 spots?
   (c) 21 spots?

2. How many **spots** has a Snodget with:
   (a) 4 stripes?
   (b) 10 stripes?
   (c) 18 stripes?

3. How old is a Snodget when its 3rd section has grown?

4. How many sections has a 12 week old Snodget?

5. Fill in the blanks in this sentence: 'For a 12 week old Snodget the ratio, spots : stripes = _____ : _____.'

6. How many spots has a 2 week old Snodget?

7. Draw a picture of a Snodget which is 49 days old.

Simplifying ratios

A ratio can be simplified if all the numbers have a common factor.
So the ratio 2 : 6 can be simplified to the ratio 1 : 3.
The ratio 3 : 6 : 15 can be simplified to the ratio 1 : 2 : 5.

Exercise 2

Write these ratios in a more simple form.

1. 10 : 5	**2.** 4 : 6	**3.** 12 : 4	**4.** 6 : 15
5. 10 : 2	**6.** 8 : 20	**7.** 14 : 8	**8.** 16 : 20
9. 3 : 18	**10.** 12 : 9	**11.** 30 : 25	**12.** 30 : 24
13. 9 : 21	**14.** 35 : 21	**15.** 32 : 40	**16.** 49 : 56
17. 48 : 36	**18.** 2 : 4 : 8	**19.** 2 : 6 : 12	**20.** 3 : 9 : 21

Ratio and sharing

● Louise is five times hungrier than Philip.
  Share 12 sweets between Louise and Philip in the ratio 5 : 1.

Louise : Philip
=   5 : 1
Total of 6 shares

Each share = 12 ÷ 6
            = 2 sweets
So Louise's share is 5 × 2 = 10 sweets
    Philip's share is 1 × 2 = 2 sweets

● Share £20 between Bill and Ben in the ratio 3 : 2.

Bill : Ben
= 3 : 2
Total of 5 shares

Each share = 20 ÷ 5
            = £4
So Bill's share : (3 × 4) : £12
    Ben's share = (2 × 4) = £8

Exercise 3

Share these quantities in the ratios given.

1. 18 apples between Tina and Gill, ratio 2 : 1

2. 30 oranges between Rachael and Sheila, ratio 2 : 3

3. 24 pears between Robert and Peter, ratio 3 : 1

4. 35 bananas between Richard and Ron, ratio 2 : 5

5. 42 teabags between David and Jacqui, ratio 5 : 1

6. 56 rulers between X and Y, ratio 2 : 5

7. 44 pencils between M and N, ratio 7 : 4

8. 63 erasers between S and T, ratio 4 : 5

9. 77 pens between F and G, ratio 1 : 6

10. 132 mints between C and D, ratio 4 : 7

11. Find the largest share in these problems
(a) £70, ratio 4 : 3
(b) 180 kg, ratio 4 : 5
(c) $225, ratio 7 : 8

12. Find the smallest share in these problems
(a) 480 g, ratio 5 : 3
(b) $510, ratio 12 : 5
(c) £380, ratio 15 : 4

Exercise 4

1. In a room, the ratio of boys to girls is 2 : 3. If there are 8 boys, how many girls are there?

2. In an office the ratio of men to women is 5 : 1. If there are 30 men, how many women are there?

3. A photo was enlarged in the ratio 2 : 3. The original photo was 8 cm long. How long was the enlarged copy?

8 cm
original

enlarged copy

4. A photocopier enlarges copies in the ratio 3 : 5. The length of a shark was 12 cm on the original. How long is the shark on the enlarged copy?

5. In a hall, the ratio of chairs to tables is 7 : 2. If there are 10 tables, how many chairs are there?

6. The ratio of squash to water in a drink is 3 : 8. How much squash is used with 4 litres of water?

7. Find the ratio (shaded area) : (unshaded area) for each diagram.

(a) 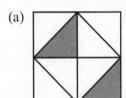   (b) 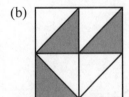   (c)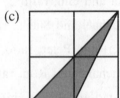

8. If $\frac{5}{8}$ of the children in a class are girls, what is the ratio of girls to boys?

9. Concrete for paths consists of cement, sand and gravel in the ratio 1 : 2 : 4 by volume. What volume of sand is needed to make 14 m^3 of concrete? Give your answer correct to 2 d.p.

10. Bread is made from flour and yeast in the ratio 30 to 1.
   (a) How much yeast is mixed with 960 g of flour?
   (b) How much flour is needed to mix with 400 g of yeast?

11. A prize of £50 000 is shared between Ken, Len and Ben in the ratio 2 : 3 : 5. How much does each person receive?

12. Divide 6000 g of gold between three prospectors in the ratio 3 : 4 : 5.

13. Lee, Mike and Neil formed a syndicate to enter a giant lottery. They agreed to share their winnings in the ratio of their contributions. Lee paid £1, Mike paid 60p and Neil paid 25p. Together they won £1 480 000. How much did Neil get?

14. The diagram shows 3 squares A, B and C. The sides of the squares are in the ratio 1 : 3 : 6.

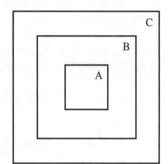

   (a) The side of square B is 9 cm. Find the sides of square A and the sides of square C.
   (b) Write this ratio in its simplest form, side of square B : side of square C
   (c) Work out the areas of squares A and C
   (d) Write this ratio, in its simplest form area of square A : area of square C.

Map scales

On a map of scale 1 : 3 000 000, Edinburgh and Newcastle appear 5 cm apart. What is the actual distance between the towns?

1 cm on map = 3 000 000 cm on land.

5 cm on map = 5 × 3 000 000 cm on land.

15 000 000 cm = 150 000 m
          = 150 km

Edinburgh is 150 km from Newcastle.

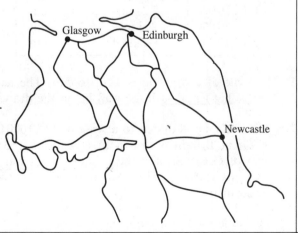

Exercise 5

1. On a map whose scale is 1 : 100 000, the distance between two villages is 7 cm. What is the actual distance in kilometres between the two villages?

2. Two towns are 9 cm apart on a map whose scale is 1 : 5 000 000. Find the actual distance between the two towns.

3. On a map whose scale is 1 : 200 000 the distance between two towns is 8·5 cm. Find the actual distance between the towns.

4. A river is 3 cm long on a map whose scale is 1 : 50 000. Find the actual length of the river.

5. The scale of a map is 1 : 10 000. Find the actual length in metres of a road which is 2 cm long on the map.

6. The distance between two towns is 20 km. How far apart will they be on a map of scale 1 : 4000?

7. The length of a lake is 120 km. How long will it be on a map of scale 1 : 100 000?

8. The distance between two points is 30 km. How far apart will they be on a map of scale 1 : 50 000?

9. The length of a section of motorway is 15 km. How long will it be on a map of scale 1 : 100 000?

10. Copy and complete the table

Map scale	Actual length on land	Length on map
(a) 1 : 5000	4 km	cm
(b) 1 : 20 000	5·2 km	cm
(c) 1 : 80 000	20 km	cm
(d) 1 : 10 000	8·4 km	cm

11. The scale of a drawing is 1 cm to 5 m. The length of a wall is 20 m. What length will the wall be on the drawing?

12.* A world map is drawn to a scale of 1 : 80 000 000, while a map of Great Britain is drawn to a scale of 1 : 3 000 000. On the map of Great Britain, the distance from Land's End to John o'Groats is 36 cm. How far apart are the two places on the world map?

13.* The scale used in a motoring atlas is '1 inch to 3 miles'. Write this in the form 1 : *n*. [1 mile = 1760 yards]

2.4 Rounding off

Significant figures

Write the following numbers correct to three significant figures (3 s.f.)

(a) $3 \cdot 3582 = 3 \cdot 36$ (to 3 s.f.)
$\uparrow$

(b) $0 \cdot 8242 = 0 \cdot 824$ (to 3 s.f.)
$\uparrow$

(c) $62\,750 = 62\,800$ (to 3 s.f.)
$\uparrow$

(d) $0 \cdot 06049 = 0 \cdot 0605$ (to 3 s.f.)
$\uparrow$

In each case we look at the number marked with an arrow to see if it is 'five or more'. We approach from the left and start counting as soon as we come to the first figure which is not zero. Once we have started counting we count any figure, zeros included.

Exercise 1

In Questions **1** to **8** write the numbers correct to three significant figures.

1. $1 \cdot 0765$ **2.** $24 \cdot 897$ **3.** $195 \cdot 12$ **4.** $0 \cdot 7648$

5. $17 \cdot 482$ **6.** $0 \cdot 07666$ **7.** $28\,774$ **8.** $2391 \cdot 2$

In Questions **9** to **16** write the numbers correct to two significant figures.

9. $6 \cdot 894$ **10.** $2 \cdot 232$ **11.** $0 \cdot 6456$ **12.** $0 \cdot 7163$

13. $0 \cdot 3443$ **14.** $7 \cdot 831$ **15.** $27 \cdot 83$ **16.** $31 \cdot 37$

In Questions **17** to **28** write the numbers to the degree of accuracy indicated.

17. $19 \cdot 72$ (2 s.f.)   **18.** $8 \cdot 314$ (1 s.f.)   **19.** $0 \cdot 71551$ (3 s.f.)   **20.** $587 \cdot 55$ (4 s.f.)

21. $1824 \cdot 7$ (3 s.f.)   **22.** $23\,666$ (2 s.f.)   **23.** $0 \cdot 0347$ (1 s.f.)   **24.** $87 \cdot 84$ (2 s.f.)

25. 2482 (2 s.f.)   **26.** $3 \cdot 0405$ (3 s.f.)   **27.** $17 \cdot 81$ (2 s.f.)   **28.** $0 \cdot 755$ (1 s.f.)

In Questions **29** to **36** use a calculator and write the answer correct to 3 significant figures

29. $17 \div 3 \cdot 1$ **30.** $0 \cdot 11 \times 6 \cdot 13$ **31.** $2 \div 0 \cdot 11$ **32.** $187 \div 19$

33. $1 \cdot 7 \times 8 \cdot 32$ **34.** $5 \div 0 \cdot 753$ **35.** $19 \div 0 \cdot 037$ **36.** $1 \div 0 \cdot 7$

Decimal places

(a) $7 \cdot 258 = 7 \cdot 26$ (to 2 d.p.)   (b) $0 \cdot 0428 = 0 \cdot 04$ (to 2 d.p.)   (c) $74 \cdot 755 = 74 \cdot 76$ (to 2 d.p.)
$\quad\quad\uparrow$ $\uparrow$ $\uparrow$

In each case we look at the number marked with an arrow to see if it is 'five or more'. Here we count figures after the decimal point.

Exercise 2

In Questions **1** to **8** write the numbers correct to two decimal places (2 d.p.)

1. 3·75821   **2.** 12·74412   **3.** 0·68214   **4.** 138·2972

5. 8·0152   **6.** 87·043   **7.** 9·0072   **8.** 0·0723

In Questions **9** to **16** write the numbers correct to one decimal place.

9. 18·7864   **10.** 8·55   **11.** 16·0946   **12.** 0·3624

13. 6·083   **14.** 19·53   **15.** 8·111   **16.** 7·071

In Questions **17** to **24** write the numbers to the degree of accuracy indicated.

17. 8·4165 (3 d.p.)   **18.** 0·7446 (2 d.p.)   **19.** 18·2149 (3 d.p.)   **20.** 0·887 (1 d.p.)

21. 17·543 (2 d.p.)   **22.** 12·732 (1 d.p.)   **23.** 8·255 (2 d.p.)   **24.** 1·126 (2 d.p.)

In Questions **25** to **32** use a calculator and write the answer correct to 2 decimal places.

25. $11 \div 7$ **26.** $213 \div 11$ **27.** $1·4 \div 6$ **28.** $29 \div 13$

29. $1·3 \times 0·95$ **30.** $1·23 \times 3·71$ **31.** $97 \div 1·3$ **32.** $0·95 \times 8·3$

33. Use a ruler to measure the dimensions of the rectangles below.
   (a) Write down the length and width in cm correct to one d.p.
   (b) Work out the area of each rectangle and give the answer in cm^2 correct to one d.p.

(i)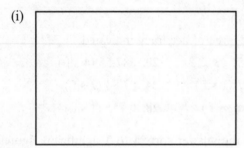

(ii)

Exercise 3

Use a calculator and write the answers to the degree of accuracy indicated.

1. $0·274 \times 1·134$ (2 d.p.)   **2.** $17·41 \div 5·24$ (2 s.f.)   **3.** $173 \times 2·35$ (3 s.f.)

4. $8·2 \div 0·89$ (1 d.p.)   **5.** $63 \div 361$ (2 s.f.)   **6.** $77·7 \times 2·4$ (1 d.p.)

7. $(8·4 - 1·47) \times 8·3$ (1 d.p.)   **8.** $(67 + 3716) \div 214$ (3 s.f.)   **9.** $(1·24 - 1·133) \times 0·61$ (2 d.p.)

10. $1 \div 0·7156$ (1 d.p.)   **11.** $81·237^2$ (3 s.f.)   **12.** $(6·14 - 3·23)^2$ (2 d.p.)

13. $8·27^2 - 11·2$ (2 d.p.)   **14.** $(8 - 0·313) \div 0·071$ (3 s.f.) **15.** $6·42^3$ (1 d.p.)

2.5 Rules of algebra

Using letters for numbers

Many problems in mathematics are easier to solve when letters are used instead of numbers. This is called using *algebra*.

It is important to remember that the *letters stand for numbers*.

- Here is a square with sides of length l cm
  The perimeter of the square in cm is $l + l + l + l$.
  If we use p cm to stand for the perimeter,
  we can write $\qquad p = l + l + l + l$
  or $\qquad\qquad\quad p = 4l$ (This means $4 \times l$)

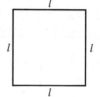

- Suppose there are a number of people in a room. Call this number N. If one more person enters the room there will be $N + 1$ people in the room.

- Suppose there are x cows in a field. After the farmer puts 3 more cows in the field there are $x + 3$ cows in the field.

- Suppose a piece of wood is l centimetres long.
  If you cut off 5 cm the length left is $l - 5$ cm.

- Suppose there are y people on a bus. At a bus stop n more people get on the bus. Now there are $y + n$ people on the bus.

- If I start with a number N and then double it I will have $2N$
  If I then add 7 I will have $2N + 7$.

- When you multiply, write the number before the letter. So write $2N$ *not* $N2$.

Remember: $4p$ means $4 \times p$ or $p \times 4$.

Exercise 1

In Questions **1** to **10** find the number I am left with.

1. I start with M and then double it.

2. I start with N and then add 6.

3. I start with e and then take away 3.

4. I start with d and then add 10.

5. I start with N and then multiply by 3.

6. I start with x, double it and then add 3.

7. I start with y, double it and then and then take away 7.

8. I start with k, treble it and then add 10.

9. I start with s and multiply by 100.

10. I start with t, multiply it by 6 and then add 11.

11. (a) The perimeter p of the square is
$$p = x + x + x + x$$
or $p = 4x.$

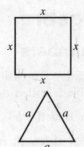

(b) Find the perimeter, p of this triangle.
Write '$p = \ldots$'

In Questions **12** to **17** find the perimeter p of the shape.

12.

13.

14.

15.

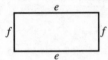

16.

17.

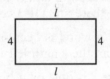

18. Draw and label a rectangle whose perimeter p is given by the formula $p = 2t + 2m.$

19. Draw and label a triangle whose perimeter is given by the formula $p = 2y + 7.$

20. Draw and label a pentagon (5 sides) whose perimeter p is given by the formula $p = 2a + 3b.$

Exercise 2

In Questions **1** to **8** find what number I am left with.

1. I start with x, add y and then take away 3.

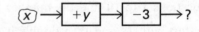

2. I start with N, double it and then add T.

3. I start with p, add it and then take away x.

4. I start with b, treble it and then add c.

5. I start with M, divide it by 2 and then add 7.

6. I start with $3x$, take away z and then add 3.

7. I start with $5N$, double it and then add M.

8. I start with p, treble it and then take away $2x$.

9. A piece of string is l cm long. If I cut off a piece 4 cm long, how much string remains?

10. A piece of wood is 25 cm long. How much remains after I cut off a piece of length x cm?

11. When a man buys a small tree it is h cm tall. During the year it grows a further t cm and then he cuts off 30 cm. How tall is it now?

12. A brick weighs w kg. How much do six bricks weigh?

13. A man shares a sum of N pence equally between four children. How much does each child receive?

14. On Monday there are n people in a cinema. On Friday there are three times as many people plus another 50. How many people are there in the cinema on Friday?

15. A prize of £x is shared equally between you and four others. How much does each person receive?

Simplifying expressions

The expression $5a + 2a$ can be *simplified* to $7a$. This is because $5a + 2a$ means five a's plus two a's, which is equivalent to seven a's.

(It can also be remembered as '5 *apples* + 2 *apples* = 7 *apples*'.)

Similarly, the expression $7c - 3c$ can be simplified to $4c$.

The expression $10x + x$ can be thought of as $10x + 1x$ which can be simplified to $11x$.

Similarly, $9a - a$ can be thought of as $9a - 1a$ which can be simplified to $8a$.

Notice that when we simplify an expression we are not finding its value when a is a particular number. We are just rewriting the expression in a simpler form.

Some expressions cannot be simplified.

The expression $7x + 2x$ consists of two *terms*, $7x$ and $2x$.

The expression $5x + 3y$ consists of two *terms*, $5x$ and $3y$.

$7x$ and $2x$ are called *like* terms.	x^2 and $3x^2$ are *like* terms.
$5x$ and $3y$ are called *unlike* terms.	x^2 and $2x$ are *unlike* terms

An expression which is the sum or difference of two terms can only be simplified if the terms are *like* terms.

Exercise 3

Simplify as many of the following expressions as possible. This exercise could be done orally.

1. $7x - 2x$
2. $4a + 5a$
3. $3a + 2b$
4. $9y - 2y$
5. $5x + 4x$
6. $5c - 2d$
7. $4x + 3$
8. $9d + d$
9. $13y - y$
10. $6d - 4$
11. $6x + 3y$
12. $4h + 2h$
13. $7y - 5y$
14. $13x - 9x$
15. $7a + a$
16. $3a + b$
17. $4 - 2x$
18. $7d - 3d$
19. $10a - 4a$
20. $17t - 2t$
21. $19b + 3b$
22. $9c + 5c$
23. $5c - c$
24. $5c - 5$
25. $9a^2 + a^2$
26. $9a + 9a^2$
27. $11b - 11$
28. $11b^2 - b^2$

Collecting like terms

- This pentagon has three sides of length a and two sides of length l. The perimeter of the shape is $a + a + a + l + l$. We can simplify this expression to $3a + 2l$.

  This is called *collecting like terms*.

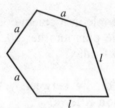

- We follow the conventions below when collecting like terms

  $4 + m + 3 + 3m = 4m + 7$ ◄——— collect in alphabetical order, with letter terms before numbers

  $s + 4 + s + 2 + t = 2s + t + 6$ ◄———

  $4p - 4$ can not be simplified.

  $3x + y - 3x = y$ ◄——— do not write 0_x do not write $1y,$

- The sign in *front* of the term is part of the term. If we change the order of terms the sign in *front* of each term *stays* with the term. We can emphasise this fact by drawing loops around each term to include the sign.

(a) Simplify $7x + 5y + 2x - 3y$

$(7x)(+5y)(+2x)(-3y) = (7x)(+2x)(+5y)(-3y)$ [group together like terms]

$\qquad\qquad\qquad = 9x + 2y$

    ↑
$\begin{bmatrix} \text{no sign} \\ \text{means} + \end{bmatrix}$

(b) Simplify $5a - 2x - a + 2x$

$(5a)(-2x)(-a)(+2x) = (5a)(-a)(-2x)\ (+2x)$ [group together like terms]

$\qquad\qquad\qquad = 4a$

Exercise 4

Simplify the following expressions as far as possible by collecting like terms.

1. $7x + 3y + 2x + 5y$ 2. $9x + 2y + 3x + y$ 3. $5a + 6y - 2a - 4y$
4. $11t + 7 - t - 4$ 5. $8y + 3 + y + 7$ 6. $9x + 2b - 8x + 7b$
7. $6a + 10 - 2a - 2$ 8. $6h - 2y + 3h + 9y$ 9. $8y - 3 + y + 9$
10. $4x + 10 - x + 3$ 11. $x + 12y + 3x - 2y$ 12. $7y + 5 + 7y - 4$
13. $3a - 2c + 5c - 2a$ 14. $5x + 2y + 7y + 5x$ 15. $7d - 4 + 10 - 6d$
16. $5a + 2c - 2a - 5d$ 17. $10x + 7 - 4x + x$ 18. $6x - 2y + x + 4$
19. $11y + 3 + 2y - 2$ 20. $a - 4c + 2a + 10c$ 21. $8d - 5 - 7d + 9$
22. $4a - 11 + 2 + 6a$ 23. $14a + 13c - 2a - 8c$ 24. $2 + 3y + 7 - 2y$
25. $4y - 2x + 8y + 5x$ 26. $6c + 13d - 7d + 4c$ 27. $8a + 5y + 2a - y$
28. $9a + c - 8a + c$ 29. $5x + 11y - 2y + 9$ 30. $6a + 3x - 2a + 10a$
31. $x^2 + 3x + 2x^2$ 32. $x^2 + 6x + 3x$ 33. $4x + 2x^2 - x$
34. $a^2 + 5a + 4a^2$ 35. $3x^2 + 2x - x^2 + x$ 36. $2x^2 - x + 3x^2 + x$

Brackets

The area of the whole rectangle
shown can be found by multiplying its
length by its width.
    Area $= 4(x + 2)$
Alternatively the area can be found by
adding together the areas of the two
smaller rectangles.
    Area $= 4x + 4 \times 2$

We see that $4(x + 2) = 4x + 4 \times 2$

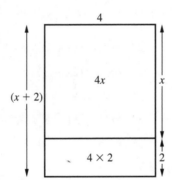

In general a number or symbol outside a pair of brackets multiplies
each of the numbers or symbols inside the brackets.

$5(x + 2) = 5x + 10$ $3(x - 2) = 3x - 6$

$4(2x + 1) = 8x + 4$ $2(1 + 3x) = 2 + 6x$

$a(x + b) = ax + ab$ $n(a + b + c) = na + nb + nc$

Remove the brackets and simplify.

(a) $3(x + 2) + 2(x + 1)$ (b) $4(x + 1) + 2(2x + 3)$
        $= 3x + 6 + 2x + 2$ $= 4x + 4 + 4x + 6$
        $= 5x + 8$ $= 8x + 10$

Note the method: First remove the brackets.
                 Second add the x terms and the number terms separately.

Exercise 5

In Questions **1** to **15** remove the brackets.

1. $3(x + 4)$ **2.** $5(x + 3)$ **3.** $4(x - 2)$

4. $6(x - 2)$ **5.** $2(2x + 1)$ **6.** $3(2x + 3)$

7. $4(3x + 1)$ **8.** $3(4x + 5)$ **9.** $9(2 - x)$

10. $2(4x - 5)$ **11.** $7(3x - 1)$ **12.** $10(2x + 5)$

13. $5(3x - 5)$ **14.** $2(3 - 2x)$ **15.** $3(x + y)$

In Questions **16** to **35** remove the brackets and simplify.

16. $2(x + 1) + 3(x + 3)$ **17.** $3(x + 4) + 2(x + 1)$

18. $4(x + 2) + 2(x + 2)$ **19.** $5(x + 1) + 3(x + 2)$

20. $2(4x + 3) + 4(3x + 4)$ **21.** $3(4x + 5) + 2(x + 5)$

22. $5(x + 1) + 3(x - 2)$ **23.** $6(2x + 1) + 3(1 + 2x)$

24. $4(3x + 1) + (2x - 1)$ **25.** $2(4 + x) + (5x - 2)$

26. $3(2x + 4) + 2(x + 1)$ **27.** $5(3 + 2x) + 10x$

28. $7(2x - 1) - 4x$ **29.** $4x + 5(2x + 1)$

30. $6x + 3(2x + 3)$ **31.** $9 + 3(3x - 1)$

32. $5(3x - 1) + 6(2x + 1)$ **33.** $8(1 + 2x) - 5$

34. $x + 6(3x + 2)$ **35.** $4(3x - 2) - 10x$

Two brackets

- Suppose we need to work out $(x + 3)(x + 2)$. We can use the area of a rectangle to help.

Total area $= (x + 3)(x + 2)$
$= x^2 + 2x + 3x + 6$
$= x^2 + 5x + 6$

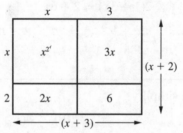

- $(2x - 1)(3x + 2) = 2x(3x + 2) - 1(3x + 2)$
$= 6x^2 + 4x - 3x - 2$
$= 6x^2 + x - 2$

[Notice that $2x \times 3x = 6x^2$.]

Exercise 6

Remove the brackets and simplify.

1. $(x+2)(x+4)$	**2.** $(x+5)(x+1)$	**3.** $(x+6)(x+2)$
4. $(y+3)(y+1)$	**5.** $(x-2)(x+4)$	**6.** $(x-3)(x+1)$
7. $(x+7)(x-2)$	**8.** $(x-2)(x-5)$	**9.** $(x-2)(x-7)$
10. $(a-3)(a+8)$	**11.** $(z+5)(z-2)$	**12.** $(a+3)(a-5)$
14. $(x-2)(x+1)$	**15.** $(k-7)(k+7)$	**16.** $(n-10)(n-1)$
16. $(2x+1)(x-3)$	**17.** $(3x+2)(x-2)$	**18.** $(4x+1)(x+3)$

19. The expression $(x+3)^2$ may be written $(x+3)(x+3)$.
Remove the brackets and simplify the following:
(a) $(x+3)^2$ (b) $(x-4)^2$ (c) $(2x+1)^2$

In Questions **20** and **21** do not use brackets.

20. In number walls each brick is made by adding
the two bricks underneath it.

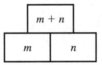

Fill in the missing expressions on these walls

(a) 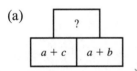   (b) 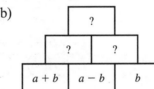   (c)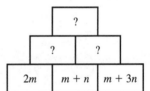

21. Here are some cards.

$2x$	$x+3$	$x \div 3$	x^2

$3x$	$3 \div x$	x^3

$x-3$	$2x+x$	$3+x$	$3-x$

(a) Which card will always be the same as $\boxed{x \times x}$?

(b) Which cards will always be the same as $\boxed{x+x+x}$?

(c) Which card will always be the same as $\boxed{\dfrac{x}{3}}$?

(d) Draw a new card which will always be the same as $\boxed{x+3x}$.

2.6 Solving equations

The main rule when solving equations is

'Do the same thing to both sides'.

You can *add* the same thing to both sides.
You can *subtract* the same thing from both sides.
You can *multiply* both sides by the same number.
You can *divide* both sides by the same number.

Solve the equations. The operations circled are performed on both sides.

(a) $3x - 1 = 5$

$(+1)$ $(+1)$

$3x = 6$

$(\div 3)$ $(\div 3)$

$x = 2$

(b) $2x + 3 = 4$

(-3) (-3)

$2x = 1$

$(\div 2)$ $(\div 2)$

$x = \frac{1}{2}$

(c) $10 + 4x = 6$

(-10) (-10)

$4x = -4$

$(\div 4)$ $(\div 4)$

$x = -1$

(d) $\qquad 6 = 14 - x$

$(+x)$ $(+x)$

$6 + x = 14$

(-6) (-6)

$x = 8$

Note: Always make the x term positive.

Exercise 1

Solve the equations

1. $3x - 2 = 13$ **2.** $5x + 2 = 12$ **3.** $7x - 4 = 3$

4. $2x + 7 = 7$ **5.** $7 + 2x = 11$ **6.** $3 + 5x = 33$

7. $6 + 4x = 8$ **8.** $6x - 3 = 15$ **9.** $2x - 11 = 10$

10. $8x - 9 = 15$ **11.** $8 + 3x = 5$ **12.** $4x + 1 = 2$

Questions **13** to **24** are more difficult.

13. $3x - 2 = 0$ **14.** $4x + 1 = 25$ **15.** $7x - 2 = -1$

16. $5 + 2x = 6$ **17.** $7 + 3x = 22$ **18.** $3 = 4x + 1$

19. $5 = 3x - 1$ **20.** $7 = 15 - 2x$ **21.** $10 = 12 - 3x$

22. $4 = 6x + 5$ **23.** $7x - 1 = -8$ **24.** $3 - x = 10$

Equations with the unknown on both sides

(a) $3x = 2x + 7$
   $\boxed{-2x}$ $\boxed{-2x}$ ← Removes the x term from R.H.S.
      $x = 7$

(b) $5x = 14 - 2x$
   $\boxed{+2x}$ $\boxed{+2x}$ ← Removes the x term from R.H.S.
      $7x = 14$
      $\boxed{\div 7}$ $\boxed{\div 7}$
      $x = 2$

(c) $3x + 5 = 2x + 7$
   $\boxed{-2x}$ $\boxed{-2x}$
   $x + 5 = 7$
   $\boxed{-5}$ $\boxed{-5}$
      $x = 2$

(d) $4x + 3 = 13 - x$
   $\boxed{+x}$ $\boxed{+x}$
   $5x + 3 = 13$
   $\boxed{-3}$ $\boxed{-3}$
      $5x = 10$
   $\boxed{\div 5}$ $\boxed{\div 5}$
      $x = 2$

Exercise 2

Solve the equations

1. $4x = 2x + 6$
2. $7x = 4x + 12$
3. $2x = x + 17$
4. $4x = 3x + 11$
5. $3x - 5 = 2x$
6. $6x - 4 = 4x$
7. $5x - 8 = 3x$
8. $9x = 10 - x$
9. $6x = 24 - 2x$
10. $9x = 18 + 3x$
11. $2x = 15 - 3x$
12. $9x - 1 = 6x$

In Questions **13** to **24**, begin by putting the x terms on one side of the equation.

13. $4x + 3 = 2x + 5$
14. $7x - 5 = 2x + 10$
15. $3x + 7 = 8x + 2$
16. $6x + 1 = 2 - 3x$
17. $7x - 2 = 1 - 3x$
18. $5 - x = 2x - 7$
19. $5x - 8 = x + 12$
20. $3x - 9 = 4x + 4$
21. $2 + 8x = 5 - x$
22. $16x + 9 = 12x - 3$
23. $1 - 10x = 6 - 5x$
24. $4 - 5x = 4 + 7x$

Equations with brackets

Many of the more difficult problems which appear later in this section involve forming equations with brackets. Once the brackets have been removed the method of solution is similar to that for the equations dealt with earlier.

(a) $3(2x - 1) = 2(5 - x)$
$6x - 3 = 10 - 2x$
$6x + 2x = 10 + 3$
$8x = 13$
$x = 1\frac{5}{8}$

(b) $2(3x - 1) - (x - 2) = 5$
$6x - 2 - x + 2 = 5$
$5x = 5$
$x = 1$

Exercise 3

Solve the equations.

1. $3(x + 2) = 18$

2. $5(x - 2) = 10$

3. $4(x + 1) = 5$

4. $4(x + 4) = 20$

5. $3(2x + 1) = 9$

6. $2(3x - 1) = 10$

7. $4(x - 3) = 2x + 6$

8. $2(3x + 1) = 5x + 7$

9. $7(x - 4) = 3x$

10. $5 = 2(5 - x)$

11. $21 = 3(2x + 5)$

12. $8 = 4(5x - 1)$

Questions **13** to **24** involve two pairs of brackets

13. $3(x + 4) = 2(x + 5)$

14. $7(x + 2) = 4(x + 6)$

15. $6(x - 4) = 2(x - 1)$

16. $3(x + 5) = 2(4 - x)$

17. $4(1 - 3x) = 9(3 + x)$

18. $7(2x + 1) = 2(5 + 4x)$

19. $8(x - 3) = 2x$

20. $2(x + 1) + x = 7$

21. $7(x - 2) - 3 = 2(1 - x)$

22. $5(x - 1) - (x + 2) = 0$

23. $2(3x - 1) - 3(x + 1) = 0$

24. $4(x + 1) + 2(1 - x) = x$

Exercise 4

Solve the equations for x.

1. $3(x - 1) = 2x - 2$

2. $4(x + 2) = 3x + 10$

3. $2(2x - 1) = x + 4$

4. $3(x - 1) = 2(x + 1) - 2$

5. $4(2x - 1) = 3(x + 1) - 2$

5. $5 + 2(x + 1) = 5(x - 1)$

7. $6 + 3(x + 2) = 2(x + 5) + 4$

8. $5(x + 1) = 2x + 3 + x$

9. $4(2x - 2) = 5x - 17$

10. $x + 2(x + 4) = -4$

11. $3x + 2(x + 1) = 3x + 12$

12. $4x - 2(x + 4) = x + 1$

Questions **13** to **24** involve different unknowns.

13. $5(2a + 1) - 5 = 3(a + 1)$

14. $3(4a - 1) - 3 = a + 1$

15. $2(a - 10) = 4 - 3a$

16. $7(n - 3) = 10 - n$

17. $3(n + 1) = 2(n + 3) - 6$

18. $5(2n - 1) = 9(n + 1) - 8$

19. $3(t + 2) = 4(1 - t)$

20. $7(t + 3) = 2(3 - t)$

21. $3(2t + 1) = 4(5 - t)$

22. $5(y + 1) = 3(y - 2) + 12$

23. $3(y + 7) = 2(y + 1) + 20$

24. $2(2y - 1) = 3(1 - 2y)$

Using equations to solve problems

Many mathematical problems are easier to solve when an equation is formed. In general it is a good idea to start by introducing a letter like 'x' or 'h' to stand for the unknown quantity.

Philip is thinking of a number. He tells us that when he doubles it and adds 7, the answer is 18. What number is Philip thinking of?

Suppose that Philip is thinking of the number x

He tells us that $\qquad\qquad\qquad 2x + 7 = 18$

Subtract 7 from both sides: $\qquad\qquad 2x = 11$

Divide both sides by 2 $\qquad\qquad\quad x = \frac{11}{2}$

$\qquad\qquad\qquad\qquad\qquad\qquad x = 5\frac{1}{2}$

So Philip is thinking of the number $5\frac{1}{2}$

Exercise 5

In each question I am thinking of a number. Use the information to form an equation and then solve it to find the number.

1. If we multiply the number by 3 and then add 2, the answer is 13.

2. If we multiply the number by 5 and then subtract 3, the answer is 9.

3. If we multiply the number by 6 and then add 11, the answer is 16.

4. If we multiply the number by 11 and then subtract 4, the answer is 7.

5. If we double the number and add 10, the answer is 30.

6. If we multiply the number by 10 and then subtract 4, the answer we get is the same as when we multiply the number by 7 and then add 2.

7. If we multiply the number by 6 and subtract 1, the answer we get is the same as when we double the number and add 5.

8. If we multiply the number by 7 and add 3, the answer we get is the same as when we multiply the number by 2 and add 5.

9. If we treble the number and add 10, we get the same answer as when we multiply the number by 9 and add 8.

10. If we double the number and subtract <u>from</u> 7 we get the same answer as when we treble the number and add 2.

11. If we treble the number and subtract from 8 we get the same answer as when we double the number and add 7.

12. If we double the number, subtract 11 and then add the original number we get the same answer as when we subtract the number *from* 9.

Steven is thinking of a number. When he doubles the number, adds 4 and then multiplies the result by 3, the answer is 13. What number is he thinking of?

Let the number he is thinking of be x.
He doubles it, adds 4, multiplies the result by 3.
We have, $3(2x + 4) = 13$
$6x + 12 = 13$
$6x = 1$
$x = \frac{1}{6}$
Steven is thinking of the number $\frac{1}{6}$.

Exercise 6

In each question, I am thinking of a number. Use the information to form an equation and then solve it to find the number.

1. If I subtract 2 from the number and then multiply the result by 5, the answer is 11.

2. If I double the number and then subtract 7, the answer is 4.

3. If I multiply the number by 4, add 3 and then double the result, the answer is −2.

4. If I treble the number, add 2 and then double the result, the answer is 9.

5. If I add 4 to the number and then multiply the result by 7, I get the same answer as when I subtract 1 from the number and then double the result.

6. If I multiply the number by 7 and subtract 10, I get the same answer as when I add 2 to the number and then double the result.

7. If I multiply the number by 5, subtract 2, and then multiply the result by 4, the answer I get is the same as when I double the number and then subtract 3.

8. If I double the number, add 3 and then multiply the result by 5, I get the same answer as when I double the number and then add 21.

Harder problems

The diagram shows a square.
Find the length of each side of the square
and hence find the area of the square.

A square has equal sides.
So: $5x - 8 = 3x + 2$
$5x - 3x = 2 + 8$
$2x = 10$
$x = 5$

The side of the square is $3x + 2$
With $x = 5$, $3x + 2 = 17$
∴ The side of the square $= 17$ units

Finally the area of the square $= 17 \times 17$
$= 289$ square units.

Exercise 7

1. The diagram shows a rectangle. Write an equation and solve it
   to find x.

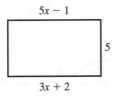

2. The length of a rectangle is three times its width. If the perimeter
   of the rectangle is 20 cm, find its width.

3. The length of a rectangle is 3 cm more than its width. If the
   perimeter of the rectangle is 30 cm, find its width.

4. In a quadrilateral ABCD, BC is twice as long as AB and AD is
   three times as long as AB. Side DC is 10 cm long. The
   perimeter of ABCD is 31 cm. Write an equation and solve it to
   find the length of AB.

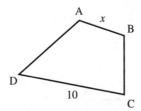

5. (a) Find x if perimeter is 18 cm.   (b) Find x if the area is 6 cm².

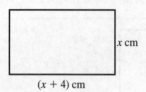

x cm

$(x + 4)$ cm

5 cm

$(x - 4)$ cm

6. Sally has 5 times as many sweets as her brother Paul, but, as she is feeling generous, she gives him 10 of hers so that they now each have the same number. How many did Paul have originally?

7. The diagram shows two angles in an isosceles triangle. Find the angles in the triangle.

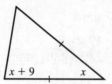

$x + 9$ x

8. In the quadrilateral, $AB = x$ cm, BC is 2 cm less than AB and CD is twice as long as BC. AD is 1 cm longer than CD. If the perimeter of the quadrilateral is 33 cm, find the length of AB.

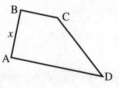

9. The total distance from P to T is 181 km. The distance from Q to R is twice the distance from S to T. R is mid-way between Q and S. The distance from P to Q is 5 km less than the distance from S to T.

Find the distance from S to T.

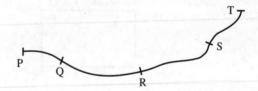

10. Ahila's prize in a competition is a giant box of Smarties. Ahila decides to share the prize equally with her friend Meera and they each start filling empty Smarties tubes with their share. After a while Meera has filled 5 tubes and has 38 Smarties left over and Ahila has filled only 3 tubes and has 152 left over. How many Smarties go into each full tube?

11. The angles of a triangle are A, B and C. Angle B is twice as big as angle A and angle C is 10 bigger than angle A.

Find the size of angle A.

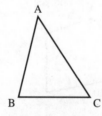

Part 3

3.1 Calculating angles

Angle facts reminder

- The angles in a triangle add up to 180°.

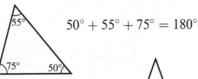

$50° + 55° + 75° = 180°$

An *isosceles* triangle has two equal angles and two equal sides. Isosceles triangles have line symmetry.

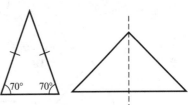

- The angles on a straight line add up to 180°.

- The angles at a point add up to 360°.

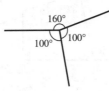

Angles in quadrilaterals

Draw a quadrilateral of any shape on a piece of paper or card and cut it out. Mark the four angles *a*, *b*, *c* and *d* and tear them off.

Arrange the four angles about a point.

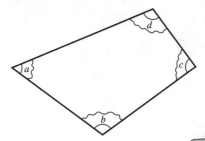

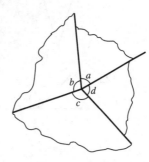

The angles in a quadrilateral add up to 360°

Exercise 1

Find the angles marked with letters.

1.

2.

3.

4.

5.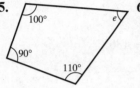

6.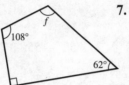

7.

8.

9.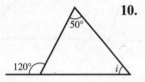

10.

11.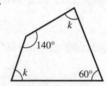

12.

13.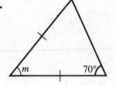

14.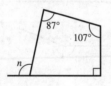

15.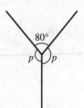

16.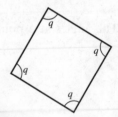

17.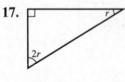

18.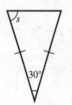

19.

20.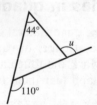

21.

22.

23.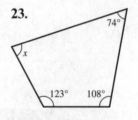

24.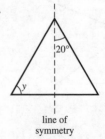

line of symmetry

Angles and parallel lines

Two straight lines are *parallel* if they never meet.
They are always the same distance apart.
In the diagram, lines AB and CD are parallel.
Lines which are parallel are marked with arrows.
The line XY cuts AB and CD.

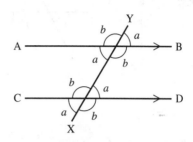

All the angles marked *a* are equal.
All the angles marked *b* are equal.
Remember:

'All the acute angles are equal and all the obtuse angles are equal.'

Many people prefer to think about 'Z' angles,
(alternate angles)

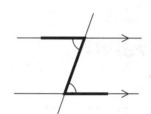

and 'F' angles (corresponding angles)

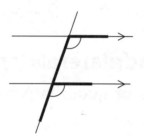

Find the angles marked with letters.

(a)

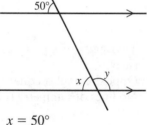

$x = 50°$
$y = 130°$

(b)

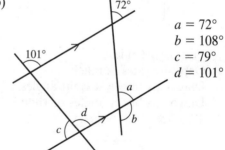

$a = 72°$
$b = 108°$
$c = 79°$
$d = 101°$

Exercise 2

Find the angles marked with letters.

1.

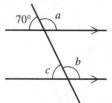

2.

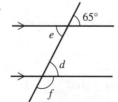

3.

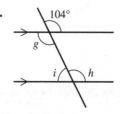

4.

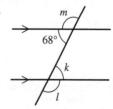

5.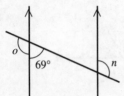

6.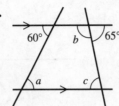

7.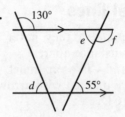

8.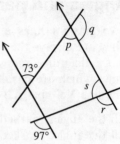

9.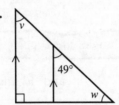

10.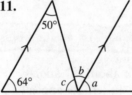

11.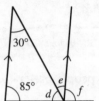

12.

3.2 Quadrilaterals and other polygons

Properties of quadrilaterals

Square: Four equal sides;
All angles 90°;
Four lines of symmetry.

Rectangle (not square): Two pairs of equal
and parallel sides;
All angles 90°;
Two lines of symmetry.

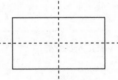

Rhombus: Four equal sides;
Opposite sides parallel;
Diagonals bisect at right angles;
Diagonals bisect angles of rhombus;
Two lines of symmetry.

Parallelogram: Two pairs of equal and parallel
sides;
Opposite angles equal;
No lines of symmetry (in general).

Trapezium: One pair of parallel sides.

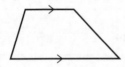

Kite: AB = AD, CB = CD;
Diagonals meet at 90°;
One line of symmetry.

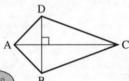

For all quadrilaterals the sum of the interior angles is 360°.

Exercise 1

1. Name each of the following shapes:
  (a) ABEH
  (b) EFGH
  (c) CDFE

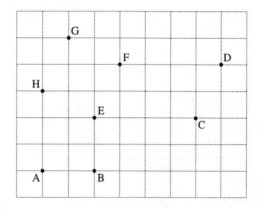

2. (a) Write down the coordinates of point D
    if ABCD is a kite
  (b) Write down the coordinates of point E
    if ABCE is a parallelogram.

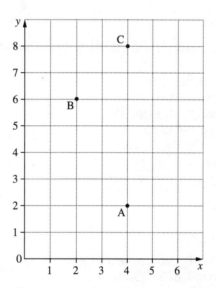

3. Copy the table and fill all the boxes with either 'Yes', 'No' or a number.

	How many lines of symmetry?	How many pairs of opposite sides are parallel?	Diagonals always equal?	Diagonals are perpendicular?
Square				
Rectangle				
Kite				
Rhombus				
Parallelogram				

4. Find the angle x.

(a)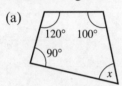

(b)
Kite

(c)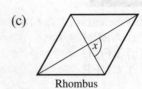
Rhombus

(d)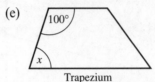
Parallelogram

(e)
Trapezium

(f)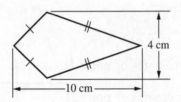
Kite

5. Find the area of the kite shown.

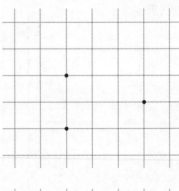

6. The diagram shows three vertices (corners) of a parallelogram. Copy the diagram and mark with crosses the *three* possible positions of the fourth vertex.

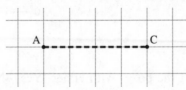

7. Line AC is one *diagonal* of a rhombus ABCD. Draw *two* possible rhombuses ABCD.

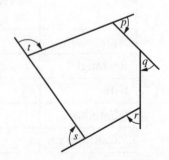

Exterior angles of a polygon

The exterior angle of a polygon is the angle between a produced side and the adjacent side of the polygon. The word 'produced' in this context means 'extended'.

If we put all the exterior angles together we see that the sum of the angles is 360°. This is true for any polygon.

- The sum of the exterior angles of a polygon = 360°.
- In a *regular* polygon all exterior angles are equal.
- For a *regular* polygon with n sides, each exterior angle $\dfrac{360}{n}$.

Exercise 2

1. Look at the polygon shown.
   (a) Calculate each exterior angle.
   (b) Check that the total of
       the exterior angles is 360°.

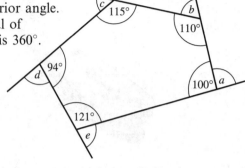

2. The diagram shows a regular decagon.
   (a) Calculate the angle *a*.
   (b) Calculate the interior angle
       of a regular decagon.

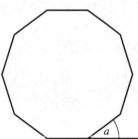

3. Find   (a) the exterior angle
          (b) the interior angle
   of a regular polygon with
   (i) 9 sides   (ii) 18 sides   (iii) 45 sides   (iv) 60 sides

4. Find the angles marked with letters.

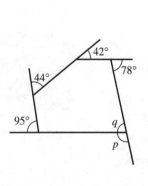
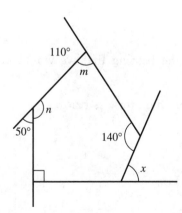

5. Each exterior angle of a regular polygon is 15°. How many sides
   has the polygon?

6. Each interior angle of a regular polygon is 140°. How many
   sides has the polygon?

7. Each exterior angle of a regular polygon is 18°. How many sides
   has the polygon?

3.3 Bearings

Bearings are used by navigators on ships
and aircraft and by people travelling in
open country.
Bearings are measured from north
in a *clockwise* direction. A bearing is
always given as a three-figure number.

A bearing of 090° is due east. If you are going south-west, you are
on a bearing 225°.

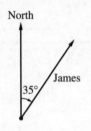

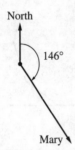

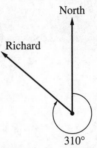

James is walking on
a bearing of 035°.

Mary is walking on
a bearing of 146°

Richard is walking on
a bearing of 310°

Relative bearings

The bearing of A *from* B is the bearing that we would take if we
wanted to travel to A *from* B.

It is helpful to draw arrows on diagrams, as below.

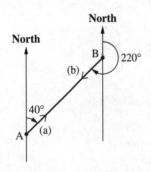

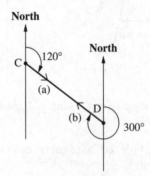

(a) The bearing of B *from* A is 040°.
(b) The bearing of A *from* B is 220°.

(a) The bearing of D *from* C is 120°.
(b) The bearing of C *from* D is 300°.

Exercise 1

1. For each diagram, write down

    (a) the bearing of B from A,
    (b) the bearing of A from B.

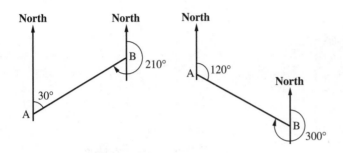
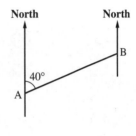

2. For each diagram, write down the bearing of C from D

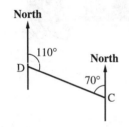
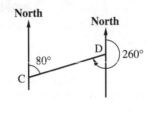
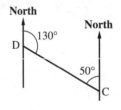

3. (a) On squared (or graph) paper mark points A and B, 8 units apart. Leave space above and below the line AB.

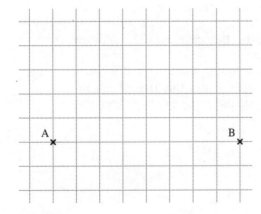

  (b) Mark the point P which is
    (i) on a bearing 070° from A
    (ii) on a bearing 320° from B.

  (d) Mark the point R which is
    (i) on a bearing 124° from A
    (ii) on a bearing 180° from B

  (c) Mark a point Q which is
    (i) on a bearing 162° from A
    (ii) on a bearing 225° from B

  (e) Measure the bearing of
    (i) P from Q
    (ii) R from Q

4. The map shows several features on and around an island. Axes are drawn to identify positions. [eg The coordinates of the cave are (9, 3).]

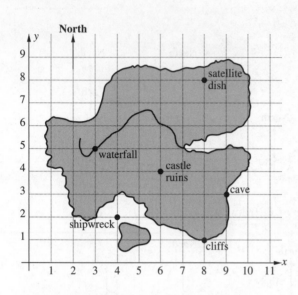

Four commandos, Piers, Quintin, Razak and Smudger, are in hiding on the island. Find the coordinates of the commandos, using the following information.

(a) The castle ruins are due south of Piers and the waterfall is due west of him.

(b) From Quintin, the bearing of the satellite dish is 045° and the shipwreck is due south of him.

(c) From Razak, the bearing of the waterfall is 315° and the bearing of the castle ruins is 045°.

(d) From Smudger, the bearing of the cave is 135° and the bearing of the waterfall is 225°.

(e) The leader of the commandos is hiding somewhere due north of the shipwreck in a hollow tree. From this tree, the castle ruins and the cliffs are both on the same bearing. Find the coordinates of this hollow tree.

Scale drawing

Some problems involving bearings can be solved using a scale drawing. Since bearings are measured from north it is convenient to use squared paper. This enables you to place your protractor accurately in a vertical position.

Begin questions by drawing a small sketch to get an idea of where the lines will go. Choose as large a scale as possible for greater accuracy.

Exercise 2

Use a scale of 1 cm to represent 1 km, unless otherwise stated.

1. Point A is 8 km due east of point B. Point C is due south of point A. The bearing of point C from point B is 137°. Find the distance between B and C.

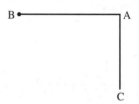

2. P is 6 km due north of Q. R is 8 km due west of Q. Find the bearing of P from R.

3. Point X is 7 km due west of point Y. Point Z is due north of point Y. The bearing of Z from X is 052°. Find the distance between X and Z.

4. A ship sails 9 km due north and then a further 6 km on a bearing 075°. How far is the ship now from its starting point?

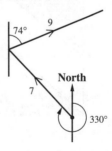

5. A ship sails 8·5 km on a bearing 118° and then a further 10 km on a bearing 021°. How far is the ship from its starting point?

6. A ship sails 7 km on a bearing 330° and then a further 9 km on a bearing 074°. How far is the ship from its starting point?

7. Point G is 9 km from F on a bearing of 130° from F. Point H is 10 km from F on a bearing of 212° from F. What is the bearing of G from H?

8. Point X is 7·2 km from Y on a bearing 215° from Y. Point X is also 8·5 km from Z on a bearing 290° *from Z*. How far is Y from Z?

3.4 Area

Rectangle

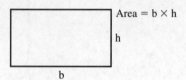

Triangle

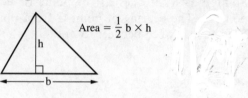

Exercise 1

Find the area of each shape All lengths are in cm.

1.

2.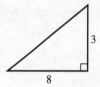

3.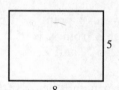

4.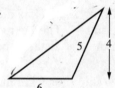

5.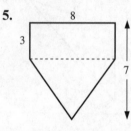

6.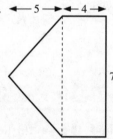

7.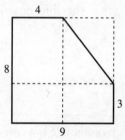

8.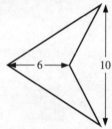

9. Find the shaded area.

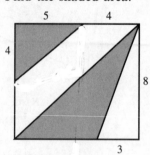

10. Find the shaded area.

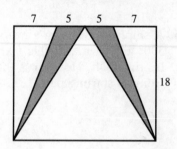

In Questions **11** to **18** the area is written inside the shape. Calculate the length of the side marked x.

11.

12.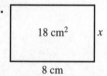

13.

14.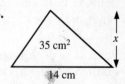

15.

16.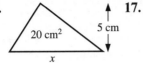

17.

18.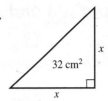

19. Here are some shapes made with centimetre squares.

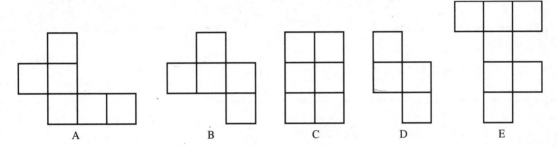

(a) Which shape has an area of $4\,\text{cm}^2$?
(b) Which shape has a perimeter of $12\,\text{cm}$?
(c) Which two shapes have the same perimeter?

20. Look at these shapes made with equilateral triangles.

  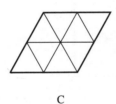 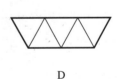 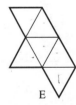

(a) Which shape has the largest area?
(b) Which shape has the same area as shape A?
(c) Which shape has the same perimeter as shape C?

21. Here are two shapes *both* with a perimeter of 32 cm.
Calculate the *area* of each shape.

length 5 3 3 width

square

22.* A gardener is spreading fertilizer on his lawn (but not the pond in the middle!). The instructions only say that 2 measures of the fertilizer will treat $10\,\text{m}^2$ of lawn. Each measure of fertilizer costs 60 p.
Find the cost of the fertilizer required.

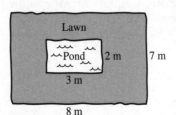

Trapezium and parallelogram

Trapezium (two parallel sides)

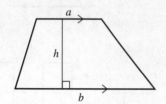

Parallelogram

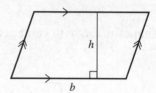

$$\text{area} = \frac{1}{2}(a + b) \times h$$

$$\text{area} = b \times h$$

Exercise 2

Find the area of each shape. All lengths are in cm.

1.
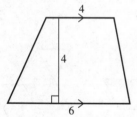

2.
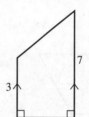

3.
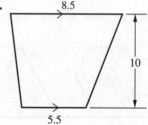

4.
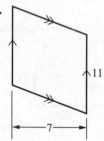

5.
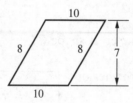

6.
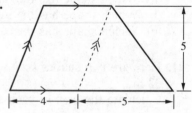

9. A triangle and a square are drawn on dotty paper with dots 1 cm apart. What is the area of the shaded region?

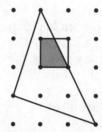

Mixed area problems

Exercise 3

1. The diagram shows a picture 20 cm by
   15 cm surrounded by a border 5 cm wide.
   What is the area of the border?

2. A rectangular lawn 17 m by 8 m is
   surrounded by a path 1 m wide. What is
   the area of the path?

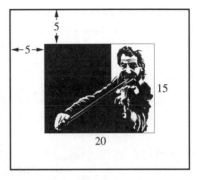

3. A wall measuring 5 m by 3·5 m is to be covered by square tiles
   measuring 50 cm by 50 cm. How many tiles are needed?

4. A rectangular area 3 m by 1·2 m is to be covered by paving slabs
   measuring 50 cm by 40 cm. What is the least number of slabs
   needed?

5. How many panes of glass 35 cm by 10 cm can be cut from a
   sheet 105 cm by 110 cm?

6. A flag has a sloping strip drawn across.
   Calculate the area of the shaded strip.

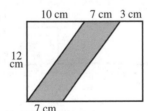

7. A rectangle has a perimeter of 28 m and a length of 6·5 m. What
   is its area?

8. The field shown is sold at £3250
   per acre. Calculate the price paid.
   [1 acre = 4840 square yards]

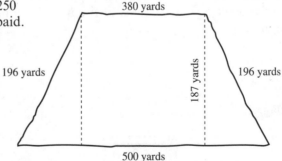

9. A groundsman has enough grass seed to cover three hectares.
   [1 hectare = 10 000 m^2]. A tennis court measures 15 m by 40 m.
   How many courts can he cover with seed?

10. A rectangular field 350 m long has an area of 7 hectares.
    Calculate the perimeter of the field.

11. A waterproofing spray is applied to the outside of the 4 walls, including the door, and the roof of the garage shown.
    (a) Calculate the total area to be sprayed.
    (b) The spray comes in cans costing £1·95 and each can is enough to cover $4\,m^2$. How much will it cost to spray this garage? [Assume you have to buy full cans].

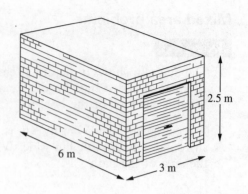

12. A gardener is using moss killer on his lawn. The instructions say that 4 measures of the mosskiller, in water, will treat $10\,m^2$ of lawn. The box contains 250 measures and costs £12·50.
    Find the area of the lawn and hence the cost of the moss killer required.

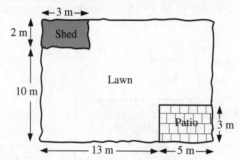

13. The shaded triangle is drawn inside a rectangle with longer side 12 cm.
    (a) If area of triangle ② = 2 × (area of triangle ①), find the length x.
    (b) If area of triangle ② = 3 × (area of triangle ①), find the length x.

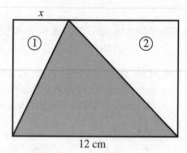

14. Here is a flag.

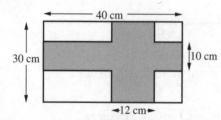

    Calculate the area of the shaded cross.

3.5 Transformations

Reflection, rotation, enlargement

- **Reflection**

  $\triangle 1$ is reflected onto $\triangle 2$

  Shape 3 is reflected onto shape 4

  The object and image are *congruent*.

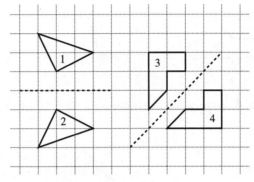

- **Rotation**

  Shape 5 is rotated 90° clockwise about the point O onto shape 6. Tracing paper is useful for rotations.

  The object and image are congruent.

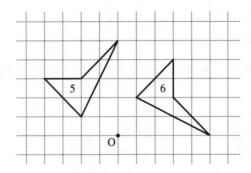

- **Enlargement**

  This picture is enlarged by a scale factor 3.

  The object and image are mathematically *similar*.

The scale factor for an enlargement can be a fraction. In this enlargement the scale factor is $\frac{1}{2}$.

In an enlargement the object and image are not congruent

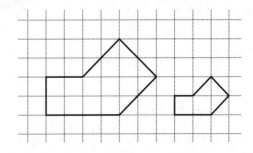

Exercise 1

In Questions **1**, **2**, **3** draw each shape and then reflect it in the broken line.

1.
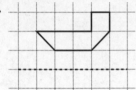

2.
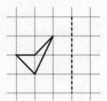

3.
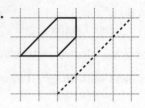

In Questions **4**, **5**, **6** draw each shape and then rotate it about the point O.

4.
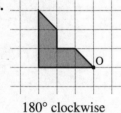

180° clockwise

5.
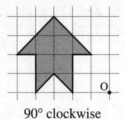

90° clockwise

6.
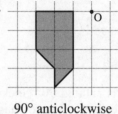

90° anticlockwise

In Questions **7**, **8**, **9** draw each shape and then enlarge it by the scale factor given.

7.

Scale factor 3

8.
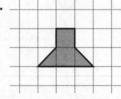

Scale factor 2

9.
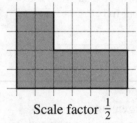

Scale factor $\frac{1}{2}$

For questions **10**, **11**, **12**, use the diagram below

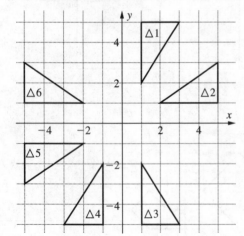

10. △1 is the image of △2 after:
    A   a reflection
    B   a rotation
    C   2 rotations
    D   2 reflections

11. △5 is the image of △2 after:
    A   rotation about (0, 0)
    B   rotation about (1, −1)
    C   reflection in $y = x$
    D   reflection in $y = -x$

12. △3 is the image of △6 after:
    A   rotation 180° about (0, 0)
    B   two reflections
    C   reflection in $y = x$
    D   reflection in $y = -x$

13. Draw axes with values from -7 to $+7$ and draw triangles with the following vertices:

$\triangle 1$: $(-6, -6)$	$(-2, -6)$	$(-2, -4)$
$\triangle 2$: $(-6, -6)$	$(-6, -2)$	$(-4, -2)$
$\triangle 3$: $(6, 2)$	$(2, 2)$	$(2, 0)$
$\triangle 4$: $(-6, 2)$	$(-2, 2)$	$(-2, 0)$
$\triangle 5$: $(6, 3)$	$(6, 7)$	$(4, 7)$

Describe fully the following rotations or reflections. For rotations, give the angle, direction and centre. For reflections, give the equation of the mirror line.

(a) $\triangle 1 \rightarrow \triangle 2$ (b) $\triangle 1 \rightarrow \triangle 3$
(c) $\triangle 1 \rightarrow \triangle 4$ (d) $\triangle 1 \rightarrow \triangle 5$

14. Draw axes with values from -7 to $+7$ and draw triangles with the following vertices:

$\triangle 1$: $(3, 1)$	$(7, 1)$	$(7, 3)$
$\triangle 2$: $(1, 3)$	$(1, 7)$	$(3, 7)$
$\triangle 3$: $(7, -1)$	$(3, -1)$	$(3, -3)$
$\triangle 4$: $(-1, -7)$	$(-3, -7)$	$(-3, -3)$
$\triangle 5$: $(-2, 2)$	$(-6, 2)$	$(-6, 0)$
$\triangle 6$: $(3, -4)$	$(3, -6)$	$(7, -6)$

Describe fully the following rotations or reflections:

(a) $\triangle 1 \rightarrow \triangle 2$ (b) $\triangle 1 \rightarrow \triangle 3$
(c) $\triangle 1 \rightarrow \triangle 4$ (d) $\triangle 1 \rightarrow \triangle 5$
(e) $\triangle 3 \rightarrow \triangle 6$

Centre of enlargement

A mathematical enlargement always has a *centre of enlargement* as well as a scale factor. The centre of enlargement is found by drawing lines through corresponding points on the object and image and finding where they intersect. For greater accuracy it is better to count squares between points because it is difficult to draw construction lines accurately over a long distance.

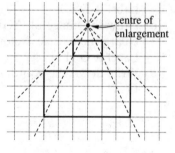

In the second diagram, $A'B'C'$ is an enlargement of ABC with scale factor 2 and centre O.

Observe that $OA' = 2 \times OA$
           $OB' = 2 \times OB$
           $OC' = 2 \times OC$

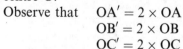

Always measure distances from the centre of enlargement.

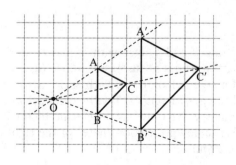

Exercise 2

In questions **1, 2, 3** copy the diagrams and then find the centre of enlargement.

1. 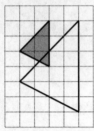   **2.**    **3.**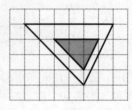

In questions **4** to **6** copy the diagram and then draw an enlargement using the scale factor and centre of enlargement given.
Leave room for the enlargement!

4.   **5.** 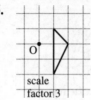   **6.**

7. Copy the diagram.
   (a) Draw the image of △ABC after an enlargement scale factor 2, centre (0, 0). Label it A′B′C′.
   (b) Draw the image of △DEF after an enlargement scale factor 2, centre (−5, 4). Label it D′E′F′.
   (c) Draw the image of △GHI after an enlargement scale factor 3, centre (−5, −2). Label it G′H′I′.
   (d) Write down the coordinates of A′, D′ and G′.

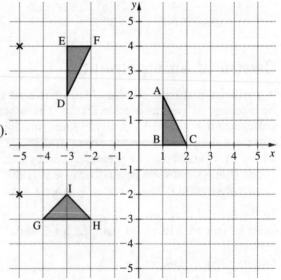

8. (a) Draw x and y axes with values from 0 to 12 and draw △1 with vertices at (6, 4), (6, 6), (5, 6).
   (b) Enlarge △1 onto △2 with scale factor 2, centre (7, 6).
   (c) Enlarge △1 onto △3 with scale factor 3, centre (6, 3).
   (d) Enlarge △1 onto △4 with scale factor 2, centre (3, 8).
   (e) Write down the coordinates of the right angled vertex of △2, △3 and △4.

Translation

In a translation an object 'shifts' from one position to another. There is no turning or reflection and the object stays the same size. A translation is described completely by its *vector*.

In the diagram:

(a) △A is mapped onto △B by the translation with vector $\begin{pmatrix} 3 \\ 2 \end{pmatrix}$.

(b) △A is mapped onto △C by the translation with vector $\begin{pmatrix} 5 \\ -2 \end{pmatrix}$.

(c) △C is mapped onto △B by the translation with vector $\begin{pmatrix} -2 \\ 4 \end{pmatrix}$.

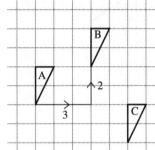

When performing a translation, concentrate your attention on *one* vertex of the shape.

The top number of a vector gives the number of units across (positive to the right). The bottom number gives the number of units up or down (positive upwards).

So $\begin{pmatrix} 5 \\ 2 \end{pmatrix}$ is 5 right → , 2 up ↑ , $\begin{pmatrix} 3 \\ -1 \end{pmatrix}$ is 3 right → 1 down ↓

Exercise 3

1. Look at the diagram shown. Write down the vector for each of the following translations:
   (a) △H → △P   (b) △E → △A
   (c) △R → △S   (d) △W → △C
   (e) △Y → △L   (f) △U → △F
   (g) △T → △A   (h) △W → △G
   (i) △O → △Y   (j) △U → △I

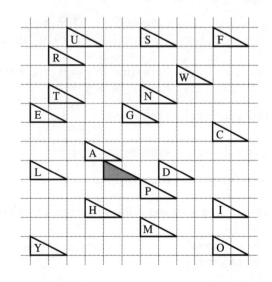

[Tracing paper will be helpful in this exercise.]

1. Copy the diagram so that you can draw construction lines.

   Draw fully each of the following transformations:
   (a) △1 → △2
   (b) △2 → △3
   (c) △3 → △4
   (d) △1 → △5
   (e) △4 → △6

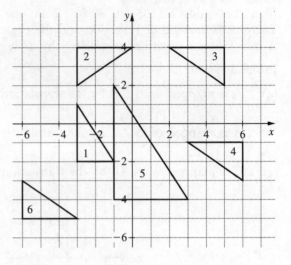

2. (a) Draw axes with x and y from -6 to $+6$.
   (b) Plot and label △1 with vertices at $(-6, -2)$, $(-6, -5)$, $(-5, -2)$.
   (c) Draw △2, △3, ... △7 as follows:
      (i) △1 → △2   Rotation in $y = x$
      (ii) △2 → △3   Rotation 180°, centre $(0, -5\frac{1}{2})$
      (iii) △3 → △4   Reflection in $y = x$
      (iv) △3 → △5   Rotation 90° anticlockwise, centre $(0, -3)$
          [Check that the right angle is at $(2, -1)$]
      (v) △5 → △6   Enlargement, scale factor 3, centre $(4, 0)$
      (vi) △5 → △7   Translation $\begin{pmatrix} -6 \\ 4 \end{pmatrix}$
   (d) Describe fully each of the following single transformations:
      (i) △7 → △6
      (ii) △1 → △4
      (iii) △2 → △5

3. (a) Draw axes with x and y from -7 to $+7$.
   (b) Plot and label △1 with vertices at $(0, 0)$, $(0, 2)$, $(3, 2)$.
   (c) Draw △2, △3, ... △7 as follows:
      (i) △1 → △2   Reflection in $y = 0$ (the x axis)
      (ii) △2 → △3   Reflection in $y = x$
      (iii) △1 → △4   Translation $\begin{pmatrix} -6 \\ 2 \end{pmatrix}$
      (iv) △4 → △5   Translation $\begin{pmatrix} 4 \\ 3 \end{pmatrix}$
      (v) △4 → △6   Reflection in $y = 0$
      (vi) △6 → △7   Reflection in $y = x$
   (d) Describe each of the following single transformations:
      (i) △1 → △3
      (ii) △1 → △5
      (iii) △2 → △7

3.6 Symmetry

Line symmetry

An object has line symmetry if we can draw a straight line through it
(usually dotted) so that it balances perfectly.

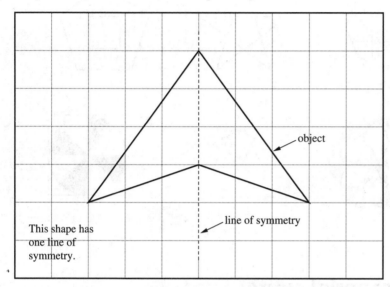

To check if a line of symmetry balances perfectly you can:-

(a) Trace over the shape on tracing paper and fold it along the line
of symmetry. If the two sections either side of the symmetry line
fit onto each other exactly, then it really is a line of symmetry.

(b) Put a small mirror onto the line of symmetry. Look into the
mirror and remove it quickly. If there was no difference in what
you saw then it must be a line of symmetry.

Rotational summetry

The shape B fits onto itself three times when rotated through a
complete turn. It has *rotational symmetry of order three*.

The shape C fits onto itself six times when rotated through a
complete turn. It has rotational symmetry of order six.

Exercise

For each shape write down (a) the number of lines of symmetry
                                     (b) the order of symmetry

1.   **2.**   **3.**   **4.**

5.   **6.** 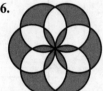 **7.**   **8.**

3.7 Metric and Imperial units

Originally measurements were made by using appropriately sized bits
of human being. The inch was measured using the thumb, (hence we
still sometimes say 'rule of thumb' when we mean rough measurement),
the foot by using the foot.

After the French Revolution in 1789 the standard unit of length
became the metre and the unit of mass became the kilogram. All the
smaller and larger units are obtained by dividing or multiplying by
ten, a hundred, a thousand and so on.

Metric units		Imperial units
Length	10 mm = 1 cm	12 inches = 1 foot
	100 cm = 1 m	3 feet = 1 yard
	1000 m = 1 km	1760 yards = 1 mile
Mass	1000 mg = 1 g	16 ounces = 1 pound
	1000 g = 1 kg	14 pounds = 1 stone
	1000 kg = 1 tonne	2240 pounds = 1 ton
Volume	1000 ml = 1 litre	8 pints = 1 gallon
	1 ml = 1 cm^3	

Exercise 1

Copy and complete

1. 57 cm =   m   **2.** 1·3 km =   m   **3.** 0·24 kg =   g   **4.** 600 g =   kg

5. 17 mm =   cm   **6.** 3000 kg =   t   **7.** 0·6 m =   cm   **8.** 14 mm =   cm

9. 2000 ml = ℓ **10.** 305 g =   kg   **11.** 80 cm =   m   **12.** 200 mm =   m

13. 2·5 t =   kg   **14.** 2·4 m =   mm   **15.** 20 g =   kg   **16.** 4·5 ℓ =   ml

17. 2 ℓ =   cm^3 **18.** 5·5 m =   cm   **19.** 56 mm =   m   **20.** 7 g =   kg

Questions **21** to **30** involve imperial units

21. 3 feet =   inches   **22.** 5 yards =   feet

23. 2 pounds =   ounces   **24.** 9 stones =   pounds

25. 24 inches =   feet   **26.** $\frac{1}{2}$ pound =   ounces

27. 2 feet 6 inches =   inches   **28.** 1 ton =   pounds

29. 8 stones 4 pounds =   pounds   **30.** 5 feet 2 inches =   inches

Questions **31** to **45** involve a mixture of metric and imperial units.

31. 0·032 kg =   g   **32.** 6 feet =   yards   **33.** 8 ounces =   pound

34. 1 mile =   feet   **35.** 235 mm =   cm   **36.** 0·42 t =   kg

37. 11·1 cm =   m   **38.** $\frac{1}{4}$ pound =   ounces   **39.** 7 litres =   ml

40. 4 yards =   feet   **41.** 7 mm =   cm   **42.** 2 gallons =   pints

43. 400 m =   km   **44.** 5 gallons =   pints   **45.** 10 miles =   yards

Converting between metric and imperial units

- It is sometimes necessary to convert imperial units into metric units and vice versa.
  Try to remember the following *approximate equivalents*:

1 inch ≈ 2·5 cm	1 kg ≈ 2 pounds
1 foot ≈ 30 cm	30 g ≈ 1 ounce
1 km ≈ $\frac{5}{8}$ mile	1 gallon ≈ 5 litres

[The '≈' sign means 'is approximately equal to'.]

- Here are some familiar objects to help you remember.

A one pound coin has a mass of about 10 grams.

A standard bag of sugar has a mass of 1 kg.

A 'tall' adult man is about 6 feet tall. [180 cm]

Exercise 2

Copy and complete using the approximate conversions given above.

1. 3 kg ≈   pounds   2. 10 inches ≈   cm   3. 4 gallons ≈   litres

4. 24 km ≈   miles   5. 5 feet ≈   cm   6. 80 kg ≈   pounds

7. 4 inches ≈   cm   8. 10 gallons ≈   litres   9. 6 feet 2 inches ≈   cm

10. All the teachers at Gibson Academy must be at least 5 feet 6 inches tall. Mr Swan is 1·70 m tall. Is he tall enough to teach at Gibson Academy?

11. A boxer must weigh no more than 10 stones just before his fight. With two days to go he weighs 65 kg.
Roughly how much weight in pounds does he have to lose to get down to the 10 stone limit?

12. A car manual states that 2 gallons of oil must be put into the engine before it is started. Roughly how much will it cost if oil costs £1·20 per litre?

13. If the speed limit on a road in Holland is 80 km/h, what is the equivalent speed limit in m.p.h.?

14. The perimeter of a farm is about 40 km. What is the approximate perimeter of the farm in miles?

15. A carpenter requires a 12 mm drill for a certain job but he has only the imperial sizes $\frac{1}{4}$, $\frac{1}{2}$ and $\frac{3}{4}$ inch.
Which of these drills is the closest in size to 12 mm?

16. At a charity cake sale all the proceeds were collected in 10p coins and then the coins were arranged in a long straight line for a newspaper photo.
If the diameter of a 10p coin is just under one inch and the line of coins was 50 metres long, roughly how much money was raised?

17.* Grass seed should be sown at the rate of $\frac{3}{4}$ of an ounce per square yard. One packet of seed contains 3 lb of seed. How many packets of seed are needed for a rectangular garden measuring 60 feet by 36 feet? [3 feet = 1 yard, 16 ounces = 1 lb]

Part 4

4.1 Representing data

Frequency charts

In the past you have learned how to draw bar charts to represent information (or *data*). In this section you will concentrate on interpreting graphs. The questions are designed to test your understanding of different situations.

The last three questions of Exercise 1 are about *Frequency Polygons*

Exercise 1

1. A nurse records the ages of all the children who visit her clinic as shown in the table. Make a tally chart to show how many children of each age were seen during the whole week.

	Ages of children in clinic								
M	2	3	1	4	7	9			
Tu	5	5	7	2	4	6			
W	6	6	3	2	4				
Th	1	1	1	1	2	1	1	1	1	1
F	4	7	8	1	3	5	4			

(a) What was the most common age of the children?
(b) The nurse thought that most of the children were aged 2 or under. Was she correct?
(c) One day of the week was reserved for a routine check-up for children of a certain age. What day do you think that was? Give a reason.

2. At a medical inspection the 11/12 year-olds in a school have their heights measured. The results are shown.

    136·8, 146·2, 141·2, 147·2, 151·3, 145·0, 155·0,
    149·9, 138·0, 146·8, 157·4, 143·1, 143·5, 147·2,
    147·5, 158·6, 154·7, 144·6, 152·4, 144·0, 151·0.

(a) Put the heights into groups

class interval	frequency
$135 \leq h < 140$	
$140 \leq h < 145$	
$145 \leq h < 150$	

(b) Draw a frequency diagram

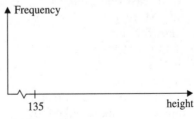

[The group '$135 \leq h < 140$' means heights greater than or equal to 135 cm and less than 140 cm]

3. The heights of the children in a
holiday camp are shown. Which of
the statements below gives the best
description of the children?

A: 'Most of the children were about
the same height.'

B: 'Most of the children were either
tall or short.'

C: 'There were far more tall children
than short children.'

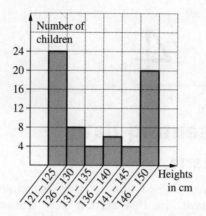

4. A class was split into two groups A and B and both groups were
given the same spelling test.

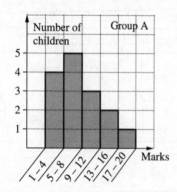
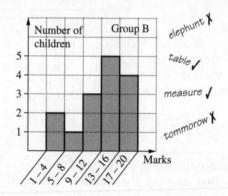

(a) How many children in group B got a mark of 13 or more?

(b) One group were allowed to learn the words on the day
before the test. Which group do you think that was?

(c) Say why you chose that group in part (b).

5. The pupils, parents and teachers at a
school baked lots of cakes for a
charity cake sale. Altogether 200
people baked at least one cake.

(a) Alice said 'More girls than boys
baked cakes for the sale.'
Decide if this statement is: 'True',
'False' or 'Cannot tell'.

(b) Explain your answer.

(c) Use the graph to work out the
mean number of cakes baked by
each of the 200 people who took
part.

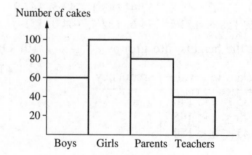

6. A farmer grows carrots in two
   different fields. In one field he uses a
   new fertilizer and in the other he uses
   the old fertilizer. The diagrams show
   the weight of the carrots he dug up
   from each field.

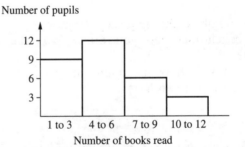

In one sentence describe what effect the new fertilizer had.

7. The graph shows the number of
   books read in one month by the
   pupils in a class.
   (a) How many pupils were in the
       class?
   (b) Can you use the graph to tell you
       exactly how many books were
       read?
   (c) Explain your answer.

8. The sport of mud wrestling is best played when the ground is
   made soft by plenty of rainfall. The World Mudwrestling
   Association (W.M.A.) have to choose a venue for the 1999
   championships. They have past rainfall data for the relevant
   month for two potential towns, Ortega and Pantena. Which
   venue would be more suitable? Explain your answer.

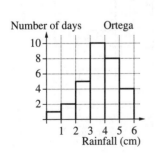

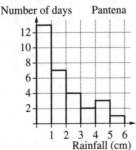

9. A teacher has a theory that pupils' test results are affected by the amount of T.V. watched at home.

With the willing cooperation of the children's parents, the pupils were split into two groups:

  Group X watched at least two hours of T.V. per day.
  Group Y watched a maximum of half an hour per day.

The pupils were given two tests: one at the start of the experiment and another test six months later. Here are the results:

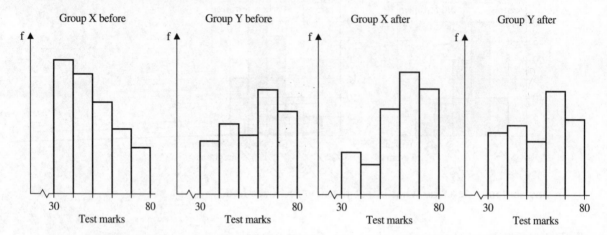

Look carefully at the frequency diagrams.

What conclusions can you draw? Was the teacher's theory correct?

Give details of how the pupils in group X and in group Y performed in the two tests.

10. A *frequency polygon* can be drawn by joining the mid-points of the tops of the bars on a frequency chart.

Frequency polygons are used mainly to compare data.

Here is a frequency chart showing the heights (or lengths!) of the babies treated at a hospital one day.

Copy the chart and complete the frequency polygon which has been started.

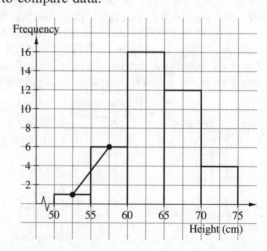

11. Using the same axes, with heights from 80 cm to 200 cm, draw frequency polygons for the heights of five year olds and sixteen year olds.

Describe briefly the main differences between the two frequency polygons.

Five year olds		Sixteen year olds	
height (cm)	frequency	height (cm)	frequency
80–90	0	120–130	0
90–100	6	130–140	2
100–110	15	140–150	3
110–120	3	150–160	4
120–130	1	160–170	7
130–140	0	170–180	6
		180–190	3
		190–200	0

12. Scientists doing research in genetic engineering altered the genes of a certain kind of rabbit. Over a period of several years, measurements were made of the adult weight of the rabbits and their lifespans. The frequency polygons below show the results.

What can you deduce from the two frequency polygons? Write one sentence about weight and one sentence about lifespan.

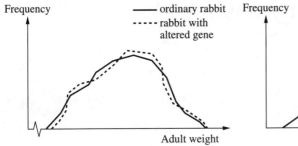

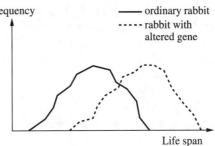

Pie charts

1. The pie chart shows the results of a survey in which 200 people were asked what they thought was the most important modern invention.
Copy this table and fill it in.

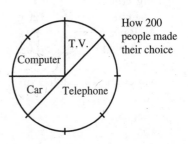

How 200 people made their choice

Choice	computer	T.V.	telephone	car
Number of people				

2. A hospital casualty department recorded the types of injuries treated one day. Altogether 200 people were treated.
(a) *About* how many people had broken bones?
(b) *About* how many people had head injuries?

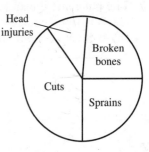

3. Lara had £24 to spend on presents.
   The pie chart shows how much she
   spent on each person.
   How much did she spend on:
   (a) her mum   (b) her dad
   (c) her brother   (d) her auntie
   (e) her friend   (f) her grandma?
   [Make sure that your answers add up to £24.]

4. This pie chart shows the afterschool activities of 200 pupils.
   (a) How many pupils do drama? [Hint: work out $360° \div 36°$]
   (b) How many pupils do sport?
   (c) How many pupils do computing?

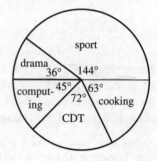

5. Opinion pollsters asked over a thousand people which TV
   channel they like best. Their answers were:

ITV	30%
Channel 4	15%
Satellite	20%
BBC1	27%
BBC2	8%

   Find the angle on a pie chart representing
   (a) Channel 4   (b) BBC1.

6. A packet of breakfast cereal weighing 480 g contains four
   ingredients:

Oats	120 g
Barley	80 g
Wheat	60 g
Rye	220 g

   Calculate the angles on a pie chart.

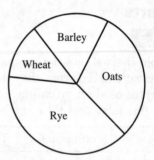

7. The pie chart illustrates the sales of four brands of petrol.
   (a) What percentage of total sales does BP have?
   (b) If Shell accounts for 35% of total sales, calculate the angles
       x and y.

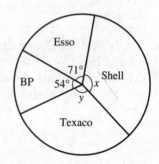

8. The children at a school were asked to state their favourite sport. Here are the results.

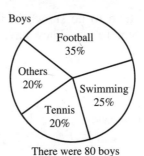

Boys

There were 80 boys

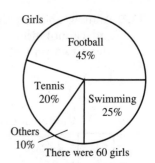

Girls

There were 60 girls

James says 'The same number of boy and girls chose tennis'.
Mel says 'More boys than girls chose swimming'.
(a) Use both charts to explain whether or not James is right.
(b) Use both charts to explain whether or not Mel is right.

9. The pie charts show how much money two shopkeepers get from selling different products.

Mr. Brown

Mrs. Evans

(a) Mr Brown gets £180 from selling ice cream. Estimate how much he gets from selling sweets.
(b) From all sales: Mr Brown gets a total of £800 and
                  Mrs Evans gets a total of £1200.
Estimate how much each shopkeeper gets from selling magazines.

10. The people in a town were asked to state which supermarket they shopped at most often. The table and the pie chart show the results.

Asda	10%
Tesco	45%
Somerfield	5%
Safeway	?
Sainsbury	?

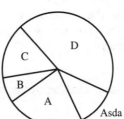

(a) Which sector, either A, B, C or D is for
  (i) Somerfield
  (ii) Tesco?
(b) In the survey more people said Sainsbury than Safeway.
  Which sector is for Sainsbury?
  Which sector is for Safeway?
(c) Estimate the percentage who said
  (i) Sainsbury
  (ii) Safeway
  [Make sure your percentages add up to 100.]

11.* Andrew and Martin intend to go snowboarding at Christmas, and cannot decide where to go. They have this information about two possible places.

Expected snow cover.

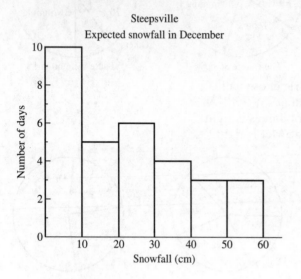

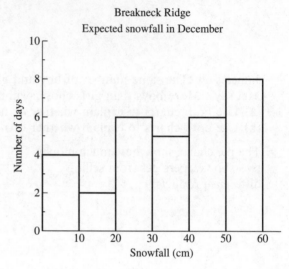

Type of slopes

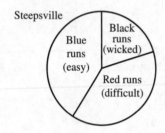

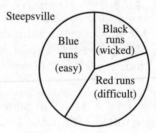

Decide where you think they should go. It doesn't matter where you decide, but you *must* say why, using the 2 types of diagram to help you explain.

12. Explain how each of the diagrams below is misleading in some way.

(a)

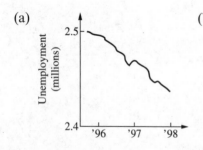

(b)

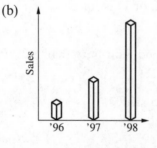

(c)

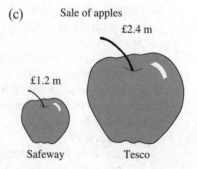

Stem and leaf diagrams

Data can be displayed in groups in a stem and leaf diagram.
Here are the marks of 20 girls in a science test.

47	53	71	55	28	40	45	62	57	64
33	48	59	61	73	37	75	26	68	39

We will put the marks into groups 20–29, 30–39,:... 70–79.
We will choose the tens digit as the 'stem' and the units as the 'leaf'.

The first four marks are shown [47, 53, 71, 55]

Stem (tens)	Leaf (units)
2	
3	
4	7
5	3 5
6	
7	1

The complete diagram is below ...... and then with the leaves in numerical order:

Stem	Leaf		Stem	Leaf
2	8 6		2	6 8
3	3 7 9		3	3 7 9
4	7 0 5 8		4	0 5 7 8
5	3 5 7 9		5	3 5 7 9
6	2 4 1 8		6	1 2 4 8
7	1 3 5		7	1 3 5

The diagram shows the shape of the distribution. It is also easy to find the mode, the median and the range.

Back-to-back stem plots

Two sets of data can be compared using a *back-to-back stem plot*.
Here are the marks of 20 boys who took the same science test as the girls above.

33	55	63	74	20	35	40	67	21	38
51	64	57	48	46	67	44	59	75	56

These marks are entered onto the back-to-back stem plot shown.

It is helpful to have a key.

Boys	Stem	Girls
1 0	2	6 8
8 5 0	3	3 7 9
8 6 4 0	4	0 5 7 8
9 7 6 5 1	5	3 5 7 9
7 7 4 3	6	1 2 4 8
5 4	7	1 3 5

key (boys)

1|5 means 51

key (girls)

2|4 means 24

Exercise 3

1. The marks of 24 children in a test are shown

41	23	35	15	40	39	47	29
52	54	45	27	28	36	48	51
59	65	42	32	46	53	66	38

Draw a stem and leaf diagram. The first three entries are shown.

Stem	Leaf
1	
2	3
3	5
4	1
5	
6	

2. Draw a stem and leaf diagram for each set of data below

(a)

| 24 | 52 | 31 | 55 | 40 | 37 | 58 | 61 | 25 | 46 |
| 44 | 67 | 68 | 75 | 73 | 28 | 20 | 59 | 65 | 39 |

(b)

| 30 | 41 | 53 | 22 | 72 | 54 | 35 | 47 |
| 44 | 67 | 46 | 38 | 59 | 29 | 47 | 28 |

Stem	Leaf
2	
3	
4	
5	
6	
7	

3. Here is the stem and leaf diagram showing the masses, in kg, of some people on a bus.
   (a) Write down the range of the masses
   (b) How many people were on the bus?
   (c) What is the median mass?

Stem (tens)	Leaf (units)
3	3 7
4	1 2 7 7 8
5	1 6 8 9
6	0 3 7
7	4 5
8	2

4. In this question the stem shows the units digit and the leaf shows the first digit after the decimal point.
   Draw the stem and leaf diagram using the following data:

2·4	3·1	5·2	4·7	1·4	6·2	4·5	3·3
4·0	6·3	3·7	6·7	4·6	4·9	5·1	5·5
1·8	3·8	4·5	2·4	5·8	3·3	4·6	2·8

key
3|7 means 3·7

Stem	Leaf
1	
2	
3	
4	
5	
6	

5. Here is a back-to-back stem plot showing the pulse rates of several people.
   (a) How many men were tested?
   (b) What was the median pulse rate for the women?
   (c) Write a sentence to describe the main features of the data.

Men		Women
5 1	4	
7 4 2	5	3
8 2 0	6	1 2
5 2	7	4 4 5 8 9
6 2	8	2 5 7
4	9	2 8

key (boys)
1|4 means 41

key (women)
5|3 means 53

4.2 Averages and range

☐ The mean
All the data is added and the total is divided by the number of items. In everyday language the word 'average' usually stands for the mean.

☐ The median
When the data is arranged in order of size, the median is the one in the middle. If there are two 'middle' numbers, the median is in the middle of these two numbers [i.e. the mean of the two numbers].

☐ The mode
The mode is the number or quality (like a colour) which occurs most often. Sometimes a set of data will have no mode, two modes or even more and this is a problem which we cannot avoid.

☐ Range
The range is not an average but is the difference between the largest value and the smallest value in a set of data. It is useful in comparing sets of data when the *spread* of the data is important.

Exercise 1

1. Find the mean, median and mode of the following sets of numbers:
(a) 4, 13, 5, 7, 9, 6, 5
(b) 6, 20, 1, 16, 2, 12, 6, 3, 8, 6, 8
(c) 13, 2, 11, 2, 10, 4, 5, 10, 8, 10

2. In several different garages the cost of one litre of petrol is
55p, 52·8p, 56·4p, 53·1p, 59p, 53·8p, 57p.
What is the median cost of one litre of petrol?

3. Six girls have heights of 1·48 m, 1·51 m, 1·47m, 1·55 m, 1·40 m and 1·59 m.
(a) Find the mean height of the six girls.
(b) Find the mean height of the remaining five girls when the tallest girl leaves.

4. The temperature outside a house was measured at midnight every day for a week. The readings were:
8°, 11°, 3°, 4°, −1°, 0°, 3°.
(a) Find the mean temperature for the whole week.
(b) Find the mean temperature for the last four days of the week.

5. Mrs Green gave birth to five babies (two girls and three boys) which weighed 1·3 kg, 1·2 kg, 1·45 kg, 1·35 kg and 1·3 kg. What was the median weight of the babies?

6. Sally throws a dice eight times and wins 20p if the median score is more than 3. The dice shows 6, 1, 2, 6, 4, 1, 3, 6. Find the median score. Does she win 20p?

7. The temperature was recorded at 0400 in seven towns across the U.K. The readings were 0°, 1°, −4°, 1°, −2°, −5°, −4°. What was the median temperature?

8. The number of occupants in the 33 houses in a street is as follows:
    2 4 3 4 1 4 2 4 1 5 2
    3 0 5 3 4 3 6 7 3 3 6
    4 1 4 2 0 1 4 3 2 5 0
    What is the modal number of occupants in the houses?

9. The test results for a class of 30 pupils were as follows:

Mark	3	4	5	6	7	8
Frequency	2	5	4	7	6	6

    What was the modal mark?

10. Find the range of the following sets of numbers:
    (a) 4, 11, 3, 8, 22, 5, 7, 30, 18
    (b) 9, 18, 100, 64, 11, 26
    (c) 4, −2, 6, 4, 5, 10, 3.

11. The range for nine numbers on a card is 60. One number is covered by a piece of blu-tac. What could that number be? [There are two possible answers.]

    55   22   13
    38   61   10
    24   44

12. There were seven people sleeping in a tent. The mean age of the people was 20 and the range of their ages was 7. Write each statement below and then write next to it whether it is *True*, *Possible* or *False*.
    (a) The oldest person in the tent was 9 years older than the youngest.
    (b) The youngest person in the tent was 18 years old.
    (c) Every person in the tent was 20 years old.

13. There were ten children on a coach journey. The mean age of the children was 11 and the range of their ages was 4. Write each statement below and then write next to it whether it is *True*, *Possible* or *False*.
    (a) The youngest child was 9 years old
    (b) Every child was 11 years old.
    (c) All the children were at least 10 years old

14.* Write down five numbers so that:
the mean is 7
the median is 6
the mode is 4.

15.* Make a list of 9 numbers (not all the same!) so that the mode, the median and the mean are all the same value.
For example: The set of numbers 5, 6, 7, 7, 10 have mode, median and mean equal to 7.
Ask a friend to check your list.

What do you understand by 'average'?

As we have seen there are three kinds of 'average' in common use: the mean, the median and the mode.
Knowing which average to choose is a matter of judgement and the choice often depends on the data.

The salaries of 9 employees of a firm are, in pounds,
8500, 8700, 8900, 9000, 9200, 9300, 9700, 13 000, 155 000.
Which 'average' salary best describes this group?

(a) There is no modal salary
(b) The median salary is £9200.
(c) The mean salary is £25 700
(d) For this set of data, the *median* is a far more typical value than the mean. The mean value is distorted by the one very high salary of £155 000.

Exercise 2

1. For the set of numbers below find the mean and the median.
3, 2, 99, 4, 1, 5, 3, 3
Which average best describes the set of numbers?

2. In a maths exam, Stephen's result was 53%. The marks obtained by the pupils in his group were

37, 39, 39, 40, 40, 41, 42, 42, 53, 90, 91, 95, 97, 99, 100 [All percentages].

When he tells his parents his mark, he also tells them what the group's 'average mark' was. Which average do you think he chose to give them if he wants his parents to think he did well? Explain your answer.

3.

The annual salaries of the workers in a small company were as follows:

25 trainees £4800 each
15 on scale A £7800 each
10 on scale B £9500 each
 2 on scale C £14 200 each
 1 manager £45 000.

The boss wants to give the impression that the average salary is fairly high. The workers' representative, on the other hand, wants to quote an average salary which is very low. Which average should each person quote?

4. In a maths exam, Joe got 54%. For the whole class the mean mark was 51% and the median mark was 57%. Which 'average' tells him whether he is in the 'top' half or the 'bottom' half of the class?

5. In an experiment, several toy cars were run until their batteries ran out of power. The length of time for which they worked was recorded. The results were

car	A	B	C	D	E	F	G	H
hours of working	12	13	11	1	10	13	14	10

(a) Find the mean and the median length of time for which the cars ran.
(b) Which figure represents the better 'average' value?

6. Which is the best average for the set of data below?

1, 1, 1, 1, 1, 1, 1, 1, 1, 2, 2, 2, 2, 3, 4, 4, 80, 110.

Give reasons for your choice.

Frequency tables

When a set of data consists of many numbers it is convenient to record the information in a frequency table. It is possible to find the mean, median and mode directly from the table as shown in the example below.

The frequency table shows the number of goals scored in 15 football matches.

number of goals	0	1	2	3	4	5 or more
frequency	2	5	4	3	1	0

(a) We *could* find the mean as follows:
$$\text{mean} = \frac{(0+0+1+1+1+1+1+2+2+2+2+3+3+3+4)}{15}$$
A better method is to multiply the number of goals by the respective frequencies.
$$\text{mean} = \frac{(0 \times 2) + (1 \times 5) + (2 \times 4) + (3 \times 3) + (4 \times 1)}{15}$$
mean = 1·73 goals (correct to 2 d.p.)

(b) The median is the 8th number in the list, when the numbers are arranged in order. The median is, therefore, 2 goals.

(c) The modal number of goals is 1, since more games had 1 goal than any other number.

Exercise 3

1. The frequency table shows the weights of 30 eggs laid by the hens on a free range farm.

weight	44 g	48 g	52 g	56 g	60 g
frequency	5	6	7	9	3

Find the mean weight of the eggs.

2. The frequency table shows the weights of the 40 pears sold in a shop.

weight	70 g	80 g	90 g	100 g	110 g	120 g
frequency	2	7	9	11	8	3

Calculate the mean weight of the pears.

3. The frequency table shows the price of a Mars bar in 30 different shops.

price	49p	50p	51p	52p	53p	54p
frequency	2	3	5	10	6	4

Calculate the mean price of a Mars bar.

4. The marks, out of 10, achieved by 25 teachers in a spelling test were as follows:

mark	5	6	7	8	9	10
frequency	8	7	4	2	3	1

mite	✗
might	✓
goal	✓
gole	✗
paralel	✗
thay	✗

Find (a) the mean mark
     (b) the median mark
     (c) the modal mark.

5. The table shows the weight of 29 parcels in a *grouped* data table.

We can obtain an *estimate* for the mean weight of the parcels by *assuming* that all the parcels in each interval have the weight at the mid-point of the interval.

So we are assuming that we have 6 parcels weighing 2·5 kg, 12 parcels weighing 7·5 kg, 8 parcels weighing 12·5 kg and so on.

Weight (kg)	Mid-point	Frequency
0–5	2·5	6
5–10	7·5	12
10–15	12·5	8
15–20	17·5	2
20–25	22·5	1

Copy and complete the working below,

$$\text{Mean weight} = \frac{(2\cdot5 \times 6) + (7\cdot5 \times 12) + (12\cdot5 \times 8) + (17\cdot5 \times 2) + (22\cdot5 \times 1)}{29}$$

$$= \boxed{} \text{ kg to 2 s.f.}$$

6. The heights of 30 children were measured and are shown in the table.
   (a) Calculate an estimate of the mean height of the children.
   (b) Why is your answer only an *estimate* of the mean height?

Height (cm)	Mid-point	Frequency
110–120	115	6
120–130		10
130–140		8
140–150		4
150–160		2

7. In an archeological dig, several Roman coins were found. The weights of the coins are shown in the table.
   Calculate an estimate for the mean weight of the coins.

Weight (g)	Mid-point	Frequency
4–7	5·5	5
7–10		10
10–13		15
13–16		7
16–19		4
19–22		2
22–25		2

4.3 Probability

Methods of estimating probability

The probability of an event is a measure of the chance of it happening. Probability is measured on a scale from 0 to 1. An event which is impossible has a probability of 0. An event which is certain has a probability of 1.

There are four different ways of estimating probabilities.

Method A

Use symmetry

- The probability of rolling a 3 on a fair dice is $\frac{1}{6}$.
  This is because all the scores 1, 2, 3, 4, 5, 6 are equally likely.
- Similarly the probability of getting a head when tossing a fair coin is $\frac{1}{2}$.

Method B

Conduct an experiment or survey to collect data

- Suppose I wanted to estimate the probability of a drawing pin landing point upwards when dropped onto a hard surface. I could not use symmetry for obvious reasons but I could conduct an experiment to see what happened in say 500 trials.

- I might want to know the probability that the next car going past the school gates has only one occupant.
  I could conduct a survey in which the number of people in cars is recorded over a period of time.

Method C

Look at past data

Suppose I wanted to estimate the probability that there will be snow in the ski resort to which a school party is going in February next year. I could look at weather records for the area over the last 10 or 20 years.

Method D
Make a subjective estimate

We have to use this method when the event is not repeatable. It is not really a 'method' in the same sense as are methods A, B, C.

- We might want to estimate the probability of England beating France in a soccer match next week. We could look at past results but these could be of little value for all sorts of reasons. We might consult 'experts' but even they are notoriously inaccurate in their predictions.

Exercise 1

In Questions **1** to **14** state which method A, B, C or D you would use to estimate the probability of event given.

1. The probability of drawing a 'king' from a pack of playing cards.

2. The probability that it will rain every day at the site where the school party is going on a camping holiday next year.

3. The probability that a person selected at random would vote 'Conservative' in a general election tomorrow.

4. The probability that your maths teacher will pick the winning six numbers in the National Lottery next week. [There are 13 983 816 ways of choosing 6 numbers from 1 to 49.]

5. The probability that a letter posted 'first class' at 8.00 a.m. today will arrive at its destination tomorrow.

6. The probability that the England cricket team will win the toss in their next three test matches.

7. The probability that someone in your class will be the parent of twins within the next 20 years.

8. The probability that you will throw a 'double' when you roll a pair of fair dice.

9. The probability that the Eurostar leaving London at 9 o'clock tomorrow will arrive in Paris within 10 minutes of the scheduled arrival time.

10. The probability that the headteacher of your school was born in the same month as the prime minister.

11. The probability that at least one person in a party of 50 will break a leg in the next school ski trip.

12. The probability that a person who smokes will suffer from lung cancer later in life.

13. The probability of spinning a '10' on a roulette wheel which is suspected of being biased.

14. The probability that sometime this week your mother will ask you to tidy your bedroom (unnecessarily!)

Working out probabilities

For simple events, like throwing a dice or selecting a ball from a bag, symmetry can be used to work out the expected probability of the event occurring.

$$\text{Expected probability} = \frac{\text{the number of ways the event can happen}}{\text{the number of possible outcomes}}$$

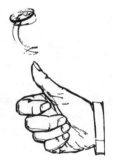

When an experiment (like rolling a dice or tossing a coin) is repeated several times, we can calculate the number of times we expect an event to occur. Call the event in which we are interested a 'success'.

Expected number of successes = (probability of a success) × (number of trials)

(a) Seven discs numbered 3, 4, 5, 7, 9, 11, 12 are placed in a bag. One disc is selected at random.

In this example there are 7 possible outcomes of a trial.
(i) $p\,(\text{selecting a '5'}) = \frac{1}{7}$
(ii) $p\,(\text{selecting an odd number}) = \frac{5}{7}$
(iii) $p\,(\text{selecting a '10'}) = 0$

(b) A fair dice is rolled 540 times. How many times would you expect to roll a '2'.

$p\,(\text{rolling a 2}) = \frac{1}{6}$
$\text{Expected number of 2's} = \frac{1}{6} \times 540$
$= 90$

Some events can either 'happen' or 'not happen'.

Probability of an event not happening = 1 − (Probability of the event happening)

(a) The spinner shown has equal sectors.

(i) p (spinning a 3) $= \frac{1}{8}$

(ii) p (not spinning a 3) $= 1 - \frac{1}{8} = \frac{7}{8}$

(b) The probability of a drawing pin landing 'point up' is 0·61.

Therefore, the probability of the drawing pin landing 'point down' is $1 - 0·61 = 0·39$.

Exercise 2

1. One card is picked at random from a pack of 52.
Find the probability that it is
(a) the Queen of diamonds
(b) a ten
(c) a diamond.

2. Ten discs numbered 1, 3, 3, 3, 4, 7, 8, 9, 11, 11 are placed in a bag. One disc is selected at random.
Find the probability that it is
(a) an even number
(b) a three
(c) less than 6.

3. David puts these numbered discs in a bag.
(a) He shakes the bag and takes one disc without looking. What number is he most likely to get?
(b) Erica wants to put discs in a bag so that it is *less likely* that she will pick a 3 than a 2.
What discs could she put in her bag?
(c) Gary has got these discs in his bag.
He wants to put some more discs in the bag to make it equally likely that he will pick a 1, a 2 or a 3. What discs should he add?

Gary's discs

4. There are 12 balls in a bag. Natasha takes a ball from the bag, notes its colour and then returns the ball to the bag. She does this 20 times.
Here are her results.

(a) What is the smallest number of red balls there *could* be in the bag?
(b) Natasha says 'There cannot be any yellow balls in the bag because there are no yellows in my table.'
Explain why Natasha is wrong.
(c) Natasha takes one more ball from the bag. What is the most likely colour of the ball?

Red	5
White	1
Green	11
Blue	3

5. This is Sarita's spinner.

(a) She thinks that the probability of spinning a 3 is $\frac{1}{5}$ because there are five numbers. Explain why this is wrong. Make a better estimate of the probability of spinning a 3.

(b) Use percentages to make a rough estimate of the probability of spinning each number. E.g. 'The probability of spinning a '1' is about 10%'

(c) How can you check that the total of the probabilities is correct?

6. A bag contains 9 balls: 3 red, 4 white and 2 yellow.

(a) Find the probability of selecting a red ball.

(b) The 2 yellow balls are replaced by 2 white balls. Find the probability of selecting a white ball.

7. Mark played a card game with Paul. The cards were dealt so that both players received two cards. Mark's cards were a five and a four. Paul's first card was a six.

Mark   Paul

Find the probability that Paul's second card was

(a) a five

(b) a picture card [a King, Queen or Jack].

8. One ball is selected at random from the bag shown and then replaced. This procedure is repeated 400 times. How many times would you expect to select:

(a) a blue ball,

(b) a white ball?

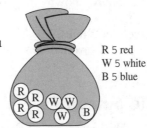

R 5 red
W 5 white
B 5 blue

9. A spinner, with 12 equal sectors, is spun 420 times. How often would you expect to spin:

(a) an E,

(b) an even number,

(c) a vowel?

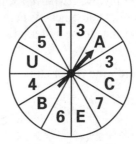

10. Heena puts 4 white balls and 1 black ball in a bag. She then takes out one ball without looking.

    (a) Heena asks her parents about the probability of getting a black.

    Her mum says,   Her dad says,
    'It is $\frac{1}{4}$ because there are   'It is $\frac{1}{5}$ because there are
    4 whites and 1 black.'   5 balls and only 1 black.'

    Which of her parents is correct?

    (b) Carl has another bag containing red and white balls. The probability of picking a red ball from Carl's bag is $\frac{4}{7}$. What is the probability of picking a white ball from Carl's bag?

    (c) How many balls of each colour *could* be in Carl's bag?

    (d) Write down another possibility for the number of balls of each colour that could be in Carl's bag.

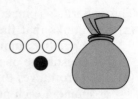

11. The number of people visiting Tower Bridge one day was 11,249. How many of these people would you expect to celebrate their birthdays on a Tuesday in the year 2000?

12. When playing Monopoly, Philip knows that the probability of throwing a 'double' with two dice is $\frac{1}{6}$. What is the probability that he does *not* throw a double with his next throw?

13. Keven bought one ticket in a raffle in which 200 tickets were sold. What is the probability that Kevin did not win the first prize?

14. A coin is biased so that the probability of tossing a head is 56%.

    (a) What is the probability of tossing a tail with this coin?

    (b) How many tails would you expect when the coin is tossed 500 times?

15.* One ball is selected from a bag containing x red balls and y blue balls. What is the probability of selecting a red ball?

16.* In a game at a fair, players pay the stall holder 25p to spin the pointer on the board shown. Players win the amount shown by the pointer.
    The game is played 960 times.
    Work out the expected profit or loss for the stallholder.

Listing possible outcomes

When an experiment involves two events, it is usually helpful to make a list of all the possible outcomes. When there is a large number of outcomes, it is important to be systematic in making the list.

- Coins
  Using H for 'head' and T for 'tail', two coins can land as:

H	H
H	T
T	H
T	T

- Two dice
  When a red dice is thrown with a white dice, the outcomes are (red dice first):
  (1, 1), (1, 2), (1, 3), (1, 4), (1, 5), (1, 6), (2, 1), (2, 2), (2, 3)...(6, 6).

The 36 equally likely outcomes can be shown on a grid. Point A shows a 4 on the red dice and a 5 on the white dice. Point B shows a 2 on the red dice and a 4 on the white dice.

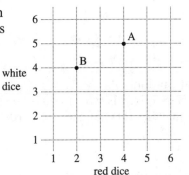

- The probability of a combined event can be found using the formula:

$$\text{probability of an event} = \frac{(\text{number of ways in which the event can happen})}{(\text{number of possible outcomes})}$$

For example the probability of getting of total of 3 when rolling two dice is $\frac{2}{36}$ because you can get a total of 3 in two different ways.

Exercise 3

1. A 10p coin and a 20p coin are tossed together. List all the possible outcomes, heads or tails, for the two coins.

2. A red dice and a white dice are thrown together.
   (a) Draw a grid to show all the possible outcomes.
   (b) How many ways can you get a total of four on the two dice?

3. Katy has these two spinners. She spins both spinners and adds up the numbers to get a total. For example a '10' and a '2' give a total of 12.
   Make a list of all the possible totals.

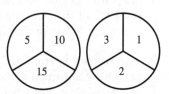

4. A bag contains a 2p coin, a 5p coin and a 10p coin. Two coins are selected at random.
   (a) List all the possible combinations of two coins which can be selected from the bag.
   (b) Find the probability that the total value of the two coins selected is
       (i)   15p
       (ii) 7p
       (iii) 20p

5. The four cards shown are shuffled and placed face down on a table.

Two cards are selected at random.
(a) List all the possible pairs of cards which could be selected.
(b) Find the probability that the total of the two cards is
  (i)   5
  (ii) 9

6. Two dice are rolled together and the
difference is found.
In the grid the point X has a difference of 3
obtained by rolling a 2 and a 5.

Find the expected probability of obtaining a
difference of   (a) 3
                  (b) 0

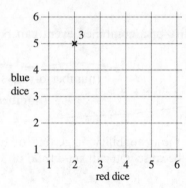

7. A coin and a dice are tossed together.
(a) List all the possible outcomes.
(b) Find the probability of getting
  (i)   a head on the coin and a 6 on the dice
  (ii) a tail on the coin and an even number on the dice.

8. Four friends, Jen, Ken, Len and Mick, each write their name on
a card and the four cards are placed in a hat. Two cards are
chosen to decide who does the washing-up that day.
(a) List all the possible combinations.
(b) What is the probability that Ken and Len are chosen?

9. The spinner is spun and the dice is rolled at the same time.
(a) Draw a grid to show all the possible outcomes.
(b) A 'win' occurs when the number on the spinner is greater
    than the number on the dice.
    Find the probability of a 'win'.

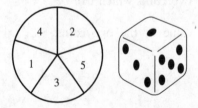

Relative frequency

Ben, Sue and Neil are rolling a dice which they suspect is biased so that it gives a 'six' more frequently than it would if it was fair.

Ben rolls 7 sixes in 20 throws
Sue rolls 20 sixes in 80 throws
Neil rolls 197 sixes in 600 throws

> If the dice shows a 'six' on x occasions out of a total number of N trials, the *relative frequency* of rolling a six is $\dfrac{x}{N}$.

For Ben, relative frequency $= \frac{7}{20} = 0.35$
For Sue, relative frequency $= \frac{20}{80} = 0.25$
For Neil, relative frequency $= \frac{197}{600} = 0.33$ (to 2 d.p.)

Whose results give the most reliable estimate for the probability of rolling a six with this particular dice?
We can take the *relative frequency* of an event occurring as an estimate of the *probability* of that event occurring. The estimate improves as the number of trials is increased.
Discuss this with your teacher.

Exercise 4

1. Karim randomly selects a card from a pack and notes whether it is a Heart, Spade, Diamond or Club. Here are his results:
   S H D S S C H C C S D H H C S
   C H C D S D H C D S H S S C H
   (a) What was the relative frequency of selecting a Heart?
   (b) What was the relative frequency of selecting a Diamond?

2. In an experiment Tom drops 12 drawing pins onto a hard floor. He does the experiment 10 times and counts how many pins land 'point up'. His results were

Number of the 12 drawing pins that landed 'point up'									
3	5	6	2	4	7	3	3	4	5

   (a) Use Tom's data to work out the probability that a *single* drawing pin will land point up.
   (b) Tom continues the experiment until he has dropped the 12 drawing pins 100 times.
   About how many drawing pins in total would you expect to land point up?

3. Four friends are using a spinner for a game and they wonder if it is perfectly fair. They each spin the spinner several times and record the results.

Name	Number of spins	Results		
		0	1	2
Alan	30	12	12	6
Keith	100	31	49	20
Bill	300	99	133	68
Ann	150	45	73	32

(a) Whose results are most likely to give the best estimate of the probability of getting each number?
(b) Make a table and collect together all the results.
Use the table to decide whether or not you think the spinner is biased or unbiased.
(c) Use the results to work out the probability of the spinner getting a '2'.

4. The RAN# button on a calculator generates random numbers between ·000 and ·999. It can be used to simulate tossing three coins. We could say any *odd* digit is a *tail* and any *even* digit is a head. So the number ·346 represents THH

Use the RAN# button to simulate the tossing of three coins

'Toss' the three coins 100 or 200 times and work out the relative frequency of getting three heads.
Compare your result with the value that you would expect to get theoretically.

Exclusive events

Events are *mutually exclusive* if they cannot occur at the same time.

Examples

- Selecting a Queen } from a pack
  Selecting a 3 } of cards

- Tossing a 'head'
  Tossing a 'tail'

- Selecting a red ball from a bag
  Selecting a white ball from the same bag.

The sum of the probabilities of mutually exclusive events is 1

The probability of something happening is 1 minus the probability of it not happening

A bag contains balls which are either red, white or green.
The probability of selecting a red ball is 0·1
The probability of selecting a white ball is 0·6
Find the probability of selecting a green ball.

The three events 'selecting a red', 'selecting a white' and 'selecting a green' are exclusive.
The sum of the probabilities is 1.

∴ p (selecting a green) $= 1 - (0·1 + 0·6)$
                         $= 0·3$

Exercise 5

1. A bag contains a large number of balls including some green balls. The probability of selecting a green ball is $\frac{1}{4}$. What is the probability of selecting a ball which is not green?

2. The spinner has 8 equal sectors. Find the probability of:
   (a) spinning a 4
   (b) not spinning a 4
   (c) spinning a 1
   (d) not spinning a 1
   (e) spinning a 3
   (f) not spinning a 3.

3. A scientist studying lions has found that the probability that a lioness gives birth to a female cub is 0·63. What is the probability that the cub will be male?

4. A bag contains balls which are either red, blue or yellow.
   The probability of selecting a red is 0·3
   The probability of selecting a blue is 0·4
   What is the probability of selecting a yellow?

4.4 Scatter graphs

Sometimes it is important to discover if there is a connection or relationship between two sets of data.

Here is a scatter graph showing the test marks of some pupils in a maths test and a science test.

We can see a connection: the pupils who got a high mark in science generally got a high mark in maths.

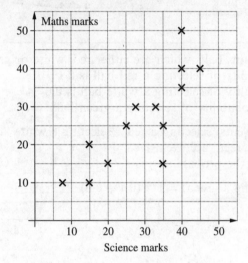

1. Here are the heights and masses of 9 people. Draw the axes shown and complete the scatter graph.

Name	Mass (kg)	Height (cm)
Alice	45	115
Fred	60	160
Jack	65	155
John	55	125
Percy	75	160
Hugh	75	170
Mabel	65	140
Diana	85	180
Cyril	52	146

(a) Who is 125 cm tall?

(b) Who weighs 52 kg?

(c) How many people are over 142 cm tall?

(d) How many people weigh less than 70 kg?

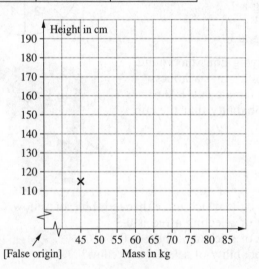

2. The scatter graph shows the number of hot drinks
sold by a cafe and the outside temperature.
(a) On how many days was it less than 12°C?
(b) How many hot drinks were sold when it was
35°C?
(c) On how many days were 40 or more hot drinks
sold?
(d) Fill the blank with either 'increases' or
'decreases': As temperature *increases* the number
of drinks sold _____.

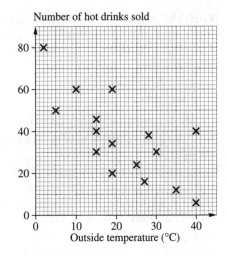

3. The graph shows the scores in a
spelling test and the shoe sizes of
14 children.
(a) How many take size 6 or less?
(b) The pass mark is 4 or more.
How many people failed?
(c) Is there a connection between
a person's shoe size and test
score?

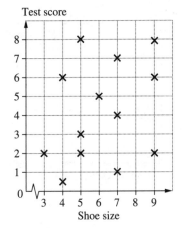

Correlation

The word correlation describes how things *co-relate*. There is
correlation between two sets of data if there is a connection or
relationship.

The correlation between two sets of data can be positive or negative
and it can be strong or weak as indicated by the scatter graphs
below.

strong positive
correlation

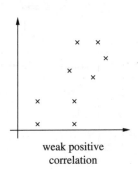

weak positive
correlation

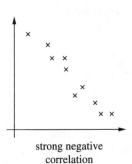

strong negative
correlation

When the correlation is positive the points are around a line which slopes upwards to the right. When the correlation is negative the 'line' slopes downwards to the right.

When the correlation is strong the points are bunched close to a line through their midst. When the correlation is weak the points are more scattered.

It is important to realise that often there is *no* correlation between two sets of data.

If, for example, we take a group of students and plot their maths test results against their time to run 800 m, the graph might look like the one on the right. A common mistake in this topic is to 'see' a correlation on a scatter graph where none exists.

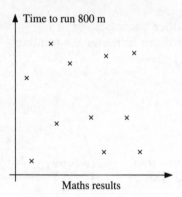

There is also *no* correlation in these two scatter graphs.

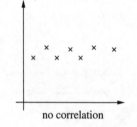

no correlation

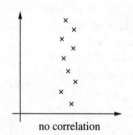

no correlation

Exercise 2

1. Make the following measurements for everyone in your class:

height	(nearest cm)
armspan	(nearest cm)
head circumference	(nearest cm)
hand span	(nearest cm)
pulse rate	(beats/minute)

For greater consistency of measuring, one person (or perhaps 2 people) should do all the measurements of one kind (except on themselves!)

Enter all the measurements in a table, either on the board or on a sheet of paper.

Name	Height	Armspan	Head
Roger	161	165	56 cm
Liz	150	148	49 cm
Gill			

(a) Draw the scatter graphs shown below

(i) arm span

height

(ii) hand span

pulse

(b) Describe the correlation, if any, in the scatter graphs you drew in part (a).

(c) (i) Draw a scatter graph of two measurements where you think there might be positive correlation.

  (ii) Was there indeed a positive correlation?

2. Plot the points given on a scatter graph, with s across the page and p up the page. Draw axes with values from 0 to 20. Describe the correlation, if any, between the values of s and p. [i.e. 'strong negative', 'weak positive' etc.]

(a)

s	7	16	4	12	18	6	20	4	10	13
p	8	15	6	12	17	9	18	7	10	14

(b)

s	3	8	12	15	16	5	6	17	9
p	4	2	10	17	5	10	17	11	15

(c)

s	11	1	16	7	2	19	8	4	13	18
p	5	12	7	14	17	1	11	8	11	5

3. Describe the correlation; if any, in these scatter graphs.

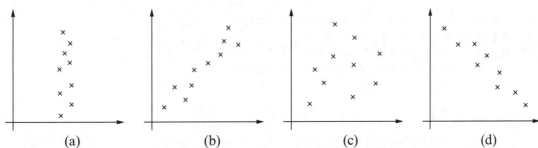

(a)   (b)   (c)   (d)

4. The table shows the marks of 7 students in the two papers of a science examination.

Paper 1	35	10	60	17	43	55	49
Paper 2	26	15	40	15	30	34	35

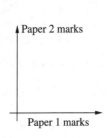

(a) Plot the marks on a scatter diagram, using a scale of 1 cm to 5 marks.

(b) A student got a mark of 25 on paper 1 but missed paper 2. What would you expect her to get on paper 2?

5. The table shows the mean weight of the apples from a certain apple tree together with the latitude of the farm where the tree was growing

Latitude (°N)	37	50	32	45	36	30	44
Mean weight of apples (g)	100	70	115	75	110	120	80

(a) Draw a scatter graph, using a scale of 1 cm to 5 g across the page and 2 cm to 5° up the page.

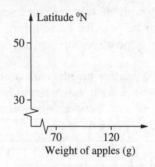

(b) What would you expect the mean weight of the apples to be on a farm at latitude 42°N?

6. Suppose scatter graphs were drawn, with the quantities below on the two axes. What sort of correlation, if any, would you expect to see in each case?
(a) height of a man; height of the man's father
(b) a person's pulse rate; a person's reaction time
(c) outside temperature; consumption of energy for heating a home
(d) value of a car; mileage of the car [for the same kind of car]
(e) price of goods in U.K; price of similar goods in Germany
(f) number of ice creams sold; outside temperature
(g) exposure to sun; degree of sunburn
(h) use of a calculator; ability to do mental arithmetic
(i) length of time sleeping; rate of growth of fingernails

Line of best fit

When a scatter graph shows either positive or negative correlation, a *line of best fit* can be drawn. The sums of the distances to points on either side of the line are equal and there should be an equal number of points on each side of the line. The line is easier to draw when a transparent ruler is used.

Here are the marks obtained in two tests by 9 students.

Student	A	B	C	D	E	F	G	H	I
Maths mark	28	22	9	40	37	35	30	23	?
Physics mark	48	45	34	57	50	55	53	45	52

A line of best fit can be drawn as there is strong positive correlation between the two sets of marks.

The line of best fit can be used to estimate the maths result of student I, who missed the maths test but scored 52 in the physics test.
We can *estimate* that student I would have scored *about* 33 in the maths test. It is not possible to be *very* accurate using scatter graphs. It is reasonable to state that student I 'might have scored between 30 and 36' in the maths test.

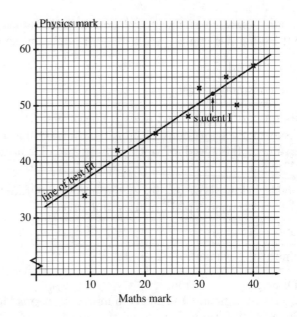

Exercise 3

1. Plot the points given on a scatter graph, with m across the page and t up the page. Draw axes with values from 0 to 20. Draw a line of best fit

m	5	16	20	2	18	16	4	7
t	12	6	3	14	4	4	12	10

What value would you expect for t when m is 12?

2. The following data gives the marks of 11 students in a French test and in a German test.

French	15	36	36	22	23	27	43	22	43	40	26
German	6	28	35	18	28	28	37	9	41	45	17

(a) Plot this data on a scatter graph, with the French marks on the horizontal axis.
(b) Draw the line of best fit.
(c) Estimate the German mark of a student who got 30 in French.
(d) Estimate the French mark of a student who got 45 in German.

3. The data below gives the petrol consumption figures of cars, with the same size engine, when driven at different speeds.

Speed (m.p.h.)	30	62	40	80	70	55	75
Petrol consumption (m.p.g)	38	25	35	20	26	34	22

(a) Plot a scatter graph and draw a line of best fit.
(b) Estimate the petrol consumption of a car travelling at 45 m.p.h.
(c) Estimate the speed of a car whose petrol consumption is 27 m.p.g.

4. The table below show details of the number of rooms and the number of occupants of 11 houses in a street.

Number of rooms	2	3	7	11	7	5	5	11	5	6	4
Number of occupants	2	8	5	2	6	2	7	7	4	0	1

(a) Draw a scatter graph
(b) Can you estimate the likely number of people living in a house with 9 rooms? If so, what is the number?
Explain your answer.

5. Look at the scatter graph of height against armspan which you drew for question **1** of the last exercise.
(a) Draw a line of best fit on your graph.
(b) A person of height 161 cm enters the room. Estimate the armspan of that person.

6. A professional golfer was thinking about the factors which might affect his golf scores. He drew the three graphs below.

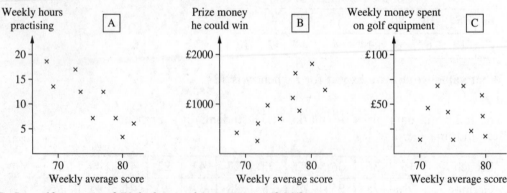

[N.B. In golf a score of 70 is *better* than a score of 80!]
(a) What does graph A show about the relationship between the weekly hours practising and his weekly average score?
(b) What does graph B show about the relationship between the amount of prize money he could win and his weekly average score?
(c) One week he spent 15 hours practising and he spent £50 on golf equipment. Explain how you could estimate the average score for that week.

4.5 Collecting data

- Statistical methods can be used to answer many questions.
  Examples: 'Which subject do people find most difficult in school?'
  'Are young people more superstitious than older people?'

- A question can often be tested by conducting a survey in which a
  large number of people respond to a questionnaire.
  When you design a questionnaire you should think ahead to how
  you will display your results. In general graphs or charts are
  easier for other people to understand than tables of numbers.
  You might use:
  Pie charts;
  Bar charts;
  Scatter graphs;
  Frequency
  polygons.

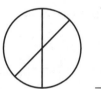

Questionnaire design

There are several points to consider when designing a questionnaire.

- Keep it as short and simple as possible.
  - People are (quite rightly) not prepared to spend a long time
    filling in forms.
- Do not ask questions if they are not relevant.
  - Do not ask for the person's name unless you have to. People
    are more likely to cooperate if their replies are anonymous.
- Try not to ask questions that require written replies.
  - You may get a hundred different points of view which
    makes analysing the answers extremely difficult. It is much
    better to ask questions that can be answered with yes/no or
    by ticking an appropriate box. Do not *only* questions which
    can be answered yes/no.
- Try to avoid personal questions.
  - If you ask someone their age, weight or income they will
    often be inclined to give you false information. A better
    approach would be to ask 'Which category do you fall
    into?'

| under 16 | 16–19 | 20–29 | 30–49 | 50 or over |

- Make sure you cover all possibilities.
  - Do not leave a person thinking 'I don't belong to any of
    those categories'.
- Do not ask questions in such a way that the person feels forced to
  agree.

Example 1.   Most people would find it difficult to say 'no' to a question such as, 'Don't you agree that the cruel and inhumane way of transporting live animals should be abolished'.

Example 2.   Do *not* ask: 'Do you agree that pupils in this school are given too much homework?'.

A better question is:

'The amount of homework set to pupils in this school is:

Tick one box.   ☐   ☐   ☐   ☐   ,

not enough   about right   too much   don't know

- Here are two questionnaires: the first is well designed but the second contains several faults.

Good

I am collecting information to see if there is any connection between a person's height and the height of their parents.

Tell people what you are doing

1. Please tick one box

Male   Female
☐   ☐

2. Age: please tick one box

13 → 15   16 → 18   19 and over
☐   ☐   ☐

Make it easy to answer.

3. Please state your height, either in feet and inches or in cm.

height
☐

4. Please state the height of your father [If you are not sure an estimate will be O.K.]

height of father
☐

Use the word 'please' frequently.

height of mother
☐

5. Please state the height of your mother

Not Good

State your name and age.

Name _____

Age _____

No introduction

Not a good idea

People often don't like to state their age

- How much television do you watch on average?

☐   ☐   ☐
not much   quite a lot   a lot

Much too vague

- Which are your favourite programmes on T.V.?

You may get 100 different answers. This will be impossible to analyse.

- Do you agree that BBC1 provides the best news coverage?

☐   ☐
agree   disagree

Question is biased towards agreeing

Needs a box for 'don't know'

Exercise 1

In Questions **1** to **6** explain why the question is not suitable for a questionnaire.

1. How much do you earn per month?

| 0–£100 | £100–£200 | £200–£500 | £400–£700 | more than £700 |

2. Wouldn't you agree that the present government is doing an appalling job?

3. For how long do you watch the television each day?

| 2–3 hrs | 3–4 hrs | 5–6 hrs |

4. Do you think that the disintegration of theological suppositions is leading to ethical degeneration?

5. Which sort of holiday do you most enjoy?

6. Some of the money from the National Lottery goes to charities. Tick one box:

The money going to charities is ☐ ☐
   Too little   Too much

7. A group of pupils were asked to design a questionnaire to find out people's views about watching sport on television. Comment on the following two pupil's efforts. Design an improved questionnaire to find out people's opinions.

(a)
```
Name ............ Sex M/F

Age ................

Do you like sport? .......... Y/N

Do you have satellite TV? ......
                         Y/N

Is there enough sport on TV?
                ........... Y/N
```

(b)
```
Do you like sport?
Not at all
Not much
A bit
Quite a lot
I love it

Do you have cable or satellite TV?
Yes/No

How often do you watch sport?
Every day
Up to three times a week
Less than twice a month

Should there be more sport on
television?
Yes/No
```

8. A new variety of soup, 'Cheese and Onion', is to be launched by a leading manufacturer. They wish to know if it will be popular and sell well. People are asked to try a free sample and comment on their impression.
Design a questionnaire to test people's opinions.

Part 5

5.1 Using a calculator

Order of operations

Here is an apparently simple calculation

$4{\cdot}52 + 3{\cdot}5 \times 6{\cdot}3$.

Working left to right on a calculator press

| 4·52 | + | 4·52 | × | 4·52 | = |

Depending on what make of calculator you use, you may get 50·526 or you may get 26·57. Which is correct?

Where there is a mixture of operations to be performed to avoid uncertainty you must follow these rules: (a) work out brackets first
(b) work out $\div$, $\times$ before $+$, $-$.

Some people use the word 'BIDMAS' to help them remember the correct order of operations.

Here are four examples

- $8 + 6 \div 6 = 8 + 1 = 9$
- $20 - 8 \times 2 = 20 - 16 = 4$
- $(13 - 7) \div (6 - 4) = 6 \div 2 = 3$
- $20 - 8 \div (5 + 3) = 20 - 8 \div 8 = 19$

Brackets
Indices
Divide
Multiply
Add
Subtract

Exercise 1

In Questions **1** to **20** do not use a calculator to work out the answer.

1. $13 + 9 \div 3$

2. $40 - 5 \times 7$

3. $8 \times 3 - 14$

4. $(8 + 3) \times 6$

5. $15 - (7 + 5)$

6. $8 + 3 \times 2$

7. $17 - 12 \div 4$

8. $24 \div (1 + 7)$

9. $3 \times 4 + 5 \times 2$

10. $30 \div 3 + 5 \times 4$

11. $3 + 20 \div 2$

12. $(10 \div 2) \div 4$

13. $16 - (8 + 3 \times 2)$

14. $(9 \div 1 - 2) \times 4$

15. $3 \times 5 - 12 \div 2$

16. $8 \times 2 - 4 \div 2$

17. $\dfrac{9 - 5}{10 - 8}$

18. $\dfrac{10 + 3 \times 2}{8 \div 2}$

19. $\dfrac{36 - 12 \div 2}{5 + 1}$

20. $\dfrac{(6 + 5) \times 2}{12 - 5 \div 5}$

Exercise 2

Use a calculator and give the answer correct to two decimal places.

1. $2 \cdot 5 \times 1 \cdot 67$ **2.** $19 \cdot 6 - 3 \cdot 7311$ **3.** $0 \cdot 792^2$

4. $0 \cdot 13 + 8 \cdot 9 - 3 \cdot 714$ **5.** $2 \cdot 4^2 - 1 \cdot 712$ **6.** $5 \cdot 3 \times 1 \cdot 7 + 3 \cdot 7$

7. $0 \cdot 71 \times 0 \cdot 92 - 0 \cdot 15$ **8.** $9 \cdot 6 \div 1 \cdot 72$ **9.** $8 \cdot 17 - 1 \cdot 56 + 7 \cdot 4$

10. $\dfrac{6 \cdot 3}{1 \cdot 84}$ **11.** $\dfrac{19 \cdot 7}{8 \cdot 24} + 1 \cdot 97$ **12.** $\dfrac{2 \cdot 63}{1 \cdot 9} - 0 \cdot 71$

In Questions **13** to **30** remember 'B I D M A S'.

13. $2 \cdot 5 + 3 \cdot 1 \times 2 \cdot 4$ **14.** $7 \cdot 81 + 0 \cdot 7 \times 1 \cdot 82$ **15.** $8 \cdot 73 + 9 \div 11$

16. $11 \cdot 7 \div 9 - 0 \cdot 74$ **17.** $7 \div 0 \cdot 32 + 1 \cdot 15$ **18.** $2 \cdot 6 + 5 \cdot 2 \times 1 \cdot 7$

19. $2 \cdot 9 + \dfrac{8 \cdot 3}{1 \cdot 83}$ **20.** $1 \cdot 7^2 + 2 \cdot 62$ **21.** $5 \cdot 2 + \dfrac{11 \cdot 7}{1 \cdot 85}$

22. $9 \cdot 64 + 26 \div 12 \cdot 7$ **23.** $1 \cdot 27 + 3 \cdot 1^2$ **24.** $4 \cdot 2^2 \div 9 \cdot 4$

25. $0 \cdot 151 + 1 \cdot 4 \times 9 \cdot 2$ **26.** $1 \cdot 7^3$ **27.** $8 \cdot 2 + 3 \cdot 2 \times 3 \cdot 3$

28. $3 \cdot 2 + \dfrac{1 \cdot 41}{6 \cdot 72}$ **29.** $\dfrac{1 \cdot 9 + 3 \cdot 71}{2 \cdot 3}$ **30.** $\dfrac{8 \cdot 7 - 5 \cdot 371}{1 \cdot 14}$

Using brackets

Most calculators (apart from those given away free with a packet of 'Honey Nut Loops') have brackets buttons like these 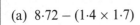 .

When you press the left hand bracket button $\boxed{[(\text{---}}$ you may see

 ignore this.

When the right hand bracket button is pressed you will see that the calculation inside the brackets has been performed. Try it.

Don't forget to press the $\boxed{=}$ button at the end to give the final answer.

(a) $8 \cdot 72 - (1 \cdot 4 \times 1 \cdot 7)$ (b) $\dfrac{8 \cdot 51}{(1 \cdot 94 - 0 \cdot 711)}$

   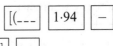

Answer $= 6 \cdot 34$ to 2 d.p.   Answer $= 6 \cdot 92$ to 2 d.p.

Exercise 3

Work out and give the answer correct to 2 decimal places.

1. $18.41 - (7.2 \times 1.3)$

2. $11.01 + (2.6 \div 7)$

3. $(1.27 + 5.6) \div 1.4$

4. $9.6 + (11.2 \div 4)$

5. $(8.6 \div 3) - 1.4$

6. $11.7 - (2.6 \times 2.7)$

7. $7.41 - \left(\dfrac{7.3}{1.4}\right)$

8. $\left(\dfrac{8.91}{1.7}\right) - 2.63$

9. $\dfrac{1.41}{(1.7 + 0.21)}$

10. $(1.56 + 1.9) \div 2.45$

11. $3.2 \times (1.9 - 0.74)$

12. $8.9 \div (1.3 - 0.711)$

13. $(8.72 \div 1.4) \times 1.49$

14. $(2.67 + 1.2 + 5) \times 1.13$

15. $23 - (9.2 \times 1.85)$

16. $\dfrac{(8.41 + 1.73)}{1.47}$

17. $\dfrac{7.23}{(8.2 \times 0.91)}$

18. $\dfrac{(11.4 - 7.87)}{17}$

In Questions **19** to **36** use the $\boxed{x^2}$ button where needed.

19. $2.6^2 - 1.4$

20. $8.3^2 \times 1.17$

21. $7.2^2 \div 6.67$

22. $(1.4 + 2.67)^2$

23. $(8.41 - 5.7)^2$

24. $(2.7 \times 1.31)^2$

25. $8.2^2 - (1.4 + 1.73)$

26. $\dfrac{2.6^2}{(1.3 + 2.99)}$

27. $4.1^2 - \left(\dfrac{8.7}{3.2}\right)$

28. $\dfrac{(2.7 + 6.04)}{(1.4 + 2.11)}$

29. $\dfrac{(8.71 - 1.6)}{(2.4 + 9.73)}$

30. $\left(\dfrac{2.3}{1.4}\right)^2$

Other useful buttons

$\boxed{+/-}$ This key changes the sign of a number from (+) to (−) or from (−) to (+).

$\boxed{\text{Min}}$ Puts the number displayed into the memory. It automatically clears any number already in the memory when it puts in the new number.

$\boxed{\text{MR}}$ Recalls the number in the memory.

$\boxed{x^y}$ Raises the number to a power. For 5^3 press

$\boxed{5}\ \boxed{x^y}\ \boxed{3}\ \boxed{=}$.

On a calculator work out:

(a) $-5{\cdot}2 + 7{\cdot}81$
   Press the keys

   Answer $= 2{\cdot}61$

(b) $7{\cdot}5 \div (-0{\cdot}04)$

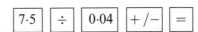

   Answer $= -187{\cdot}5$
   Notice that we do not *need* the
   brackets buttons. You may use them if
   you prefer.

Exercise 4

Work out the following. Give the answer correct to one decimal
place where appropriate.

1. $-7 \times 3{\cdot}2$

2. $-5 \times (-2{\cdot}3)$

3. $8 \div (-4{\cdot}5)$

4. $13 \times (-4{\cdot}5)$

5. $-2 \times (-8{\cdot}9)$

6. $-12 \div (3{\cdot}2)$

7. $-5 \times (-4{\cdot}4)$

8. $-8 - 11{\cdot}7$

9. $-7 + 20{\cdot}3$

10. $-9 + 30 - 17{\cdot}4$

In questions **11** to **19** use the x^y button, where needed.

11. $3{\cdot}7^3$

12. $2{\cdot}1^4$

13. $3{\cdot}1^5 + 112$

14. $1{\cdot}64^5$

15. $(1{\cdot}81 + 2{\cdot}43)^4$

16. $19{\cdot}8 + 1{\cdot}96^3$

17. $1{\cdot}7^3 + 2{\cdot}4^3$

18. $200 - 3{\cdot}7^4$

19. $3{\cdot}2 + 3{\cdot}2^2 + 3{\cdot}2^3$

In Questions **20** to **34** think ahead and use your calculator as
efficiently as possible.

20. $\dfrac{5{\cdot}65}{1{\cdot}21 + 3{\cdot}7}$

21. $\dfrac{8{\cdot}7}{13} + \dfrac{4{\cdot}9}{15}$

22. $14{\cdot}6 - (3{\cdot}9 \times 2{\cdot}62)$

23. $12{\cdot}94 - \sqrt{8{\cdot}97}$

24. $\dfrac{5{\cdot}41 + 7{\cdot}82}{9{\cdot}82 - 3{\cdot}99}$

25. $\sqrt{\dfrac{100{\cdot}9}{9{\cdot}81 + 56}}$

26. $11{\cdot}2\%$ of $9{\cdot}6^3$

27. $\frac{2}{7}$ of $\left(\dfrac{4{\cdot}2}{1{\cdot}95 - 0{\cdot}713}\right)$

28. $\frac{1}{6} + \frac{1}{7} + \frac{1}{8} + \frac{1}{9}$

29. $\dfrac{\sqrt{8{\cdot}74} + \sqrt{7{\cdot}05}}{\sqrt{3{\cdot}14} + \sqrt{2{\cdot}76}}$

30. $\dfrac{900}{101 - 2{\cdot}9^4}$

31. $(15\%$ of $22{\cdot}36)^3$

32. 18% of $9{\cdot}1\%$ of 1150

33. $2{\cdot}8^5 - \sqrt{\dfrac{9{\cdot}7}{11{\cdot}4}}$

34. $\frac{2}{3}$ of $\left(\dfrac{9{\cdot}81}{1{\cdot}25^2}\right)^3$

Calculator words

• When you hold a calculator display upside down some numbers appear to form words: 4508 spells "Gosh"

0.70 spells "Old"

(ignoring the decimal point)

Exercise 5

Translate this passage using a calculator and the clues below:

" ① !" shouted Olag out of the window of his ② . "I need some ③ / ④ for my dinner. Do you ⑤ them?"
" ⑥ did" ⑦ / ⑧ "I even took off the ⑨ for free. ⑩ / ⑪ / ⑫ they were. The problem is that all the ⑬ were eaten in the ⑭ , mostly by ⑮ . ⑯ / ⑰ such a ⑱ / ⑲ lately. ⑳ and ㉑ are always ㉒ because of the amount of ㉓ they drink every night"

" ㉔ well, he is the ㉕ I suppose" Olag grumbled "Roast ㉖ again tonight then ..."

Clues to passage

①: $2(9 - 4)$
②: $(3 \div 40) + 0.0011$
③: $\frac{3}{8} - (39.2 \div 10^4)$
④: $5 \times 12 \times 100 - 7$
⑤: $(90 \times 80) + (107 \times 5)$
⑥: $\sqrt{0.01} \times 10$
⑦: $(68 + 1.23) \div 200$
⑧: $101^2 - (5 \times 13) - 2$
⑨: $750^2 + (296\,900 \div 20)$
⑩: $2^3 \times 5^2 \times 3 + 16.3 + 1.7$
⑪: $(70\,000 \div 2) + (3 \times 2)$
⑫: $11\,986 \div 2$
⑬: $(600^2 - 6640) \div 10$
⑭: $200^2 - 685$
⑮: $(0.5^2 \times 0.6)$
⑯: $\sqrt{289} \times 2$
⑰: $836.4 \div 17 + 1.8$
⑱: $30^2 + 18$
⑲: $5^3 \times 64.6$
⑳: $(63\,508 \times 5) - 3$
㉑: $\sqrt{(1160 - 4)}$
㉒: 1.3803×0.25
㉓: $(32 \times 10^3) + 8$
㉔: $2^3 \times 5$
㉕: $(5^3 \times 2^2 \times 11) + 8$
㉖: $7 \times 10^7 - 9\,563\,966$

5.2 Percentages

The use of percentages is very important in mathematics but unfortunately they are misunderstood by many people in everyday life. Recent surveys, conducted among adults, have shown that the number of people who do not understand basic percentages is alarming.

(a) Work out 18% of £5600

Either: 18% of £5600   Or: 18% of £5600
$= \frac{18}{100} \times \frac{5600}{1}$ $= 0.18 \times 5600$
$= £1008$ $= £1008$

(b) Change a mark of 17 out of 40 into a percentage.
To change a fraction to a percentage, multiply by 100.
∴ Answer $= \frac{17}{40} \times 100$
$= 42.5\%$

(c) Work out 6·3% of £68·99, correct to the nearest penny.

6·3% of £68·99
$= \frac{6.3}{100} \times \frac{68.99}{1}$
$= £4.34637$
$= £4.35$ (to the nearest penny)

Exercise 1

1. Work out.
   (a) 11% of £245   (b) 18% of £2300
   (c) 74% of £6100   (d) 7·5% of £350
   (e) 4% of £6·50   (f) 130% of £85

2. Work out, correct to the nearest penny.
   (a) 3% of £8·24   (b) 11% of £18·99
   (c) 39% of £59·95   (d) 18% of £5·90
   (e) 4·6% of £18·99   (f) 12·5% of £6·95

3. (a) Work out the volume of a standard size box of Corn Flakes.
   (b) What is the volume of a *special offer* box of Corn Flakes which is 40% bigger?
   (c) The standard size box contains enough Corn Flakes to fill 20 cereal bowls. How many bowls can be filled from the 'special offer' box of Corn Flakes?

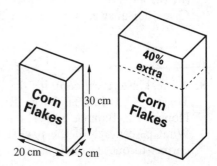

4. Change these fractions to percentages
(a) $\frac{1}{5}$ (b) $\frac{3}{4}$ (c) $\frac{7}{8}$ (d) $\frac{17}{20}$
(e) $\frac{44}{80}$ (f) $\frac{63}{120}$ (g) $\frac{71}{100}$ (h) $\frac{19}{25}$

5. The letters shown on the right are each given a number as either a fraction, a decimal or a percentage.
In (a), (b), (c) below the numbers 1, 2, 3, ... give the positions of the letters in a sentence. So 1 is the first letter, 2 is the second letter and so on.
Find the letter whose value is the same as the number given, and write it in the correct position.

A	24%	N	0·9
E	0·05	O	0·625
F	0·32	R	0·6
G	$\frac{3}{20}$	S	$\frac{7}{20}$
H	0·36	T	0·02
I	3%	U	$\frac{3}{25}$
L	0·49	V	0·1%
M	$\frac{3}{4}$	Y	99%

For example in part (a) number 1 is $\frac{3}{5}$.
Since $\frac{3}{5} = 0·6$, letter R goes in the first box.
Find the sentence in each part.

(a)

1	2	3	4	5	6	7	8	9	10	11	12
R											

1. $\frac{3}{5}$ 2. 0·24   3. 2%   4. 0·03   5. $\frac{5}{8}$ 6. 0·35
7. $\frac{6}{25}$ 8. 60%   9. $\frac{1}{20}$ 10. 32%   11. 0·12   12. $\frac{9}{10}$

(b)   1. 15%   2. $62\frac{1}{2}\%$ 3. 49%   4. $\frac{8}{25}$ 5. $\frac{3}{100}$ 6. 35%
     7. 0·75   8. 0·99   9. 0·15   10. 0·24   11. 75%   12. 5%

(c)   1. $(0·6)^2$ 2. $0·2 + 0·04$ 3. $\frac{1}{2}$ of 0·98   4. 32%   5. $\frac{5}{8}$ 6. $\frac{8}{25}$
     7. $0·2 \div 10$ 8. 5%   9. 90%   10. $\frac{15}{500}$ 11. 50% of $\frac{7}{10}$ 12. $\frac{64}{200}$
     13. $3 \div 100$ 14. $\frac{1}{1000}$ 15. $(0·2)^2 + (0·1)^2$

6. In a Physics test, Sima got 52 out of 80. What was her mark as a percentage?

7. What percentage of the letters in the box are
(a) vowels?
(b) the letter R?
Give your answers correct to 1 d.p.

S	M	O	K	I	N	G	I	S
N	O	T	P	A	R	T	I	C
U	L	A	R	L	Y	G	O	O
D	F	O	R	Y	O	U	O	K

8. A breakfast cereal contains the following ingredients by weight:
Toasted Oat Flakes 720 g, Raw Sugar 34 g, Oat Bran 76 g, Honey 26 g, Banana 57 g, Hazelnuts 12 g.
What percentage of the packet is Oat Bran? Give your answer correct to one decimal place.

9. The table shows the results when three makes of car were tested for a particular fault in the ventilation system.
   (a) What percentage of the cars which failed were Fords?
   (b) What percentage of the Rolls Royce cars failed?

	Rolls Royce	Renault	Ford
Failed	2	13	25
Passed	17	474	1756
Total			

10. Copy and complete the table.

	Fraction	Decimal	Percentage
(a)	$\frac{4}{5}$		
(b)		0.125	
(c)			2%
(d)	$\frac{2}{3}$		

Increasing or decreasing by a percentage

Mathematicians always look for quick ways of solving problems. The question in the box below is solved first by an 'ordinary' method and secondly by a 'quick' method. You can choose for yourself which method you prefer.

The price of a computer costing £955 is to be increased by 6%. Find the new price.

Method 1.   Increase in price = 6% of £955
$$= \frac{6}{100} \times \frac{955}{1}$$
$$= £57 \cdot 30$$
New price = £955 + £57·30
$$= £1012 \cdot 30$$

Method 2.   New price = 100% of £955 + 6% of £955
$$= 106\% \text{ of } £955$$
$$= 1 \cdot 06 \times 955$$
$$= £1012 \cdot 30$$

(a) Increase a price of £6800 by 17%

New price = 100% of £6800
          +17% of £6800
= 117% of £6800
= 1·17 × 6800
= £7956

(b) Decrease a price of £584 by 2%

New price = 100% of £584
          −2% of £584
= 98% of £584
= 0·98 × 584
= £572·32

Exercise 2

1. (a) Increase £120 by 35%
   (b) Increase 80 kg by 40%
   (c) Decrease $400 by 15%
   (d) Decrease 350 km by 60%

2. The 1995 price of a motor bike is £8580.
   Calculate the 1996 price, which is
   5% higher.

3. Find the new price of a necklace
   costing £85, after the price is
   reduced by 7%.

4. The 'Hairy Scarebellies' debut C.D. cost £12 when it was first
   released, but it is so rare that copies have increased 40% in
   value since then. What are they worth now

5. A jacket costing £130 is reduced by 25% in the latest sale. Find
   its sale price.

6. Stan is delighted to find out that his guitar has increased 60% in
   value. He bought it in 1988 for £450. What is it worth now?

7. Alfonse has found that most new cars are worth only 40% of
   their original value after 3 years.
   (a) How much will a £13,500 car be worth after 3 years?
   (b) How much, in pounds, has it lost in value?

8. 'Gloddings' stately home was
   valued at £800 000 when Lord and
   Lady Campbell first bought it.
   Since then it has increased by
   48% in value. What is it worth
   now?

9. Rajesh bought 500 shares in 'Ruthless Incorporated'. at £2·31
   each.

   (a) Find the total value of his shares.
   (b) Find the total value of his shares after a drop of 27% in
       value.

10. Sita bought 300 shares in 'Carling P.L.C.' at £1·65 each.

    (a) Find the total value of her shares.
    (b) Find the new value of her shares after an increase of 56% in
        value.

Percentage change

Suppose the price of a car
was increased from £8000 to
£8100 and the price of a pair
of speakers was increased from
£200 to £300. The *actual* increase
of £100 is the same for both
items but the increase is far
more significant for the speakers!
A good way of comparing price
changes (up or down) is to work
out the *percentage* change.

For an increase use the formula,

$$\text{percentage increase} = \left(\frac{\text{actual increase}}{\text{original value}}\right) \times 100$$

For a decrease,

$$\text{percentage decrease} = \left(\frac{\text{actual decrease}}{\text{original value}}\right) \times 100$$

Percentage profit or loss are calculated in the same way, changing
the words 'increase' to 'profit' and 'decrease' to 'loss'.

For the car above, percentage increase $= \left(\dfrac{100}{8000}\right) \times 100$

$$= 1\tfrac{1}{4}\%$$

For the speakers, percentage increase $= \left(\dfrac{100}{200}\right) \times 100 = 50\%$

(a) Waitrose reduce the price of their
own label cheesecake from £1·60 to
£1·12.
Find the percentage decrease.

The actual decrease = £0·48

Percentage decrease $= \left(\dfrac{0·48}{1·60}\right) \times 100$

$\qquad\qquad = 30\%$

(b) The owner of a sports shop buys tennis
rackets for £32 and sells them for
£69·99.
Find the percentage profit.

The actual profit = £37·99.

Percentage profit $= \left(\dfrac{37·99}{32}\right) \times 100$

$\qquad\qquad = 118·7\%$ (1 d.p.)

Exercise 3

Give answers correct to 1 decimal place, where necessary.

1. Find the percentage increase when the price of a house goes up from £120 000 to £144 000.

2. Vijay's wages were increased from £115 per week to £130 per week. What was the percentage increase?

3. Calculate the percentage increase or decrease in each case.

	Original price	Final price
(a)	£160	£176
(b)	£200	£206
(c)	£410	£630
(d)	£240	£210
(e)	$880	$836
(f)	$22·50	$18·00

4. One year a leading dancer from the Royal Ballet earned £39 600. In the year after she returned from dancing in Paris and Rome, she was paid £65 000. Calculate her percentage increase in pay.

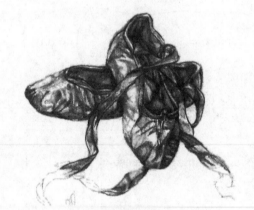

5. During a season when Liverpool were near the top of the league, their average crowd was 31 750. In the following season, they suffered a loss of form and the average attendance went down to 27 430. Calculate the percentage fall in the attendance.

6. A man bought a car in an auction for £6350 and then quickly sold it for £7295. Calculate the percentage profit.

7. Find either the percentage profit or loss, correct to the nearest whole number.
   (a) old price = £70, new price = £105
   (b) old price = £40, new price = £75
   (c) old price = £90, new price = £52
   (d) old price = £190, new price = £152

8. The 'Greasy Spoon' cafe buys its ingredients at the costs shown below, and then charges according to the menu. Find the percentage profit on each item.

	Item	Bought for	Menu price
(a)	Can of Cola	15p	50p
(b)	Portion of chips	8p	60p
(c)	Burger	40p	£1·20
(d)	Cup of tea	5p	40p

9. Karim buys a car for £430 from 'Dodgy Motors Ltd.' 4 Weeks later it fails its M.O.T. and he sells it for scrap rather than pay for it to be repaired. Find his percentage loss if the scrap value is £60.

10. In January the greatest weight a weightlifter could manage was 155 kg. After feeding on a special diet of raw meat and raw fish, he managed to lift 168 kg. Work out the percentage improvement in his performance.

11. A box has a square base of side 20 cm and height 10 cm. Calculate the percentage increase in the volume of the box after the length and width of the base are both increased by 20% and the height is increased by 15%.

12.* The receptionist at a bank earns £14 200 per year and the chairman of the bank earns £315 600 per year.
  (a) Calculate the actual increase in each person's pay if they are given a 4% pay rise.
  (b) The chairman decided to take only the same actual increase as the receptionist. Calculate the percentage increase in his pay when he did this.

13.* A sports centre recorded the number of girls and boys who were admitted in 1995 and 1996.

	1995	1996	Total
Girls	22 414	20 904	43 318
Boys	18 715	27 404	46 119
Total	41 129	48 308	89 437

  (a) What was the percentage increase in the number of boys admitted between 1995 and 1996?
  (b) What was the overall percentage increase in admissions between 1995 and 1996?

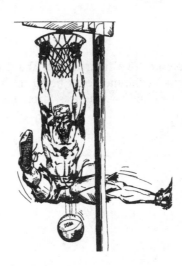

14. It is possible to do some 'easy' percentages in your head.
Remember $10\% = \frac{1}{10}$, $25\% = \frac{1}{4}$, $33\frac{1}{3}\% = \frac{1}{3}$ etc.

Work these out in your head:

(a) 10% of £230
(b) 25% of £880
(c) 80% of £5000
(d) $33\frac{1}{3}\%$ of £120
(e) 5% of £2000
(f) 75% of £12

15. *Estimate* the following (do NOT use a calculator). Show your working.

(a) 10% of £24·95
(b) 20% of £494
(c) 75% of £398·75
(d) 33% of £239·99
(e) 2% of 40 105 kg
(f) 9·7% of £68 400.

5.3 Long multiplication and division

Long multiplication

- Seventeen 23s is the same as ten 23s plus seven 23s
  17×23 is the same as $10 \times 23 + 7 \times 23$

(a)
$$\begin{array}{r} 23 \\ \times 10 \\ \hline 230 \end{array}$$

(b)
$$\begin{array}{r} 23 \\ \times 7 \\ \hline 161 \end{array}$$

(c)
$$\begin{array}{r} 230 \\ +161 \\ \hline 391 \end{array}$$

Quick method
$$\begin{array}{r} 23 \\ \times 17 \\ \hline 230 \quad \longleftarrow 10 \times 23 \\ 161 \quad \longleftarrow 7 \times 23 \\ \hline 391 \end{array}$$

- $16 \times 35 = 10 \times 35 + 6 \times 35$

(a)
$$\begin{array}{r} 35 \\ \times 10 \\ \hline 350 \end{array}$$

(b)
$$\begin{array}{r} 35 \\ \times 6 \\ \hline 210 \\ \tiny{3} \end{array}$$

(c)
$$\begin{array}{r} 350 \\ +210 \\ \hline 560 \end{array}$$

Quick method
$$\begin{array}{r} 35 \\ \times 16 \\ \hline 350 \quad \longleftarrow 10 \times 35 \\ 210 \quad \longleftarrow 6 \times 35 \\ \hline 560 \end{array}$$

- $2·5 \times 1·3$

  Ignore the decimals.

  Work out
  $$\begin{array}{r} 25 \\ \times 13 \\ \hline 250 \\ 75 \\ \hline 325 \end{array}$$

  There are two figures after the decimal points in the members being multiplied. So there are two figures after the point in the answer.
  $$2·5 \times 1·3 = 3·25$$

Exercise 1

Work out

1. 15×23	**2.** 14×31	**3.** 16×32	**4.** 17×14
5. 18×33	**6.** 19×24	**7.** 17×31	**8.** 13×52
9. 21×24	**10.** 27×32	**11.** 26×28	**12.** 27×21
13. 32×25	**14.** 33×27	**15.** 36×14	**16.** 35×27
17. 34×41	**18.** 42×61	**19.** 31×47	**20.** 53×21
21. 123×32	**22.** 291×42	**23.** 804×61	**24.** 74×243

Questions **25** to **32** contain decimals

25. 4.5×6.2	**26.** 8.4×0.13	**27.** 6.9×4.2	**28.** 1.51×0.22
29. 4.6×82	**30.** 0.73×37	**31.** 0.44×1.1	**32.** 3.14×1.3

Long division

A Use the method for 'short division' with working at the side.

$$24 \text{ remainder } 1$$
$$17)\overline{40^{6}9}$$

$$\begin{array}{r} 17 \\ \times 2 \\ \hline 34 \end{array}$$

$$\begin{array}{r} 17 \\ \times 4 \\ \hline 68 \end{array}$$

B In this method we set it out so that the remainders are easier to find

$$\begin{array}{r} 24 \\ 17)\overline{409} \\ -34 \downarrow \\ \hline 69 \\ -68 \\ \hline 1 \end{array}$$

17 into 40 goes 2 times
$2 \times 17 = 34$
$40 - 34 = 6$
'bring down' 9
17 into 69 goes 4 times
$4 \times 17 = 68$
$69 - 68 = 1$
Answer is 24 remainder 1

Exercise 2

1. $13)\overline{275}$	**2.** $14)\overline{311}$	**3.** $16)\overline{498}$	**4.** $17)\overline{544}$
5. $14)\overline{452}$	**6.** $15)\overline{634}$	**7.** $19)\overline{669}$	**8.** $21)\overline{698}$
9. $17)\overline{459}$	**10.** $15)\overline{516}$	**11.** $14)\overline{672}$	**12.** $17)\overline{550}$
13. $451 \div 22$	**14.** $276 \div 24$	**15.** $517 \div 23$	**16.** $558 \div 26$
17. $317 \div 31$	**18.** $547 \div 25$	**19.** $886 \div 42$	**20.** $963 \div 33$

21. $557 \div 26$ **22.** $528 \div 45$ **23.** $118 \div 52$ **24.** $785 \div 63$

25. $32\overline{)715}$ **26.** $18\overline{)924}$ **27.** $25\overline{)776}$ **28.** $53\overline{)781}$

29. $64\overline{)696}$ **30.** $27\overline{)583}$ **31.** $15\overline{)667}$ **32.** $98\overline{)694}$

Word problems

A minibus can take 16 passengers. How many minibuses are needed for 214 passengers?

(a) Work out $214 \div 16$

$$
\begin{array}{r}
13 \text{ remainder } 6 \\
16\overline{)214} \\
\underline{16} \\
54 \\
\underline{48} \\
6
\end{array}
$$

(b) You have to think carefully about what the remainder means. If you used 13 minibuses there would be 6 people left over. So you need 14 minibuses altogether.

Exercise 3

To do these questions you have to multiply or divide. Do not use a calculator.

1. Work out the total cost of 45 pens at 22p each. Give your answer in pounds.

2. A box of 15 golf balls costs 975 pence. How much does each ball cost?

3. There are 23 rooms in a school and each room has 33 chairs. How many chairs are there altogether?

4. A shop owner buys 52 tins of paint at 84p each. How much does he spend altogether?

5. Eggs are packed twelve to a box. How many boxes are needed for 444 eggs?

6. Figaro the cat eats one tin of cat food every day. How much will it cost to feed Figaro for 31 days if each tin costs 45p?

7. How many 23-seater coaches will be needed for a school trip for a party of 278?

8. Steve wants to buy as many 24p stamps as possible. He has £5 to spend. How many can he buy and how much change is left?

9. It costs £972 to hire a boat for a day. A trip is organised for 36 people. How much does each person pay?

10. Tins of spaghetti are packed 24 to a box. How many boxes are needed for 868 tins?

11. On average a school needs 87 exercise books a week. How many books are needed for 38 weeks?

12. A prize of 470 chocolate bars is shared equally between 18 winners. How many bars does each winner get and how many are left over?

13. Each class of a school has 31 pupils plus one teacher and there are 15 classes in the school.
    The school hall can take 26 rows of chairs with 18 chairs in a row. Is that enough chairs for all the pupils and teachers?

14. When Philip was digging a hole in his garden he struck oil! The oil came out at a rate of £17 for every minute of the day and night. How much does Philip receive in a 24-hour day?

5.4 Finding a rule

- Here is a sequence of shapes made from sticks

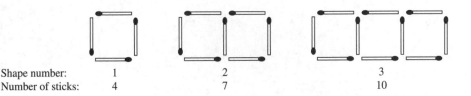

Shape number:	1	2	3
Number of sticks:	4	7	10

- There is a *rule* or *formula* which we can use to calculate the number of sticks for any shape number.

'The number of sticks is three times the shape number add one'.

Check that this rule works for all the shapes above and also for shape number 4 which you can draw.

Exercise 1

1. Here is a sequence of triangles made from sticks.

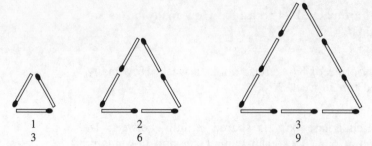

Shape number: 1   2   3
Number of sticks: 3   6   9

    (a) Draw shape number 4 and count the number of sticks.
    (b) Write down and complete the rule for the number of sticks
        in a shape: 'The number of sticks is _____ times the shape
        number'.

2. Here is a sequence of 'steps' made from sticks

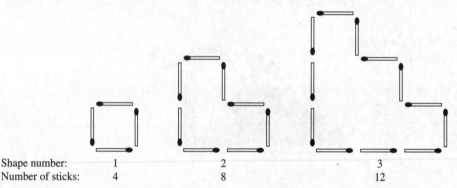

Shape number: 1   2   3
Number of sticks: 4   8   12

    (a) Draw shape number 4 and count the number of sticks.
    (b) Write down the rule for the number of sticks in a shape.
        'The number of sticks is _____ times the shape number'.

3. Louise makes a pattern of triangles from sticks.

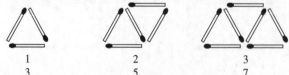

Shape number: 1   2   3
Number of sticks: 3   5   7

    (a) Draw shape number 4 and shape number 5

    (b) Make a table:

shape number	1	2	3	4	5
number of sticks	3	5	7		

    (c) Write down the rule for the number of sticks in a shape.
        'The number of sticks is _____ times the shape number and
        then add _____.'

4. Here is a sequence of houses made from sticks

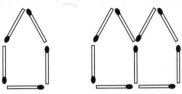 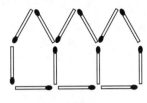

Shape number: 1   2   3
Number of sticks: 5   9   13

(a) Draw shape number 4.

(b) Make a table:

shape number	1	2	3	4
number of sticks	5	9	13	

(c) Write down the rule.
  'The number of sticks is _____ times the shape number and then add _____.'

5. Paul makes a pattern of squares from dots.

Shape number: 1   2   3
Number of dots: 4   6   8

(a) Draw shape number 4 and shape number 5.
(b) *Without* drawing the diagram, state the number of dots in shape number 10.
(c) Write the rule:
  'The number of dots is ....'
(d) Use the rule to calculate the number of dots in shape number 25.

6. Here is another sequence made from dots.

Shape number: 1   2   3
Number of dots: 6   10

(a) Draw shape numbers 4 and 5 and make a table.

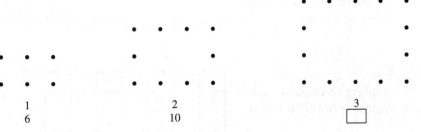

shape number	number of dots
1	6
2	10
3	
⋮	

(b) P.T.O.

(b) Decide which of the following is the correct rule for the number of dots:
  'the shape number times 3 and then add 3'
  or 'the shape number times 2 and then add 4'
  or 'the shape number times 4 and then add 2'.

7. In this sequence black squares are surrounded by white squares.

Black squares:	$b = 1$	$b = 2$	$b = 3$
White squares:	$w = 8$	$w = 10$	$w = 12$

(a) Draw the next diagram in the sequence and make a table.

black squares, b	1	2	3	4
white squares, w	8	10	12	

(b) The rule is: 'The number of white squares is two times the number of black squares and then add 6.'

(c) Work out the number of white squares in the diagram which has 20 black squares.

(d) Write the formula, without words, for the number of white squares. Use b for the number of black squares and w for the number of white squares.
Write '$w =$ '.

8. (a) Write in the missing numbers to continue the sequences across the page.

3		4		5		
7		10		13		
1		2		3		

(b) You could write letters in the spaces like this.

e
n
f

The rule is: 'To find n you double e and add on f'

(c) Write the rule without using words.

Finding a formula using algebra

The sequence of diagrams below shows rectangles made from sticks.

  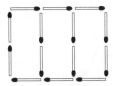

Suppose we wanted a formula connecting the number of sticks with the number of rectangles.

- Let the number of sticks be s.
  Let the number of rectangles be r.

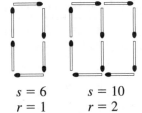 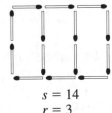 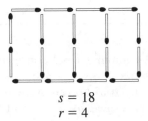

$s = 6$ $\quad$ $s = 10$ $\quad\quad$ $s = 14$ $\quad\quad\quad$ $s = 18$
$r = 1$ $\quad$ $r = 2$ $\quad\quad$ $r = 3$ $\quad\quad\quad$ $r = 4$

- Count the number of sticks and the number of rectangles in several diagrams.

- Record the values of r and s in a table.

- If the numbers in the r column are consecutive and the numbers in the s column go up (or down) by the same number each time, the formula connecting r and s is *linear*. This means that there are no terms in r^2, r^3 or anything more complicated. The graph of the formula will be a straight line.

r	s
1	6
2	10
3	14
4	18

In this case, the numbers in the s column increase by 4 each time. This suggests that a column for $4r$ will be helpful.
From this table it is clear that s is two more than $4r$.
The formula linking r and s is $\boxed{s = 4r + 2}$

r	s	$4r$
1	6	4
2	10	8
3	14	12
4	18	16

The table shows values for two variables n and t. Find the formula linking n and t.

n	t
3	7
4	10
5	13
6	16

The values of n are consecutive and the values of t go up by 3 each time. Write a new column for $3n$.
The table shows that t is 2 less than $3n$
The formula is $t = 3n - 2$.

n	t	$3n$
3	7	9
4	10	12
5	13	15
6	16	18

If the numbers in the left column are not consecutive the method has to be adapted. In harder questions you need an open mind and the ability to find a formula by trial and improvement. Sometimes you can see how the pattern is formed by looking at the diagrams.

Exercise 2

1. Here is a table for x and y.

x	y
1	2
2	6
3	10
4	14
5	18

Since y goes up by 4 each time, add a column for $4x$.

x	y	$4x$
1	2	4
2	6	8
3	10	12
4	14	16
5	18	20

What is the formula connecting x and y? Write '$y = $ '.

In Questions **2** to **17** you are given a table. Copy the table and make an extra column. Find the formula connecting x and y. Write '$y = $ '.

2.

x	y
1	5
2	7
3	9
4	11
5	13

3.

x	y
1	3
2	6
3	9
4	12
5	15

4.

x	y
1	5
2	8
3	11
4	14
5	17

5.

x	y
1	6
2	8
3	10
4	12
5	14

6.

x	y
1	5
2	9
3	13
4	17
5	21

7.

x	y
1	1
2	4
3	7
4	10
5	13

8.

x	y
1	6
2	11
3	16
4	21
5	26

9.

x	y
1	7
2	12
3	17
4	22
5	27

10.

x	y
6	14
7	17
8	20
9	23
10	26

11.

x	y
8	4
9	$4\frac{1}{2}$
10	5
11	$5\frac{1}{2}$
12	6

12.

x	y
4	15
5	18
6	21
7	24

13.

x	y
12	8
13	$8\frac{1}{2}$
14	9
15	$9\frac{1}{2}$

The last four are more difficult.

14.

x	y
2	6
3	4
4	2
5	0

15.

x	y
1	17
2	14
3	11
4	8
5	5

16.

x	y
1	25
2	20
3	15
4	10
5	5

17.

x	y
1	1
2	4
3	9
4	16
5	25

Exercise 3

1. In the diagrams below we count the number of circles c and the number of dots d, where the circles intersect.

$c = 2$
$d = 2$

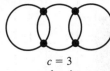

$c = 3$
$d = 4$

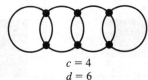
$c = 4$
$d = 6$

c	d
2	2
3	4
4	6
5	

Draw the next diagram in the sequence and write the values for c and d in a table, like the one shown. What is the formula connecting c and d? Write it as 'd = …'.

2. Here is a sequence of triangles t made from a number of matches m.

$t = 1$
$m = 3$

$t = 2$
$m = 5$

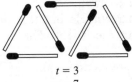
$t = 3$
$m = 7$

t	m
1	3
2	5
3	7
4	

Draw the next diagram in the sequence and write the values for t and m in a table. Find a formula connecting t and m, in the form 'm = …'.

3. Crosses are drawn on rectangular 'dotty' paper. The length l of each arm of the cross is recorded together with the total number of dots d on each cross.

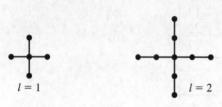

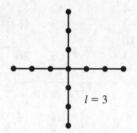

l	d
1	5
2	9
3	13

Find a formula connecting l and d.
Write it as '$d = \ldots$'.

4. Look at the tables below. In each case, find a formula connecting the two letters.

(a)

n	h
2	10
3	13
4	16
5	19

write '$h = \ldots$'

(b)

n	p
3	12
4	17
5	22
6	27

write '$p = \ldots$'

(c)

m	s
2	4
3	$4\frac{1}{2}$
4	5
5	$5\frac{1}{2}$

write '$s = \ldots$'

5. In each diagram below, a number of white squares n surrounds a rectangle of black squares. The length of each rectangle is one unit more than the height h.

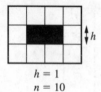

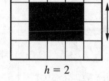

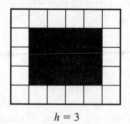

h	n
1	10

Make a table of values of h and n use it to find a formula connecting h and n. Write it as '$n = \ldots$'

6. In a sequence of diagrams similar to the one in Question **5**, white squares surround a rectangle but this time the length of the black rectangle is twice the height. The diagram with $h = 2$ is shown.

Draw the sequence of diagrams and make
a table of values of h and n.
Write the formula connecting h and n
in the form '$n = \ldots$'

7. In the diagrams below rectangles are joined together and dots are drawn around the outside with 2 dots on a long side and one dot on a short side.

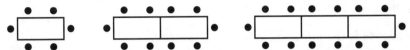

Call the number of dots *d* and the number of rectangles *r*.

Find a formula connecting *d* and *r*.

8. Find the new formula connecting *d* and *r* when the rectangles are joined along their longer sides.

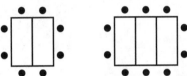

9.* In each diagram there are *w* white squares and *b* black squares.

$b = 2$
$w = 2$

$b = 3$
$w = 6$

  (a) Draw the next diagram in the sequence and make a table of values.

b	w
2	
3	
4	
5	

  (b) Sam and Lars each think they have a formula connecting *b* and *w*
      Sam's rule is 'To find *w* multiply *b* by 4 and then subtract 6'.
      Lar's rule is 'To find *w* multiply *b* by $(b - 1)$'.
      Whose rule is correct?
  (c) Use the correct rule to calculate the number of white squares in the diagram with 10 black squares.

10. In these diagrams 'steps' are made from sticks.

  (a) Draw the next diagram in the sequence.
  (b) Count the number of sticks *s* for each value of *h*, the height of the steps. Make a table.

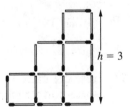

$h = 1$ $h = 2$ $h = 3$

  (c) Decide which of the following is the correct formula:
      A: 'To find *s* you multiply *h* by $(h + 3)$.'
      B: 'To find *s* you multiply *h* by 6 and then subtract 2'.
  (d) Use the correct formula to calculate *s* when $h = 7$.

The nth term in a sequence

- For the sequence 4, 8, 12, 16, ... the terms are found by multiplying the term number by 4.
  So the 10th term is 40, the 15th term is 60.

  A *general* term in the sequence is the nth term, where n stands for any number.

  The nth term of this sequence is $4n$.

- In the sequence 4, 7, 10, 13, ... the terms increase by 3 each time.
  So, the 5th term is $(3 \times 5) + 1 = 16$
  the 10th term is $(3 \times 10) + 1 = 31$
  the nth term is $(3 \times n) + 1 = 3n + 1$

Exercise 4

1. Write down each sequence and select the correct formula for the nth term from the list given.

(a) 5, 10, 15, 20, ...
(b) 10, 20, 30, 40, ...
(c) 7, 14, 21, 28,
(d) 9, 18, 27, 36, ...
(e) 100, 200, 300, 400, ...
(f) 8, 16, 24, 32, ...
(g) 11, 12, 13, 14, ...
(h) 3, 4, 5, 6, ...

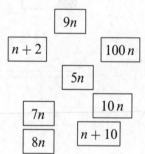

In Question **2** to **9** look carefully at how each sequence is formed.
Write down: (a) the 10th term
            (b) the nth term

2. 101, 201, 301, 401, ...   **3.** $1^2, 2^2, 3^2, 4^2, ...$

4. 12, 22, 32, 42, 52, ...   **5.** $(1 \times 2), (2 \times 3), (3 \times 4), (4 \times 5), ...$

6. $\frac{1}{100}, \frac{2}{100}, \frac{3}{100}, \frac{4}{100}, ...$ **7.** $\frac{1}{2}, \frac{2}{3}, \frac{3}{4}, \frac{4}{5}, ...$

8. $2^1, 2^2, 2^3, 2^4, ...$ **9.** 10, 100, 1000, 10000, ...

10. Here are three sequences and three expressions.
Write down each sequence and select the correct expression for its nth term.

A: 4, 7, 10, 13, ...
B: 1, 3, 5, 7, 9, ...
C: 2, 4, 8, 16, 32, ...

$(2n - 1)$

$(3n + 1)$

$(2n)$

Quadratic sequences

- In the sequence below we have written the first and second differences.

Sequence	9		15		25		39		57
First difference		6		10		14		18	
Second difference			4		4		4		

- If the second difference is constant it tells us about terms involving n^2.

+2	tells us it is	n^2
+4	tells us it is	$2n^2$
+6	tells us it is	$3n^2$

- Make a table

n	$2n^2$	Sequence
1	2	9
2	8	15
3	18	25
4	32	39

We see that the nth term of the sequence is $2n^2 + 7$.

Exercise 5

Use differences to help you find the nth term of these sequences.

1. 3, 9, 19, 33, 51, ...

2. 4, 7, 12, 19, 28, ...

3. 1, 7, 17, 31, 49, ...

4. 7, 16, 31, 52, 79, ...

5. 4, 16, 36, 64, 100, ...

6. 7, 13, 23, 37, 55

7. Here are three sequences and three expressions.
Write down each sequence and select the correct expression for its nth term.

A: 2, 6, 12, 20, ...
B: 5, 9, 13, 17, ...
C: 5, 8, 13, 20, ...

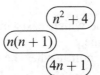

$n^2 + 4$

$n(n + 1)$

$4n + 1$

5.5 Using formulae

Substituting into formulae

- When a calculation is repeated
  many times it is often helpful to use
  a formula.

- A mobile phone company might
  use a formula like '£18 per month
  plus 20 pence per minute of call
  time'

  Let B = Phone Bill and
  m = call time in minutes.
  The formula is $B = 18 + 0.2m$

  (a) If $m = 10$, $B = 18 + 0.2 \times 10$
  $\qquad\qquad\quad B = 18 + 2$
  $\qquad\qquad\quad B = 20$
  (b) If $m = 35$, $B = 18 + 0.2 \times 35$
  $\qquad\qquad\quad B = 18 + 7$
  $\qquad\qquad\quad B = 25$

Exercise 1

1. Employees at 'Save-A-Lot' superstores are paid using the
   formula $W = 3.5h$, where W = Wage in £ and h = hours
   worked.
   (a) Find the wage for Bill who worked 8 hours
   (b) Find the wage for Sue who worked 40 hours.

2. Gary's Garage charges £30 call
   out charge plus an hourly rate of
   £25 per hour to attend roadside
   car breakdowns.
   The formula linking C (cost)
   and h (hours worked) is
   $C = 25h + 30$.
   (a) Find C if $h = 2$
   (b) Find C if $h = 10$

3. Serge has a mobile phone which costs him £15 per month plus
   20p per minute of call time.
   Find his total bill for a month when he has 30 minutes of call
   time.

4. Ayesha has a mobile phone contract with a different company.
   The formula linking B (phone bill) and C (call time in minutes)
   is $B = 28 + 0.05C$.
   (a) Find B, when $C = 100$
   (b) Find B, when $C = 10$

5. Here is a formula $c = 7t - 3$.
   Find the value of c when
   (a) $t = 2$ (b) $t = 10$ (c) $t = \frac{1}{2}$

6. Using the formula $p = 70 - 4x$, find the value of p when
   (a) $x = 1$ (b) $x = 10$ (c) $x = 20$

7. Below are several different formulae for z in terms of x.
   Find the value of z in each case.
   (a) $z = 15x - 60$, $x = 4$
   (b) $z = 2(3x + 5)$, $x = -1$
   (c) $z = \dfrac{10 - x}{2}$, $x = 5$

8. Here are two formulas involving the sides of a square:
   Perimeter, $P = 4L$
   Area, $A = L^2$

   (a) Find P, if $L = 15$
   (b) Find A, if $L = 9$
   (c) Find L, if $P = 80$
   (d) Find L, if $A = 100$

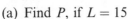

9. The perimeter of a rectangle (P) is linked to the length of its
   base (b) and height (h) by the formula $P = 2b + 2h$.
   (a) Find P, if $b = 5$ and $h = 3$.
   (b) Find P, if $b = 8$ and $h = 1$.
   (c) Find b, if $P = 30$ and $h = 5$

10. The charge, £C, made by a chef to cook for a group of p people
    is given by the formula

    $C = 7p + 65$.

    (a) What is the charge for a group of 20 people?
    (b) How many people are in the group if the charge is £282?

Exercise 2

1. Sophie's electricity bill consists of a 'Standing charge' of £11·20
   plus 8 pence for each unit used. The formula linking T (Total
   cost) and U (number of units used) is
   $T = 11.20 + 0.08U$
   (a) Find T if $U = 400$
   (b) Find Sophie's bill for 1000 units
   (c) Find the number of units used for a bill of £62·40.

2. The formula for the area of a
   triangle is $A = \frac{1}{2}BH$
   (a) Find A, if $B = 10$ and $H = 6$
   (b) Find B, if $A = 20$ and $H = 4$

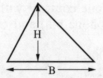

3. In the formulae below t is given in terms of n and a.
   Find the value of t in each case.
   (a) $t = 3a - 10n$; $a = 5$, $n = 1$
   (b) $t = 20a + 7n - 4$; $a = 1$, $n = 2$
   (c) $t = an + 11$; $a = 4$, $n = 3$
   (d) $t = 5(3a + 8n)$; $a = 0$, $n = 1$

4. Find the value of c, using the formulae and values given.
   (a) $c = mx + 9$; $m = -2$, $x = -3$
   (b) $c = 13t - t^2$; $t = 3$
   (c) $c = 3pq + p^2$; $p = 5$, $q = 0$
   (d) $c = (2a + b)^2$; $a = 1$, $b = 3$

5. If $T = 3y + 4y^2$, find the values of T when
   (a) $y = 1$ (b) $y = 3$ (c) $y = -1$
   [Remember $4y^2 = 4(y^2)$]

6. If $A = d^2 - 3d + 5$, find the values of A when
   (a) $d = 2$ (b) $d = 5$ (c) $d = 10$

7. The velocity, v, of an
   accelerating snowmobile is
   given by the formula
        $v = u + at$.
   Find v when $u = 0$, $a = 22.5$
   and $t = 3$.

8. An approximate formula linking temperatures in Fahrenheit and
   Celsius is $F = 2C + 30$, where F is temperature in degrees
   Fahrenheit and C is temperature in degrees Celsius.
   (a) Find F, if $C = 8$
   (b) Find C, if $F = 56$

9. The weight w of the brain of a
   Stegosaurus is connected to its
   age, A, and its intelligence
   quotient, I, by the formula
   $$w = \frac{A^2 + I/A}{5000}$$
   Find w, when $A = 20$ and $I = 2$.

Expressions

An expression does *not* have an equals sign. For example: $3x - 7$; $x^2 + 7y$; $ab - c^2$. These are all expressions.

Below are three expressions involving a, b, c and d. Find the value of each expression given that $a = 5$
$b = -2$
$c = 3$

(i) $3a - c$
$= 3 \times 5 - 3$
$= 15 - 3$
$= 12$

(ii) $2b + a$
$= 2(-2) + 5$
$= -4 + 5$
$= 1$

(iii) $3c - 4b$
$= 3(3) - 4(-2)$
$= 9 + 8$
$= 17$

Notice that the working goes *down* the page, not across. This helps to avoid errors.

Exercise 3

Find the value of the expressions given that $a = 5$
$b = -2$
$c = 3$
$d = -1$

1. $5a - c$ **2.** $2b + a$ **3.** $a + d$ **4.** $3c + b$

5. $4b + c$ **6.** $2d - a$ **7.** $5b + 10$ **8.** $a + b + c$

9. $b + c$ **10.** $7 - 2a$ **11.** $25 + 5b$ **12.** $3a + 4d$

13. $a^2 + b^2$ **14.** $ac + b$ **15.** $6 - 2c$ **16.** $d^2 + 4$

17. $ab + c$ **18.** $5d - 2c$ **19.** $b^2 + cd$ **20.** $5a + b + d$

21. $bd + c^2$ **22.** $2(a - c)$ **23.** $3(a + d)$ **24.** $a(c + b)$

In Questions **25** to **44** find the value of the expressions given that $m = 2$
$n = 0$
$p = -3$
$q = 4$

25. $mn + q$ **26.** $p + q$ **27.** $2m + p$ **28.** pq

29. $p^2 + n^2$ **30.** $2n - p$ **31.** $mp + n$ **32.** $4(p + q)$

33. $5(m + p)$ **34.** $10 - 2q$ **35.** $m - p$ **36.** $m(m + q)$

37. m^3 **38.** $p + p^2$ **39.** $5m + p + q$ **40.** p^3

41. $q(p + m)$ **42.** $m + m^2 + m^3$ **43.** $3q - 2p$ **44.** $n(m^2 - pq)$

45. Given that $x = 3$ and $y = -4$, find the value of each of the following expressions.
(a) $4x + y$ (b) $x^2 + y^2$ (c) $3x - y$
(d) $y^2 - x$ (e) $xy + 12$ (f) $5(x - y)$

46. Given that $p = -2$ and $q = 5$, find the value of each of the following expressions.

(a) $2p + q$ (b) $p - q$ (c) $3(p + q)$

(d) $p^2 - 2q$ (e) $pq + 12$ (f) $p(2q + 1)$

47. Given that $m = 6$ and $n = -1$, find the value of each of the following expressions.

(a) $m^2 + n^2$ (b) $3mn + 20$ (c) $m(5 - n)$

(d) $m + n + 1$ (e) $n(m^2 - n^2)$ (f) $mn(5m + 2n)$

'Make your Million' board game

Rules: You are given £10 at the start of the game. The object is to earn as much money as possible by substituting your dice score into the expression on your new square. The person with the biggest balance *when landing on the finish square* wins.

Example. Throwing a 5, then a 1.

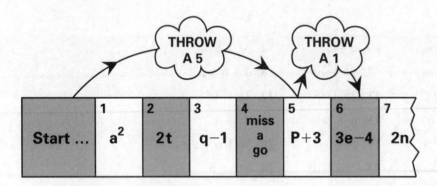

Score on dice	Expression on square	Value of expression using dice score	Balance £
—	—	—	10
5	P + 3	$5 + 3 = 8$	$10 + 8 = 18$
1	3e − 4	$(3 \times 1) - 4 = 3 - 4 = -1$	$18 - 1 = 17$
.	.	.	.
.	.	.	.

Note:

(i) Landing on 'miss a go' means that your balance remains the same.

(ii) Landing on 'back to start' means that your balance becomes *zero*.

BOARD FOR 'MAKE YOUR MILLION'

START ...	1 a^2	2 $2t$	3 $q-1$	4 MISS A GO	5 $p+3$	6 $3e-4$	7 $2m+3$

8 $3r$

17 $2e+5$	16 n^4	15 $3(b-2)$	14 c^3	13 MISS A GO	12 BACK TO START	11 $q-4$	10 f^2-9	9 $3n-1$

18 $2m+1$

19 $q-3$	20 f^2-16	21 $3n-5$	22 BACK TO START	23 $p+2$	24 a^2	25 $2t$	26 MISS A GO	27 $6-d$

28 $3r$

37 $8-d$	36 f^2-4	35 $p+5$	34 $6e-20$	33 $3n-4$	32 x^5	31 $2(b-3)$	30 $2m+4$	29 $2-d$

38 MISS A GO

39 a^2	40 $3(b-1)$	41 $2t$	42 f^2-9	43 MISS A GO	44 $p+1$	45 $6c$	46 $5e+4$	47 $2m+1$

48 $4-3e$

57 $p+6$	56 $3r$	55 $q-5$	54 BACK TO START	53 10^x	52 a^2	51 MISS A GO	50 $10-d$	49 $5(b-4)$

58 $12-2d$

59 MISS A GO	60 10^n	61 $q-1$	62 $p+4$	63 $2m+3$	64 $2t$	65 BACK TO START	... FINISH

Changing the subject of a formula

The method for changing the subject of a formula is generally the same as the method for solving an equation. The examples below are written side by side to make comparison easy.

(a) Solve the equation

$$3(x - 1) = 5$$

$3x - 3 = 5$ [Multiply out the brackets]

$3x = 5 + 3$ [Get the x term on its own]

$x = \dfrac{8}{3}$ [Divide by the coefficient of x]

(b) Make x the subject of the formula

$$a(x - b) = t$$

$ax - ab = t$

$ax = t + ab$

$x = \dfrac{t + ab}{a}$

Exercise 4

In Questions **1** to **12** make x the subject.

1. $x - a = e$

2. $x + t = h$

3. $a + b = x - g$

4. $v + x = m^2$

5. $h + x = 2h + n$

6. $s - t = t + x$

7. $x - y^2 = y$

8. $x - pq = m$

9. $n = x - mn$

10. $ax = c$

11. $mx + c = y$

12. $bx = a + c$

In Questions **13** to **24** make y the subject.

13. $my - c = n$

14. $5b = ay + b$

15. $a + c = ky - c$

16. $e + d = b + cy$

17. $t^2 + ty = p^2$

18. $ay - z = z$

19. $-m = fy$

20. $pqy = \pi r^2$

21. $aby = m + n$

22. $c^2 + d^2y = a^2$

23. $mty + c = d$

24. $xyz - p2 = q^2$

In Questions **25** to **36** make the letter in brackets the subject.

25. $a + tb = e$ $[t]$

26. $ab + kn = a^2$ $[k]$

27. $n + mw = 2n$ $[w]$

28. $s(y + a) = b$ $[y]$

29. $p(a + x) = b$ $[x]$

30. $z(c + d) = e$ $[z]$

31. $m(r + s) = t$ $[m]$

32. $b = a(m + n)$ $[n]$

33. $b^2 = w(y - a)$ $[y]$

34. $s = (u + v)t$ $[u]$

35. $m^2(a + e) = n^2$ $[e]$

36. $ab(a + x) = c$ $[x]$

5.6 Compound measures

Speed

When a cyclist moves at a constant speed of 30 metres per second, it means that he moves a distance of 30 metres in 1 second. In 2 seconds he moves 60 metres. In 3 seconds he moves 90 metres and so on. We see that the distance moved is equal to the speed multiplied by the time taken.

Remember: $\left(\text{distance} = \text{speed} \times \text{time}\right)$ ...①

We obtain two other formulas from ①:

Divide both sides by time: $\left(\dfrac{\text{distance}}{\text{time}} = \text{speed}\right)$ ...②

Divide both sides by speed: $\left(\dfrac{\text{distance}}{\text{speed}} = \text{time}\right)$ ...③

These three important formulas can be remembered using a triangle as shown. [D is at the top]

To find S: cover S, and you have $\dfrac{D}{T}$

To find T: cover T, and you have $\dfrac{D}{S}$

To find D: cover D, and you have S × T

Note: The above formulas can only be used for objects moving at a constant speed.

The units used for speed, distance and time in a question must be compatible.

- If the speed is in miles per hour, the distance must be in miles and the time must be in hours.
- If the speed is in metres per second, the distance must be in metres and the time must be in seconds.

(a) A speedway rider is travelling at a steady speed of 25 m/s.
  (i) How far does the rider travel in 3·2 s?
  (ii) How long does it take him to travel a distance of 11 m?

  (i) distance travelled = speed × time
                          = 25 × 3·2
                          = 80 m
  (ii) time taken = $\dfrac{\text{distance}}{\text{speed}}$
                   = $\frac{11}{25}$ = 0·44 s

(b) A bird flies at a speed of 8 m/s for 10 minutes. How far does it fly?

Change 10 minutes into 600 seconds.
distance = speed × time
         = 8 × 600
The bird flies 4800 m.

(c) A train travels 15 000 m in 20 minutes. Find the speed of the train in km/h.

Change 15 000 m into 15 km.
Change 20 minutes into $\frac{1}{3}$ hour.

speed of train = $\dfrac{\text{distance}}{\text{time}}$
              = $\dfrac{15}{\frac{1}{3}}$
              = 45 km/h

Exercise 1

1. A tram travels a distance of 200 m at a speed of 25 m/s. How long does it take?

2. A man runs at a speed of 7·5 m/s. How far will he run in 4 seconds?

3. An arctic tern flies a distance of 245 km in 9 hours. how fast does it fly?

4. A steamroller takes 180 seconds to travel 60 m. What is its speed, in m/s?

5. How long does it take a train to travel 270 km at a constant speed of 90 km/h?

6. A partridge flies 3 miles in 15 minutes. What is its speed in m.p.h.?

7. An aircraft flies at a speed of 940 km/h.
How far does it fly in $2\frac{1}{2}$ hours?

8. If a train travels 60 km in 20 minutes, how far does it go in one hour at the same speed?

9. A horse runs for $1\frac{1}{2}$ hours at a speed of 8 m.p.h. How far does it run?

10. A cyclist takes 30 minutes to travel 11 miles. At what speed does he cycle in m.p.h.?

11. Eurostar goes 420 km from London to Paris in just 3 hours. Find the average speed of the train.

12. Find the distance travelled:
(a) 65 m.p.h for 2 hours
(b) 8 cm/day for 5 days
(c) 5 m/s for 1 minute [units!]

13. A car takes 15 minutes to travel 20 miles. Find the speed in m.p.h.

14. A greyhound runs for 20 s at a speed of 22 m/s. How far does it run?

15. In the 1996 Olympics Donovan Bailey won the 100 m in 9·81 seconds and Michael Johnson won the 200 m in 19·37 seconds. Who ran at the faster average speed?

16. Find the time taken:
(a) 260 km at 20 km/h
(b) 2 km at 10 m/s
(c) 4 miles at 8 m.p.h.

17. A T.G.V. travels 567 km from Bordeaux to Paris at an average speed of 252 km/h. Find the arrival time in Paris, if it leaves Bordeaux at 1410.

18. A boat sails at a speed of 13 knots for 2 days. How far does it travel? [1 knot = 1 nautical mile per hour].

19. In a grand prix, the winning car passed the chequered flag 0·3 seconds ahead of the next car. Both cars were travelling at 84 m/s. What was the distance between the two cars?

20. * (a) Sam drives from Liverpool to York at an
average speed of 30 m.p.h.
How long will it take in hours and minutes?

(b) Mike takes $2\frac{1}{2}$ h to drive from Hull to
Newcastle. What was his average speed?

(c) Nikki drives from Preston to Newcastle at
an average speed of 42 m.p.h. and the
journey takes 2 h 40 min. What is the
distance from Preston to Newcastle?

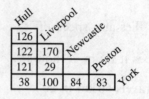

21. * A train leaves London at 0815 and arrives in York, 193 miles
away, at 1100. Find the average speed of the train.

Other compound measures

Exercise 2

In Questions **1** to **7** use
the exchange rates for
foreign currency shown.

Country	Rate of exchange
France (franc)	F 8·8 = £1
Germany (mark)	DM 2·65 = £1
Spain (peseta)	Pta 220 = £1
Italy (lire)	lire 2600 = £1
U.S.A. (dollar)	$ 1·6 = £1

1. Change the pounds into the foreign currency stated.
(a) £10 [marks]   (b) £1000 [lire]   (c) £20 [dollars]
(d) £100 [francs]   (e) £4 [pesetas]   (f) £1 million [marks]

2. A lorry costs £35 000 in Britain.
What is the price in marks?

3. A bottle of a certain wine costs
1100 pesetas in Spain and £6·99 in
Britain. In which country is the
wine cheaper?

4. A C.D. costs £13·99 in Britain
and $16 in the United States.
How much cheaper, in British
money, is the C.D. when bought
in the USA?

5. (a) Change DM 265 into pounds.
(b) Change DM 1 into pounds, to the nearest penny.

6. (a) Change $5000 into pounds, to the nearest penny.
(b) Change Lire 10 000 into pounds, to the nearest penny.

7. A motorist is fined 1000F in France for speeding. Can he pay
the fine if he has £150?

In Question **8** to **10**
use the formulas shown.

$$\text{Density} = \frac{\text{Mass}}{\text{Volume}} \quad \text{or} \quad \text{Mass} = \text{Density} \times \text{Volume}$$

8. Find the density of a metal if $100\,\text{cm}^3$ weighs 800 grams.

9. The density of copper is $9\,\text{g/cm}^3$. Find the mass of a copper bar of volume $20\,\text{cm}^3$.

10. A silver ring has a volume of
    $3\,\text{cm}^3$ and a mass of 36 grams.
    Find the density of the silver.

Questions **11** to **17** involve a variety of compound measures.

11. Heavy duty cable costs £1·50 per m. Find the cost of laying 3000 m of this cable.

12. A powerful mainframe computer
    can be hired at £55 per second.
    How much will it cost to hire the
    computer for 1 hour?

13. Gold plating costs £6 per cm^2.
    How much will it cost to plate
    this lid?

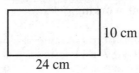

10 cm

24 cm

14. A gambler lost $3·2 million in one year. On average how much did the gambler lose per day? Give your answer to the nearest thousand dollars.

15. Good farmland is sold at £4000 per hectare (1 hectare $= 10\,000\,\text{m}^2$). Bacon farm has a rectangular field measuring 300 m by 80 m. Find the cost of the field.

16. The open box shown is made
    from metal weighing $5\,\text{g/cm}^2$.
    Find the weight of the box.

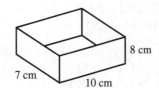

8 cm

7 cm

10 cm

17. The table shows the land area and population
    for four countries.
    (a) Work out the number of people per km^2
        for Ireland.
    (b) Which country has the *most* people per km^2?
    (c) Suppose all the people in Portugal had
        an equal area of land. How much would each
        person have in m^2? [$1\,\text{km}^2 = 1\,000\,000\,\text{m}^2$].

Country	Area in km^2	Population
Italy	301 000	58·3 million
Portugal	91 600	10·7 million
Ireland	68 900	3·4 million
Brazil	8 510 000	122·6 million

5.7 Mental arithmetic

Mental calculation strategies

In this section we will look at strategies for adding and subtracting numbers mentally. The introduction is followed by 12 questions to practise the new techniques.

A. 'Easy-to-add' numbers
When numbers are added the order of the numbers does not matter:

$$23 + 17 \quad = 17 + 23$$
$$41 + 9 + 110 = 110 + 9 + 41$$

Many pairs of numbers are easy to add together mentally

e.g. $17 + 23 = 40,$ $18 + 32 = 50,$ $33 + 7 = 40$

Practice questions
Look for 'easy-to-add' pairs of numbers in the following. If necessary change the order of the numbers in your head and then write down the answer without working.

1. $5 + 17 + 15$	**2.** $8 + 27 + 12$	**3.** $17 + 13 + 16$
4. $22 + 48 + 11$	**5.** $9 + 87 + 11$	**6.** $19 + 41 + 37$
7. $17 + 15 + 25$	**8.** $18 + 2 + 57$	**9.** $16 + 3 + 24$
10. $90 + 110 + 58$	**11.** $75 + 37 + 25$	**12.** $215 + 49 + 51$

B. Splitting the numbers
- $23 + 48$: $20 + 40 = 60$ and $3 + 8 = 11$
      So $23 + 48 = 60 + 11 = 71$

- $255 + 38$: $250 + 30 = 280$ and $5 + 8 = 13$
      So $225 + 38 = 280 + 13 = 293$

- Other way
   $23 + 48 = 23 + 40 + 8 = 63 + 8 = 71$
  $255 + 38 = 255 + 30 + 8 = 285 + 8 = 293$

  $576 - 43 = 576 - 40 - 3 = 536 - 3 = 533$
  $95 - 48 = 95 - 40 - 8 = 55 - 8 = 47$

Practice questions

1. $34 + 47$	**2.** $65 + 28$	**3.** $78 + 23$	**4.** $57 + 24$
5. $88 - 31$	**6.** $97 - 42$	**7.** $84 + 17$	**8.** $82 - 35$
9. $66 + 37$	**10.** $58 + 34$	**11.** $62 - 44$	**12.** $206 + 105$

C. Add/subtract
9, 19, 29 ... 11, 21, 31, ..., adjusting by one.

- $54 + 19 = 54 + 20 - 1 = 63$
- $77 + 41 = 77 + 40 + 1 = 118$
- $63 + 59 = 63 + 60 - 1 = 122$
- $54 - 31 = 54 - 30 - 1 = 23$
- $77 - 39 = 77 - 40 + 1 = 38$
- $95 - 29 = 95 - 30 + 1 = 66$

49 + 47 :
50 + 47 = 97
97 - 1 = 96

Practice questions
1. $67 + 21$
2. $37 + 51$
3. $36 + 39$
4. $76 + 29$
5. $45 + 29$
6. $70 - 21$
7. $80 - 41$
8. $44 + 58$
9. $33 + 96$
10. $91 - 37$
11. $53 + 41$
12. $48 - 23$

D Doubling large numbers: work from the left
- double 63 = double 60 + double 3 = 120 + 6 = 126
- double 79 = double 70 + double 9 = 140 + 18 = 158
- double 127 = double 100 + double 20 + double 7 = 200 + 40 + 14 = 254
- double 264 = double 200 + double 60 + double 4 = 400 + 120 + 8 = 528

Practice questions
1. double 54
2. double 38
3. double 67
4. double 73
5. double 28
6. double 79
7. double 115
8. double 126
9. double 87
10. double 66
11. double 237
12. double 342

E (a) Multiplying by doubling and then halving:
- 23×5 $23 \times 10 = 230$ $230 \div 2 = 115$
- 7×45 $7 \times 90 = 630$ $630 \div 2 = 315$
- 11×15 $11 \times 30 = 330$ $330 \div 2 = 165$

9 x 35
9 x 70 = 630
630 ÷ 2 = 315

(b) To multiply by 50, multiply by 100, then halve the result.
- 23×50 $23 \times 100 = 2300$ $2300 \div 2 = 1150$
- 38×50 $38 \times 100 = 3800$ $3800 \div 2 = 1900$

(c) To multiply by 25, multiply by 100, then divide by 4
- 44×25 $44 \times 100 = 4400$ $4400 \div 4 = 1100$
- 56×25 $56 \times 100 = 5600$ $5600 \div 4 = 1400$

Test 1

1. Add together 15, 25 and 70.

2. How many millimetres are there in a kilometre?

3. Find the length of the perimeter of a regular hexagon of side 20 cm.

4. Find the change from £10 when you buy two magazines for 75p each.

5. Give a rough estimate for the square root of 405.

6. Find the cost of 60 eggs at £1 per dozen.

7. A car is travelling at a steady speed of 30 m.p.h. How far does it go in 30 minutes?

8. Find the difference between $8\frac{1}{2}$ and 20.

9. Work out $1 + 2^2 + 3^3$.

10. Through what angle does the minute hand of a clock move between 8·50 and 9·00?

11. Work out roughly the area of a circle of radius 10 cm.

12. A bridge was built in Paris in 1780. How many years ago was that?

13. What is 40% as a fraction?

14. How many items costing £25 each can you buy with £200?

15. What five coins make 75p?

16. Calculate the length of the perimeter of a rectangular field measuring 110 m by 80 m.

17. Work out 0·03 multiplied by 1000.

18. Increase a price of £700 by 1%.

19. Answer true or false: $\left(\frac{1}{3}\right)^2$ is greater than $\frac{1}{3}$.

20. A large brick weighs 1 kg. Roughly what does it weigh in pounds?

21. Work out 1% of £150.

22. A plant grows 5 cm every day. How many days will it take to grow 60 cm?

23. A charity collection is made into a pile of 1000 20p coins. How much was collected?

24. Add together 67 and 77.

25. True or false: At a steady speed of 30 m.p.h. you go 1 mile every 2 minutes.

26. Glen has one of each of the coins from 1 p to 1 pound. What is their total value?

27. Three angles of a quadrilateral are 80°, 120° and 60°. What is the fourth angle?

28. How many inches are there in a foot?

29. A pie chart has a pink sector representing 25% of the whole chart. What is the angle of the sector?

30. Write down the next prime number after 31.

Test 2

1. Which of these fractions is the larger: $\frac{2}{3}$ or $\frac{3}{4}$?

2. True or false: a weight of 5 stones is less than 50 kg.

3. Work out 1% of £45.

4. Write in words the answer to $10 \times 100 \times 1000$.

5. Add together 5, 6, 7 and 8.

6. A car travels 30 miles in 30 minutes. How far will it travel at this speed in $\frac{3}{4}$ hour?

7. Sam spends 40% of his money on tapes and 50% of his money on clothes. If he had £5 left, how much did he have at first?

8. Write as a decimal: $\frac{1}{5}$ plus $\frac{1}{10}$.

9. A bucket contains 2 litres of milk. How much is left, in ml, after 100 ml is removed?

10. How many hours and minutes is it from 8·15 a.m. until noon?

11. One bag weighs 250 g. How many bags weigh 5 kg?

12. If 20 drinks cost £28, find the cost of 5.

13. A magazine costing 47p was paid for with a £1 coin. Which three coins were given as change?

14. What is the number which is 200 less than 2000?

15. Find the change from a £5 note after buying 3 pounds of apples at 20p per pound.

16. A girl faces West and turns clockwise through 1 right angle. In which direction is she now facing?

17. A film, lasting $1\frac{1}{2}$ hours, starts at 6·20. When does it finish?

18. Work out $100 - 4·9$.

19. Name the date which is 4 months before the 1st of February.

20. Write down the next prime number after 20.

21. Write $\frac{9}{10}$ as a percentage.

22. Of the people in a room, a half were French, ten per cent were German and the rest were Irish. What percentage were Irish?

23. In January, Steve weighs 70 kg. By July his weight is reduced by 10%. What does he weigh in July?

24. Find the total surface area of a cube of side 1 cm.

25. Work out $98 + 67$.

26. Write 1·6 recurring correct to one decimal place.

27. A 10p coin is 1·7 mm thick. What is the height of a pile of coins worth £1?

28. Estimate the length of a side of a square of area 50 cm².

29. Work out $\frac{2}{3}$ of £120.

30. True or false: 15 cm is about 6 inches.

Test 3

1. If I have 35 pence change from a ten pound note, how much have I spent?

2. My train leaves at 1618. How many minutes do I have to wait if I arrive at the station at 15.55?

3. The area of a triangle is 20 cm². Its base measures 10 cm. What is the height of the triangle?

4. One eighth of the children in a class walk to school. What percentage of the class is this?

5. A man was born in 1939. How old will he be in the year 2000?

6. A piece of string 54 cm long is cut into four equal parts. How long is each part?

7. True or false: Five miles is about the same as eight km.

8. The time in Miami is 5 hours earlier than the time in England. If I want to telephone Miami at 13.30 their time, what time will it be here?

9. I think of a number, multiply it by 2 and subtract 8. The result is 12. What number am I thinking of?

10. A plank of wood measures 2 metres by 50 cm. What is the area of the plank in square metres?

11. Which is largest: $\frac{1}{9}$ or 10%?

12. A bar of chocolate costs 18p. I buy as many as I can for 50p. How much change will I receive?

13. Add together 1, 2, 3, 4, 5, 6.

14. Write down ten million millimetres in kilometres.

15. By how much does a half of 130 exceed 49?

16. Work out two squared plus three squared.

17. Work out 5% of £40.

18. Two angles in a quadrilateral are each 80° and a third angle is 100°. What is the fourth angle?

19. Give an *estimate* for $291·4 \times 0·486$.

20. What number is a quarter of 140?

21. What is a half of a half of £60?

22. Rosie is going on a 2 week holiday. She leaves on the 5th of July. On what date will she return?

23. What is 2% as a simplified fraction?

24. What is the fraction exactly half way between $\frac{1}{4}$ and $\frac{1}{2}$?

For the last six questions you may write down the numbers in the question.

25. Work out 15% of £60.

26. I think of a number, subtract 8 and then divide by 2. The result is 1. What number am I thinking of?

27. My newspaper costs 45p per day from Monday to Friday and 50p on Saturday. How much do I spend on papers from Monday to Saturday?

28. The coordinates of the 4 corners of a rectangle are (1, 1), (5, 1), (5, 4) and (1, 4). What is the area of the rectangle in square units?

29. How many seconds are there in 1 hour?

30. A train journey of 480 miles took 4 hours. What was the average speed of the train?

Test 4

1. How many 20 pence coins are needed to make £8?

2. What number is mid-way between 0·1 and 0·2?

3. Work out 5% of £320.

4. True or false: one yard is approximately one metre.

5. Work out 2·2 divided by 10.

6. One sector of a pie chart represents 10% of the whole chart. what is the angle of the sector?

7. Find the approximate area of a circle of diameter 6 cm.

8. I pay for a pen costing £3.40 with a £20 note. What change do I receive?

9. Who is taller: Jan who is 5 feet tall or Sam who is 1 metre 10 tall?

10. A jar contains 1000 5p coins. Find the total value of the coins.

11. A rectangle measures 2·4 m by 10 cm. What is its perimeter in cm?

12. A rope of length 1 foot 4 inches is cut in half. How long is each piece?

13. A film started at 7·10 and finished at 10·55. How long was the film in hours and minutes?

14. Which has the longer perimeter: a square of side 10 cm or a circle of diameter 10 cm?

15. What fraction is equivalent to 40%?

16. Find the cost of 4 litres of wine at £1·25 per litre.

17. How many 24p stamps can be bought for £3?

18. Add together 34 and 164.

19. How long will it take to travel 60 miles at a speed of 30 m.p.h.?

20. Work out $3 \times 30 \times 30$.

21. What is the angle between the hands of a clock at 4 o'clock?

22. Find the cost of buying a newspaper for 40 days if each paper costs 20p.

23. Work out two fifths of £40.

24. How many prime numbers are there between 10 and 20?

25. I am thinking of a number. If I double it, add one and then square the result the answer is 25. What number am I thinking of?

26. Work out $\frac{1}{4}$ plus $\frac{1}{2}$ and give the answer as a decimal.

27. Divide one million by 100.

28. A rectangle has area 12 cm^2. What is the area of a rectangle whose sides are twice as long as those of this rectangle?

29. In a quiz, David got 15 out of 20. What percentage is that?

30. Increase a price of £300 by 10%.

5.8 Cross numbers

Make three copies of the pattern below and complete the puzzles using the clues given. To avoid confusion it is better not to write the small reference numbers 1, 2, ... 19 on your patterns. Write any decimal points on the lines between squares.

Part A

Across

1. 15% of 23
2. Next prime number after 23
4. One-third of 2409
5. Solve the equation $\dfrac{x}{5} = 3.8$
6. Area of a circle of diameter 30 cm (to 3 s.f.)
7. 11×466
9. $245^2 - (3^3 \times 2^2)$
13. $7 + 7^2 + 7^3$
15. $\frac{1}{4} + 3 \times 13$
17. Last 3 digits of (567×7)
18. 50 m written in cm
19. $75 \div 6$

Down

1. Volume of a cube of side 15 cm
2. One minute to midnight on the 24 hour clock
3. $\dfrac{5\cdot2}{0\cdot21} + \dfrac{17}{0\cdot31}$ to 3 s.f.
5. $(11\frac{1}{4})^2$ to the nearest whole number
8. $12 - \frac{1}{100}$
10. Prime number
11. $2^5 - 3$
12. $\frac{3}{7}$ of 3675
13. North-west as a bearing
14. $\frac{3}{4}$ of 11% of 12 000
16. Number of minutes between 1313 and 1745.

Check: There should be 5 decimal points in the puzzle.

Part B

Across

1. $\left(0.5 \div \frac{1}{2}\right) \times 123$
2. $1001 \div 77$
4. $200 - (4 \div 0.5)$
5. $\left(2^3 - 1\right)^2$
6. $33\frac{1}{3}\%$ of 2802
7. $8.14 - (1.96 \times 0.011)$ to 4 s.f.
9. 7391×11
13. $1^1 + 2^2 + 3^3 + 4^4$
15. $10^4 - [2 \times 20^2 + 9 \times 7]$
17. Number of minutes between 0340 and 1310.
18. $80^2 + 9^2 + 1^2$
19. 5% of 388

Down

1. (1 across) × (2 across)
2. $\frac{1}{2} + \frac{1}{3} + \frac{1}{4} + \frac{1}{5}$ to 3 d.p.
3. $20^2 - \sqrt{4}$
5. $42.2 - (8.1 \times 0.13)$ to 3 s.f.
8. 143×7
10. Inches in a foot.
11. $(2^3 \times 3^2) + 2^2 + 2$
12. Number of hours in a leap year.
13. 13% of £22.80, to the nearest penny
14. Next in the sequence 0.858, 8.58, 85.8, ...
16. 113×0.3

Check: There should be 6 decimal points in the puzzle.

Part C

Across

1. South-west as a bearing.
2. Inches in a yard
4. Last three digits of $(11^2 + 2^2)^2$
5. 4 score plus ten
6. $\left(26\frac{1}{2}\right)^2$, to the nearest whole number
7. $\frac{24.3}{1.9} + \frac{357}{24} + \frac{87.04}{3.7}$, correct to 2 d.p.
9. (13 across)^2 + (5 across)^2 + 103
13. $800 - 694$
15. $(550 - 3) \times 11$
17. $4 - 0.95$
18. $\frac{392.2}{(4.97 + 2.66)}$, correct to 2 d.p.
19. Next in the sequence 3, 5, 9, 17, 33, 65

Down

1. A quarter of 1110.
2. 11% of £323.11, to the nearest penny
3. $\frac{1.23}{1.4 - 0.271}$, correct to 2 d.p.
5. $30 \times 31 - 11$
8. Area, in cm^2, of a rectangle measuring 1.2 m by 11 cm
10. (A square number) − 1
11. 80% of 50
12. $\sqrt{(4 \text{ across})} \times (13 \text{ across}) + (10 \text{ down})$
13. Angle in degrees between the hands of a clock at 2.30
14. A quarter share of a third share of a half share of £152.16
16. $76.8 \div 0.4$

Check: There should be 7 decimal points in the puzzle.

Find the letters

Perform each calculation and write down the corresponding letter
from the list below, to make a sentence.

A. $5-8$; $-3-2$; $(-2)^2$; 3^2-20; $6\div(-6)$; $(-2)^2+3$; $-5+(-3)$; $(-49)\div(-7)$;
$-3-(-5)$; $(-5)\times(-1)$; $-7+11$; 4^2-4; $-1+13$; $(-1)^2\times4$; $30\div(-10)$;
$-2+9$; $(-3\frac{1}{2})\times2$; $(-8)\div(-2)$; $(-1)\div\frac{1}{10}$; $8-11$; $(-7)^2+(-1)^2$; $-6-5$;
$(-10)\times\frac{1}{2}$; $-3+10$; $(-2)^3-2$; $3-(-5)$; $(-3)\times(-4)$; $(-16)\div(-2)$; $2\div(-4)$?
$(-6-2)\times(-1)$; $2\times(-5)^2$; $(-6)^2\div3$; $(-2)\times(-2)\times2$; $-5+13$; $-12-(-2)$.

B. $-11+8$; $-3+(-2)$; $(-2)^2$; $1-12$; $3\times(-1)$; $1-(-6)$; $-2+4$; $(-3)\times(-4)$;
$6\div(-6)$; $(-16)\div2$; $(-3\frac{1}{2})\times-2$; 2^2-2; $1\div(\frac{1}{2})$; $-7-(-7)$; $(-3)^2-1$;
$-3-8$; $(-14)\div(-2)$; $-3+8$; $-8+15$; $(-1)^2+(-1)^2$; $(-5)\times2$; $-1-10$;
$(-2)\div(-\frac{1}{2})$; $-2-2-1$; 2^3; $4+(-6)$; $(-1)^5$; $-3+10$; $(-6)\div(-1)$; $2-(-3)$;
$(-3-4)\times(-1)$; $19-22$; $(-5)\times0$?
$(-2)^3\div(-2)$; $-2+7$; $1-(-6)$; $3\times(-1)$; $(-50)\div(-10)$; 0.1×20; $3^2+2^2-1^2$;
$(-1)\div(-\frac{1}{4})$; $(-2)^3-3$; $\frac{1}{7}\times49$; 4^3-66.

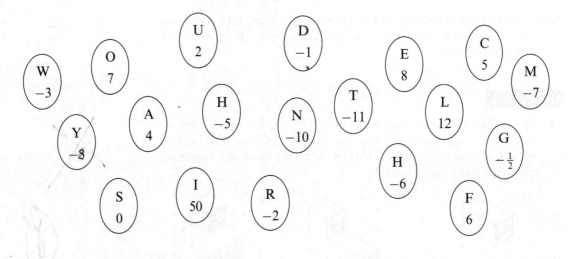

Part 6

6.1 3-D Objects

A drawing of a solid is a 2-D representation of a 3-D object. Below are two pictures of the same object.

(a) On squared paper.

(b) On isometric dot paper.

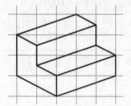

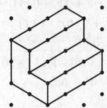

N.B. Most of the questions in this section are easier, and more fun to do, when you have an ample supply of 'unifix' or 'multilink' cubes.

Exercise 1

1. On isometric paper make a copy of each object below. Underneath each drawing state the number of 'multilink' cubes needed to make the object. (Make sure you have the isometric paper the right way round!)

(a)   (b) 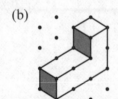 (c)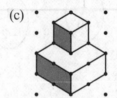

2. Using four cubes, you can make several different shapes. A and B are different shapes but C is the same as A.

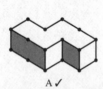   

A ✓   B ✓   C ✗

Make as many different shapes as possible, using four cubes, and draw them all (including shapes A and B above) on isometric paper.

3. Make the object shown using cubes.
Now draw the object *from a different view*.

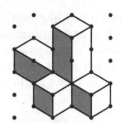

4. A   B   C   D

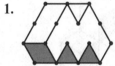

Build your own 3-D models of shapes A, B, C and D above. If possible use a different colour for each one.

Decide which of the shapes below are the same as shape A.
Repeat for shapes B, C and D.
Which shape is neither A, B, C nor D?

1.

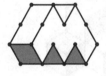

2.

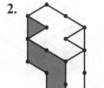

3.

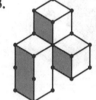

4.

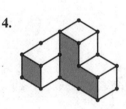

5.

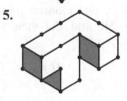

6.

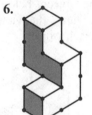

7.

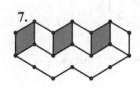

8.

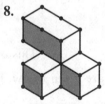

9.

10.

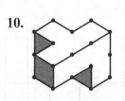

11.

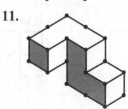

12.

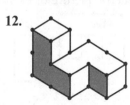

5. You need 27 small cubes for this question.
Make the four shapes below and arrange them into a $3 \times 3 \times 3$
cube by adding a fifth shape, which you have to find. Draw the
fifth shape on isometric paper. (The number next to each shape
indicates the number of small cubes in that shape).

(a)

(b)

(c)

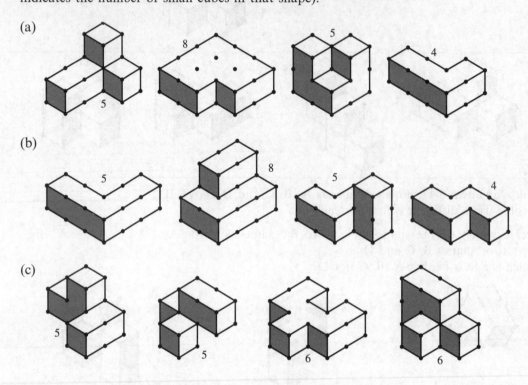

6. Make the objects below, using cubes. On squared paper, draw
the plan view, the view from the left and the view from the
right of each object.

(a)

(b)

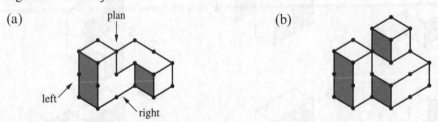

This object consists of 5 cubes   This object consists of 7 cubes.

7. Make each of the objects whose views are given below. Draw an
isometric picture of each one.

(a)   plan   left   right   (b)   plan   left   right

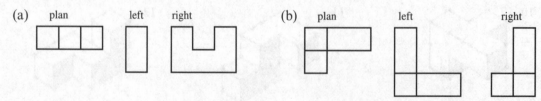

Nets for making shapes

- If the cube shown was made of cardboard, and you cut along some of the edges and laid it out flat, you would have a *net* of the cube.

  There is more than one net of a cube as you will see in the exercise below.

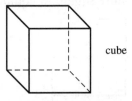

cube

- To make a cube from card you need to produce the net shown below complete with the added 'tabs' for glueing purposes.

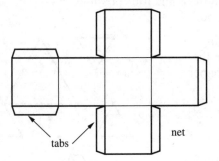

net

tabs

- In this section you will make several interesting 3D objects. You will need a pencil, ruler, scissors and either glue (Pritt Stick) or Sellotape.
  Score all lines before cutting out the net. This makes assembly of the object easier. Don't forget the tabs!

Exercise 2

1. Here are several nets which may or may not make cubes. Draw the nets on squared paper, cut them out and fold them to see which ones do make cubes.

(a)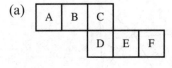

(b)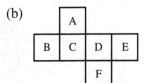

(c)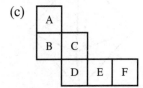

(d)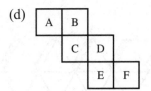

(e)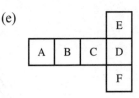

2. For the nets which *did* make cubes in Question 1, state which of the faces B, C, D, E or F was opposite face A on the cube.

3. Each diagram below shows *part* of the net of a cube. Each net needs one more square to complete the net.

(a) 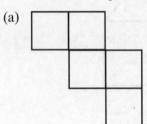   (b)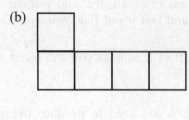

Cut out each of the shapes given and then draw the four possible nets which would make a cube with each one.

4. Some interesting objects can be made using triangle dotty paper. The basic shape for the nets is an equilateral triangle. With the paper as shown the triangles are easy to draw.

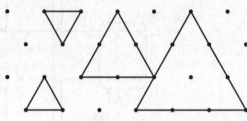

Make the sides of the triangles 3 cm or 4 cm long so that the objects are easy to make.
Here is the net of a tetrahedron.
Draw it and then cut it out.

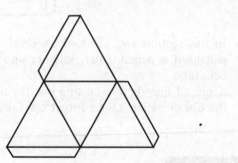

5. Here are two more.
   (a) Octahedron (octa: eight; hedron: faces)   (b) Icosahedron (an object with 20 faces)

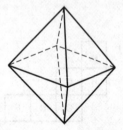

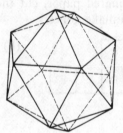

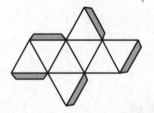

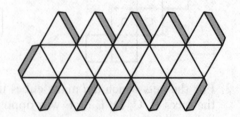

6.2 Circles

Circumference

- The perimeter of a circle is called *circumference*

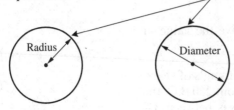

- The distance from the centre of a circle to the circumference is called *radius*

- The distance across a circle through its centre is called *diameter*

- The diameter is twice the radius. If we write d for diameter and r for radius then $d = 2r$

---

22 cm

A piece of string 22 cm long will make:

About 7 cm

A circle whose diameter is just over 7 cm.

If you divide the circumference of a circle by its diameter the number you obtain is always just over three.

$$\frac{\text{circumference}}{\text{diameter}} \approx 3$$

which means

Circumference $\approx 3 \times$ diameter

This provides a fairly good *estimate* for the circumference of any circle.

Pi

- For any circle, the exact value of the ratio $\left(\dfrac{\text{circumference}}{\text{diameter}}\right)$ is a number denoted by the Greek letter π.

  Since $\dfrac{c}{d} = \pi$, we can write $\boxed{c = \pi \times d}$. Learn this formula.

  Most calculators have a $\boxed{\pi}$ button, which will give the value of π correct to at least 7 significant figures: 3·141593.

- The number π has fascinated mathematicians for thousands of years. The Egyptians had a value of 3·16 in 1500 BC. In about 250 B.C. the Greek mathematician Archimedes showed that π was between $3\frac{10}{71}$ and $3\frac{10}{70}$. He considered regular polygons with many sides. As the number of sides in the polygon increased, so the polygon became nearer and nearer to a circle.

  Ludolph Van Ceulen (1540–1610) obtained a value of π correct to 35 significant figures. He was so proud of his work that he had the number engraved on his tombstone.

'Lovely sunny Greece, home of Pi'

Exercise 1

Make a table and complete it for Questions **1** to **12**. Make sure you write the correct units.

Number	Radius r	Diameter d	Estimated circumference	Calculated circumference
1	2 cm			
2				

1. 2 cm

2. 5 cm

3. 9 m

4. 30 mm

5. 8 km

6. 20 m

7. 25 m

8. 23 mm

9. 50 cm

10. 37 m

11. 68 km

12. 10 mm

A circular tin of diameter 9 cm rolls along the
floor for a distance of 3 m. How many times
does it rotate completely?

circumference $= \pi \times 9$

$\qquad = 28 \cdot 274334$ cm

$\qquad 3\,\text{m} = 300$ cm

Number of rotations $= \dfrac{300}{28 \cdot 274334}$

$\qquad\qquad\qquad = 10 \cdot 61$

The tin makes 10 *complete* rotations.

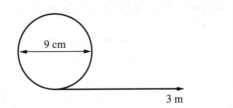

Exercise 2

Give your answers correct to 3 s.f. unless told otherwise.

1. The tip of the minute hand of a clock is 8 cm
   from the centre of the clock face. Calculate
   the distance moved by the tip of the minute
   hand in one hour.

2. A bicycle wheel of diameter 80 cm makes 20 complete rotations
   as the bicycle moves forward in a straight line. Find the
   circumference of the wheel and work out how far the bicycle
   moves forward. Give your answers in metres.

3. A tennis ball of diameter 7 cm and a golf ball of diameter
   4·25 cm roll in a straight line so that each ball makes 10
   complete revolutions. Which ball will go further and by how
   much? Give your answer to the nearest cm.

4. Which has the longer perimeter and by how much:
   an equilateral triangle of side 10 cm or a circle of diameter
   10 cm?

5. A tin of tomatoes has diameter 7·5 cm. The
   tin is wrapped in a paper cover which is long
   enough to allow 1 cm overlap for fixing.
   How long is the cover?

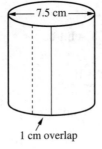

6. The wheels on Gill's bike have a diameter of
   62 cm. Gill rolls forward a distance of 1200 cm.
   Calculate how many times the wheels go
   round *completely*.

7. In a coin rolling competition Gemma rolls a one pound coin on
   its edge a distance of 4·2 m. A one pound coin has diameter
   2·2 cm. How many times did the coin rotate completely?

8. A car tyre has a radius of 37 cm.
   (a) How long is its circumference
       in cm?
   (b) How many complete rotations
       will the tyre make if the car
       travels 2 km?

9. A push chair has wheels of diameter 66 cm
   at the back and wheels of diameter 18 cm
   at the front. The pushchair travels in a
   straight line and the rear wheels rotate
   completely 84 times.

   (a) How far in metres does the chair travel?
   (b) How many complete rotations do the
       front wheels make?

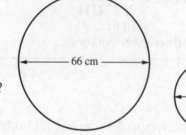

10. A newt walks around the edge of a circular pond at a speed of
    2 cm/s. How long will it take to walk all the way round if the
    radius of the pond is 1·3 m?

11. A trundle wheel can be used for measuring distances along roads
    or pavements. A wheel of circumference one metre is pushed
    along and distance is measured by counting the number of
    rotations of the wheel.
    Calculate the diameter of the wheel to the nearest mm.

12. The perimeter of a circular pond is 11·7 m. Calculate the
    diameter of the pond to the nearest cm.

13. The tip of the minute hand of Big Ben is 4·6 m from the centre
    of the clock face. Calculate the distance, in km, moved by the
    end of the minute hand in one year (365 days).

Perimeters

Calculate the perimeter of the shape.

The perimeter consists of a semi-circle
and 3 straight lines.

Length of semi-circle $= \dfrac{\pi \times 10}{2}$

$= \pi \times 5 \, \text{cm}$

∴ Perimeter of shape $= (\pi \times 5) + 4 + 10 + 4$

$= 33\cdot7 \, \text{cm (to 3 s.f.)}$

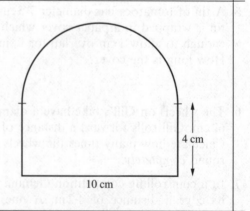

Exercise 3

Calculate the perimeter of each shape. All arcs are either semi-circles
or quarter circles.

1.

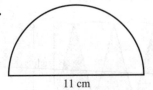

11 cm

2.

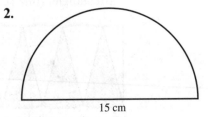

15 cm

3.

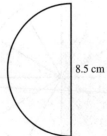

8.5 cm

4.

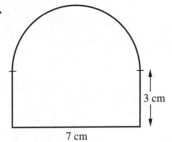

3 cm

7 cm

5.

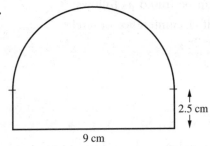

2.5 cm

9 cm

6.

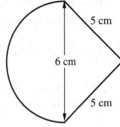

5 cm

6 cm

5 cm

7.

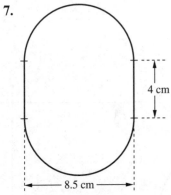

4 cm

8.5 cm

8.

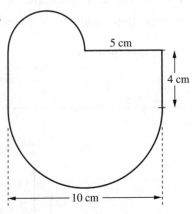

5 cm

4 cm

10 cm

9.

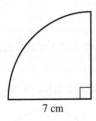

7 cm

10.

7.2 cm

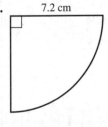

11.

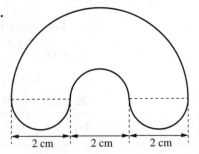

2 cm   2 cm   2 cm

12.

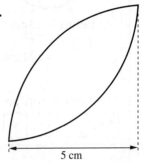

5 cm

Area of a circle

(a) The circle below is divided into 12 equal sectors

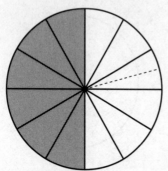

(b) The sectors are cut and arranged to make a shape which is nearly a rectangle. (one sector is cut in half).

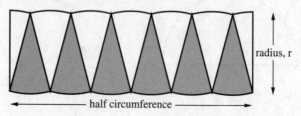

(c) The approximate area can be found as follows:

length of rectangle ≈ half circumference of circle

$$\approx \frac{\pi \times 2r}{2}$$

$$\approx \pi r$$

width of rectangle ≈ r

∴ area of rectangle ≈ $\pi r \times r$

$$\approx \pi r^2$$

If larger and larger numbers of sectors were used, this approximation would become more and more accurate.

This is a demonstration of an important result.

Area of a circle = πr^2 *Learn* this formula.

Note: πr^2 means $\pi(r^2)$.

Find the area of each shape.

(a)

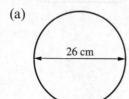

radius = 13 cm

area = πr^2

= 531 cm² (3 s.f.)

On a calculator, press:

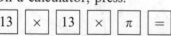

(b)

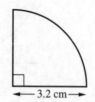

3.2 cm

The shape is a quarter circle

area = $\dfrac{\pi(3 \cdot 2)^2}{4}$

= 8·04 cm² (3 s.f.)

On a calculator, press:

| 3·2 | × | 3·2 | × | π | ÷ | 4 | = |

Exercise 4

In Questions **1** to **8** calculate the area of each circle correct to 3 s.f.

1.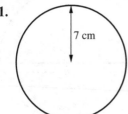
7 cm

2.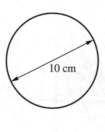
10 cm

3.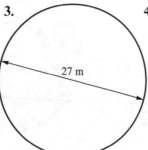
27 m

4.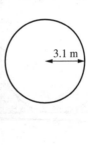
3.1 m

5.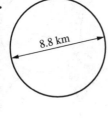
8.8 km

6.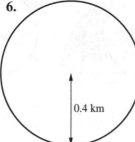
0.4 km

7.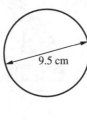
9.5 cm

8.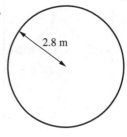
2.8 m

In Questions **9** to **22** give your answers correct to 3 s.f., where necessary.

9. When hunting for food, an eagle flies over a circular region of radius 3·5 km. What is the area of this region in km^2?

10. A carton of 'Verdone' weedkiller contains enough weedkiller to treat an area of $100 \, m^2$. A circular lawn at Hampton Court has a radius of 16·5 m. How many cartons of weedkiller are needed to treat this lawn?

In Questions **11** to **14** find the area of each shape. All arcs are either semi-circles or quarter circles and the units are cm.

11.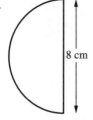
8 cm

12.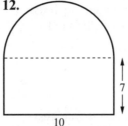
7
10

13.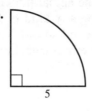
5

14.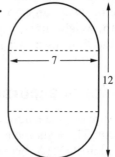
7
12

In Questions **15** to **20** find the shaded area. Lengths are in cm.

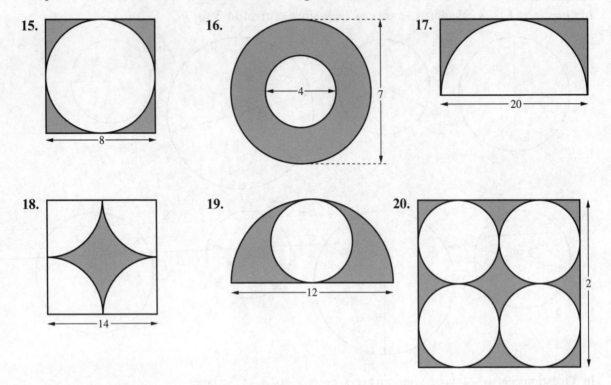

15.

8

16.

4

7

17.

20

18.

14

19.

12

20.

2

6.3 Errors in measurement

Errors

Whenever a quantity is measured the measurement is never *exact*. If you measure the thickness of a wire with a ruler, you might read the thickness as 2 mm. If you use a more accurate device for measuring you might read the thickness as 2·3 mm. An even more accurate device might give the thickness as 2·31 mm. None of these figures is precise.

They are all approximations to the actual thickness. This means that there is always an error in making any kind of measurement such as length, weight, time, temperature and so on. An error of this kind is not the same as making a mistake in a calculation!

Limits of accuracy

(a) Suppose the length of a book is measured at 22 cm to the nearest cm. The actual length could be from 21·5 to *almost* 22·5. We say 'almost' 22·5 because a length of 22·499 999 9.... would be

rounded off to 22 cm. The number 22·499 999.... is effectively
22·5 and we take 22·5 as the *upper limit*.
So in this case the *limits of accuracy* are 21·5 cm and 22·5 cm.
The maximum possible error is 0·5 cm.

(b) Using a ruler, the length of the nail shown
is measured at 3·8 cm to the nearest 0·1 cm.
In this case the limits of accuracy are
3·75 cm and 3·85 cm.

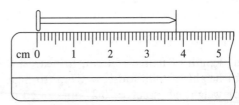

(c) Sometimes measurements are given 'to the nearest 10, 100, etc.'
Suppose the length of a lake is measured at 4200 m to the
nearest 100 m. The limits of accuracy are 4150 m and 4250 m.

(d) Summary. In (a), (b) and (c) above:

> The maximum possible error is always half of the level of accuracy.

In part (a) the level of accuracy is the nearest cm. The maximum
possible error is 0·5 cm.

In part (b) the level of accuracy is the nearest 0·1 cm. The maximum
possible error is 0·05 cm.

(e) Here are some further examples:

	lower limit	upper limit
(i) The weight of an apple is 43 g to the nearest gram	42·5 g	43·5 g
(ii) The temperature of a room is 22·9 °C to one decimal place	22·85 °C	22·95 °C
(iii) The length of a road is 780 m to the nearest 10 m	775 m	785 m

Exercise 1

1. The height of a table is measured at 84 cm to the nearest cm
write down the least possible height of the table.

2. A postmaster weighs a parcel at 5·2 kg to the nearest 0·1 kg.
Write down the greatest possible weight of the parcel.

3. The length and width of a rectangle
are measured to the nearest 0·1 cm,
as shown.
   (a) Write down the upper limit for
       the length of the rectangle.
   (b) Write down the lower limit for
       the width of the rectangle.

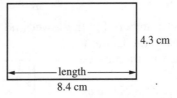

4. The height of a man is measured at 5 feet 8 inches, to the nearest
inch. Write down the greatest possible height of the man.

5. A scientist weighs a bird's egg at 3·7 g, correct to one decimal
place. What is the least possible weight of the egg?

6. A book states that the distance from the Earth to the Sun is 93 million miles correct to the nearest million miles. What is the shortest possible distance?

7. In a 200 m race a sprinter is timed at 20·63 seconds to the nearest 0·01 seconds. Write down the least possible time.

8. Copy and complete the table:

	lower limit	upper limit

(a) length of nail = 5·6 cm, to nearest 0·1 cm
(b) height of lighthouse = 37 m, to nearest m
(c) weight of insect = 0·27 mg, to 2 d.p.
(d) temperature in oven = 230 °C, to nearest 10 °C
(e) length of oil pipeline = 315 km, to nearest km

9. The length of a post is 15·4 cm, to the nearest mm. The length lies between:

A	B	C
15·3 cm and 15·5 cm	15 cm and 16 cm	15·35 cm and 15·45 cm

10. The weight of a coin is 7 g, to the nearest gram. The weight lies between:

A	B	C
6 g and 8 g	6·9 g and 7·1 g	6·5 g and 7·5 g

11. The thickness of some glass is 3·22 cm, to the nearest 0·01 cm. The thickness lies between:

A	B	C
3·215 and 3·225 cm	3·21 cm and 3·23 cm	3·219 cm and 3·221 cm

12. Chuck and Dave each weigh a different frog and they both say that their frog weighs 27 grams to the nearest gram.
What is the greatest possible difference in the actual weights of the two frogs?

13. The diagram shows the frame for a picture. The width inside the frame is 32 cm to the nearest cm.
(a) Write down the smallest possible real width of the frame.
(b) The number line shows all the possible real widths of the frame.

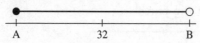

Write down the correct numbers for the lower and upper limits.
(c) The glass to go inside the frame is measured at 31·5 cm to the nearest tenth of a cm.
What is the greatest possible real width of the glass?
(d) Can you be sure that the glass will fit in the frame? Explain your answer.

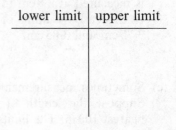

32 cm

Frame

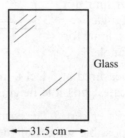

Glass

31.5 cm

6.4 Volume

- Volume is a measure of how much physical space an object takes up.
  The volume of a container, like a bottle or a tin, is the quantity of liquid it could contain.

- We measure volume in cubic centimetres. This is a natural choice because we measure length in centimetres, and area in square centimetres.

Exercise 1

For Questions **1** to **6** copy the object onto paper and write down the volume of the object. All the objects are made from centimetre cubes.

1.

2.

3.

4.

5.

6.

Find the volume of each object

7.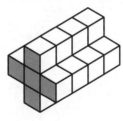

8.

9.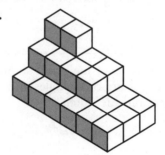

10.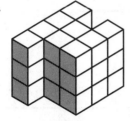

11.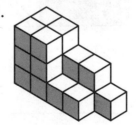

12.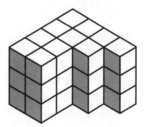

Cuboids

To find the volume of a cuboid, you
multiply the length by the width
by the height.

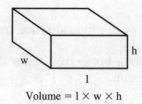

Volume = l × w × h

The volume of a cuboid measuring 2 cm by 3 cm by 5 cm is 30 cm³.
(pronounced '30 centimetres cubed')

Prisms

The volume of the object shown can
be found by dividing the object into
layers, indicated by the thick lines.
Each layer contains 6 cubes and there
are 4 layers. The volume of the object
is 24 cm³.

An object which can be cut into identical layers like this is called a
prism.
A prism has the same cross section throughout its length.

Volume of a prism = (Area of cross section) × (length)

Any cuboid is a prism since it has the same cross section throughout
its length.

Find the volume of the prism shown.
All the angles are right angles and
the dimensions are in cm.

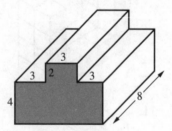

Area of cross section = 4 × (3 + 3 + 3) + (3 × 2)
$$= 42 \text{ cm}^2.$$
Volume of prism = 42 × 8
$$= 336 \text{ cm}^3$$

Liquids

The volume of a liquid is usually given in litres or millilitres (ml)

$1000 \, \text{ml} = 1$ litre

and $1 \, \text{ml}$ is the same as $1 \, \text{cm}^3$.

The diagram shows a cubic metre of water.

$$1 \, \text{m}^3 = 100 \times 100 \times 100 \, \text{cm}^3$$
$$= 1\,000\,000 \, \text{cm}^3$$
So $1 \, \text{m}^3 = 1\,000\,000 \, \text{ml}$
$$= 1000 \text{ litres}$$

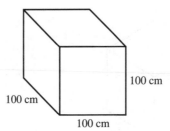

100 cm

100 cm

100 cm

Exercise 2

Find the volume of each prism.

1. Area of end = 3 cm²

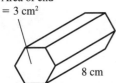

8 cm

2. Area of end = 7 m²

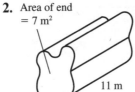

11 m

3.

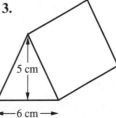

5 cm

←—6 cm—→

4.

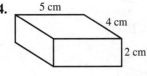

5 cm

4 cm

2 cm

5.

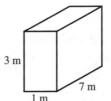

3 m

1 m

7 m

6.

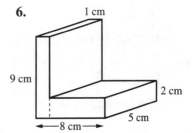

1 cm

9 cm

2 cm

5 cm

←—8 cm—→

In Questions **7** to **9** find the volume of each prism. All the angles are right angles and the dimensions are in centimetres.

7.

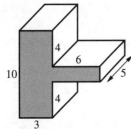

10

4

6

5

4

3

8.

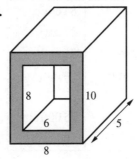

8

10

6

5

8

9.

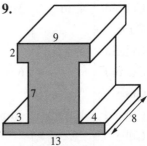

9

2

7

3

1

4

8

13

Finding an unknown length

(a) Find the height of the cuboid, given that its volume is 25 cm³.

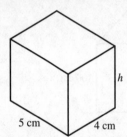

5 cm   4 cm

$$5 \times 4 \times h = 25$$
$$20h = 25$$
$$h = \tfrac{25}{20}$$
$$h = 1.25 \text{ cm}$$

(b) A box with a square base has a height of 5 cm and a volume of 80 cm³. Find the length of each side of the square base.

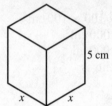

5 cm

$$x \times x \times 5 = 80$$
$$x \times x = \tfrac{80}{5}$$
$$x \times x = 16$$
$$x = 4 \text{ cm}$$

Exercise 3

1. Find the length x.

(a)

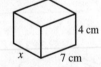

4 cm

x 7 cm

volume 5 70 cm³

(b)

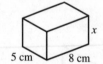

x

5 cm   8 cm

volume 5 120 cm³

(c)

x

2 cm   6 cm

volume 5 18 cm³

(d)

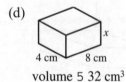

x

4 cm   8 cm

volume 5 32 cm³

(e)

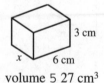

3 cm

x 6 cm

volume 5 27 cm³

(f)

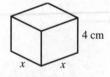

4 cm

x x

volume 5 100 cm³

2. Copy and complete the table.

	Shape	Length	Width	Height	Volume
(a)	Cuboid	4 cm	3 cm		84 cm³
(b)	Cube				27 cm³
(c)	Cuboid	5 m		2 m	75 m³
(d)	Cuboid		6 mm	3 mm	54 mm³
(e)	Cube	5 cm			
(f)	Cuboid	100 cm	50 cm		25 000 cm³
(g)	Cube				1000 cm³

3. 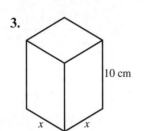 The box shown has a square base of side x cm and height 10 cm. Find x if the volume of the box is 490 cm³.

10 cm

x x

4. The solid metal cuboid shown is melted down and recast as a solid cube. How long is each side of the cube?

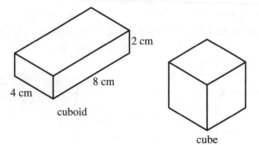

2 cm

8 cm

4 cm

cuboid

cube

5. 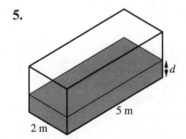 A children's paddling pool has a base 2 m by 5 m. There is 5 m³ of water in the pool.
Calculate the depth of water d in the pool, stating the units clearly.

d

5 m

2 m

6. A solid sculpture weighing 6 kg is made from metal and 1 cm³ of the metal weighs 10 g.
(a) Find the volume of the sculpture.
(b) The sculpture is melted down and made into a solid cuboid measuring 3 cm × 2 cm × x cm. Find x.

7. The inside of a spaceship orbiting the earth is a cuboid measuring 2 m by 3 m by 2 m. Unfortunately air is leaking from the spaceship at a rate of 1000 cm³/sec. How long will it take for all the air to leak out?

Cylinders

A cylinder is a prism because it
has the same cross section throughout
its length.

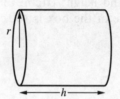

Volume = (area of cross section) × (length)

$$\text{Volume} = \pi r^2 h$$

(a) A cylinder has radius 3 cm and
length 10 cm.
Find the volume of the cylinder.

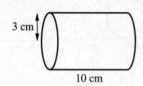

$V = \pi r^2 h$
$V = \pi \times 3^2 \times 10$
$V = 283 \text{ cm}^3$ (to 3 s.f.)

(b) Find the capacity, in litres, of the oil
drum shown

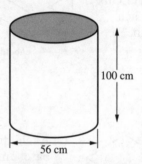

The oil drum is a cylinder.
Volume of oil drum $= \pi \times 28^2 \times 100$
$\qquad\qquad\qquad = 246\,000 \text{ cm}^3$ (to 3 s.f.)
Capacity of oil drum $= 246$ litres (to 3 s.f.)

Exercise 4

Give answers correct to 3 significant figures, where necessary.

1. Find the volume of each cylinder.

(a)
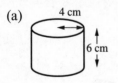

(b)
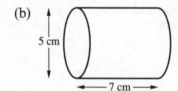

(c)
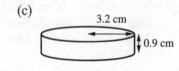

(d)
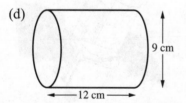

(e)
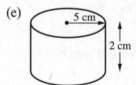

(f)
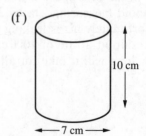

2. Cylinders are cut along the axis of symmetry. Find the volume of each object.

(a)

(b)

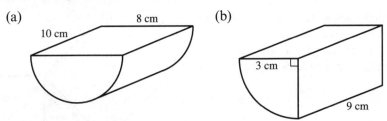

3. Find the volume in litres of a cylindrical tank of radius 40 cm and height 35 cm.

4. The lead in an unsharpened pencil is in the shape of a cylinder of diameter 2 mm and length 16 cm. Find the volume of the lead in cm³.

5. A mine shaft 200 m long is dug with the cross-section shown. Calculate the volume of earth which must be removed to make way for the shaft.

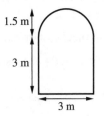

6. Water is poured from the full cylinder A into the empty tank B. Will all the water go in?

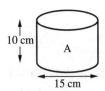
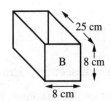

7. An empty cylindrical tank of height 70 cm and diameter 1 metre is to be filled from a tap which delivers water at the rate of 150 ml per second. How long will it take to fill the tank? Give your answer to the nearest minute.

8. How many times can the cylindrical glass be filled from the large drum which is full of milk?

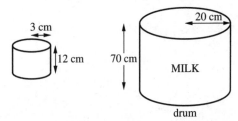

6.5 Pythagoras' theorem

Below are two dissections which demonstrate a result called
Pythagoras' theorem. Pythagoras was a famous Greek
mathematician who proved the result in about 550 B.C.
The first dissection works only for isosceles right angled
triangles.

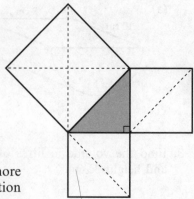

The second dissection, which is Perigal's dissection, is more
impressive. It has been left for you to complete as a demonstration
of Pythagoras' Theorem.

- Copy triangle ABC on dotted paper.

- Find the point X which is the centre of square ①

- Draw PQ parallel to AB and draw RS perpendicular to
  PQ.

- Cut out square ② and the four pieces of square ①

- Rearrange these five pieces to fit exactly into square ③

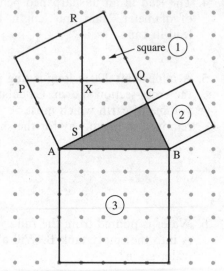

Both of these dissections demonstrate Pythagoras' theorem....

> *'In a right angled triangle, the square on the hypotenuse is equal to
> sum of the squares on the other two sides.'*

The 'hypotenuse' is the longest side in a right angled triangle.

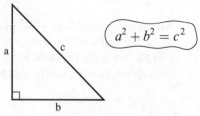

$$a^2 + b^2 = c^2$$

The theorem can be used to calculate the third side of a right angled triangle when two sides are known.

Find the length x

(a)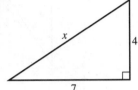

$x^2 = 4^2 + 7^2$
$x^2 = 16 + 49$
$x^2 = 65$
$x = \sqrt{65}$
$x = 8 \cdot 06$ (3 s.f.)

(b)

$x^2 + 3^2 = 6^2$
$x^2 + 9 = 36$
$x^2 = 27$
$x = \sqrt{27}$
$x = 5 \cdot 20$ (3 s.f.)

Remember: (The side on its own in the equation is the hypotenuse)

Exercise 1

Give your answers correct to 3 s.f. where necessary. The units are cm unless you are told otherwise.

1. Find x.

(a)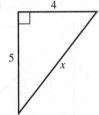

(b)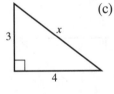

(c)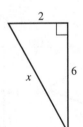

(d)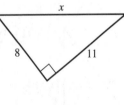

(e)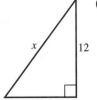

(f)

(g)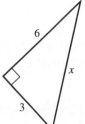

(h)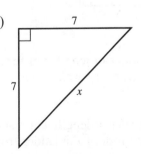

2. Find y.

Hint: In part (a) write $y^2 + 4^2 = 8^2$

(a)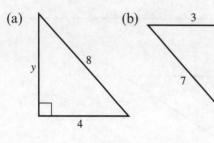

(b)

(c)

(d)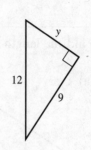

(e)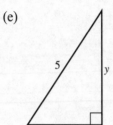

(f)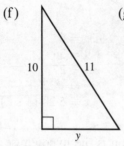

(g)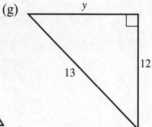

(h)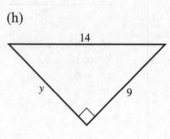

3. Find the side marked with a letter. It may be the hypotenuse or one of the other sides.

(a)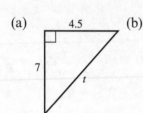

(b)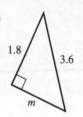

(c)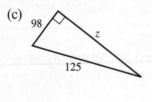

(d)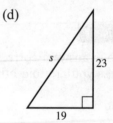

(e)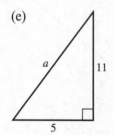

(f)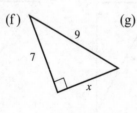

(g)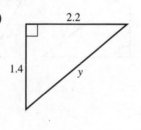

(h)

4. A ladder of length 5 m rests against a vertical wall, with its foot 2 m from the wall. How far up the wall does the ladder reach?

5. A ladder of length 4 m reaches 3·2 m up a vertical wall. How far is the foot of the ladder from the wall?

6. A boat sails from the harbour to the lighthouse. The lighthouse is 11 km to the south and 8 km to the east of the harbour.
Calculate the distance between the harbour and the lighthouse.

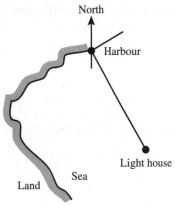

7. A farmer digs a drainage ditch across a rectangular field.
How long is the ditch, to the nearest metre?

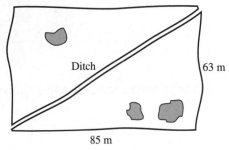

8. The square and the rectangle have the same perimeter. Which has the longer diagonal and by how much?

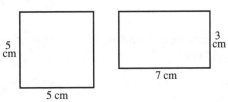

Exercise 2

Give answers correct to 3 s.f. where necessary. The units are cm unless you are told otherwise.

1. Find the side marked with a letter

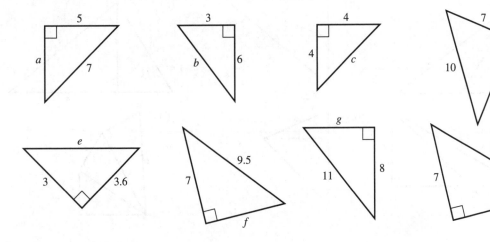

2. A ship sails 40 km due south and then a further 65 km due east. How far is the ship from its starting point?

3. A square has diagonals of length 24 cm. Find the length of a side of the square to the nearest cm.

4. What is the longest shot you could have to play on a snooker table measuring 12 feet by 6 feet?

5. Calculate the height of the isosceles triangle shown.

6. Calculate the vertical height and hence the area of an equilateral triangle of side 14 cm.

7. Calculate the length of a side of the largest square which can be drawn inside a circle of radius 10 cm.

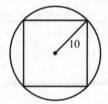

8. [More difficult] Find the length x

(a)
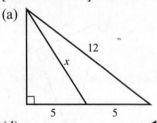

(b)
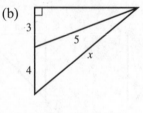

(c)
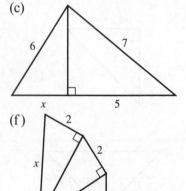

(d)
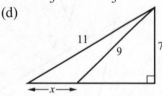

(e)
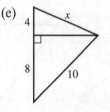

(f)

6.6 Constructions

There are several ways in which different triangles can be described.
By convention we use:
S   when a side is given,
A   when an angle is given,
R   when a right angle is given,
H   when the hypotenuse of a right angled triangle is given.

Here are five examples.

1.
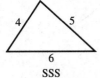
SSS

[All 3 sides]

2.

SAS

[2 sides and the included angle]

3.

ASA

[2 angles and one side]

4.

RHS

[right angle, hypotenuse and side]

5.

SSA

[2 sides and an angle (not included)]

Exercise 1

1. Using a ruler, protractor and a pair of compasses construct each of the triangles **1**, **2**, **3** and **4** above.
   Label the triangles SSS, SAS, ASA, RHS.

2. Construct triangle **5** above and, using a pair of compasses, show that it is possible to construct two different triangles with the sides and angle given.

3. Construct the triangle shown. You are given SSA.
   Show that you can construct two different triangles with the sides and angle given.

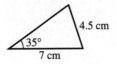

4. Copy and complete these two sentences:

   'When we are given SSS, SAS, ☐ or ☐ the constructed triangle is unique.
   When we are given ☐ the triangle is not unique and it is sometimes possible to construct two different triangles.'

Standard constructions (using compasses)

(a) Perpendicular bisector of a line segment AB.

With centres A and B draw two arcs.
The perpendicular bisector is shown as a broken line.

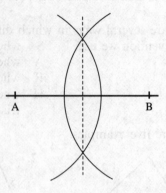

(b) Perpendicular from a point P to a line.

With centre P draw an arc
to cut the line at A and B.

Construct the perpendicular
bisector of AB.

(c) Perpendicular from a point P on a line.

With centre P draw arcs to cut the
line at A and B. Now bisect AB
as above in (a).

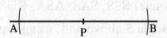

(d) Bisector of an angle

With centre A draw arc PQ.
With centres at P and Q draw two more arcs.
The angle bisector is then drawn.

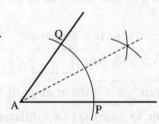

Exercise 2

Do not use a protractor.

1. Draw a line AB of length 6 cm. Construct the perpendicular bisector of AB.

2. Draw a line and a point P about 5 cm away. Construct the line which passes through P which is perpendicular to the line.

P.

_____

3. Draw a line and on it mark a point Q. Construct the perpendicular from Q.

4. Draw an angle of about 70° and construct the bisector of the angle.

5. Construct an equilateral triangle of side 6 cm.

6. Draw *any* triangle KLM and construct (a) the perpendicular bisector of KL
   (b) the perpendicular bisector of KM
   Mark the point of intersection X.

   Take a pair of compasses and, with centre at X and radius KX, draw a circle through the points K, L and M.
   This is the *circumcircle* of triangle KLM.

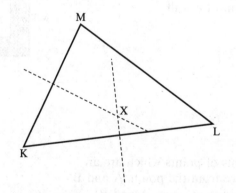

Repeat the construction for another triangle of different shape.

7. Draw any triangle ABC and construct the bisectors of angles B and C to meet at point Y.

   With centre at Y draw a circle which just touches the sides of the triangle.
   This is the *inscribed* circle of the triangle.

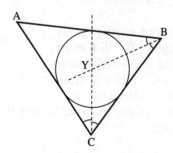

6.7 Locus

A locus is the set of points which fit a certain description. Sometimes a locus can be described in words, sometimes it is better to draw a diagram. The plural of locus is loci.

(a) Suppose television reception is 'good' within 100 km of a transmitter T. The diagram shows the locus of points where the reception is 'good'.

Here the locus is the boundary and all the points inside the circle.

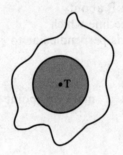

(b) In this diagram the shaded region shows the locus of points inside a room which are within 1 m of a wall.

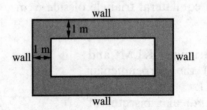

(c) Find the locus of points which are an equal distance from the points A and B. (we say 'equidistant' from A and B).

A•

•B

> This is an important and common locus construction.

Take a pair of compasses and set the radius at more than half the length AB. With centre A draw two arcs. With the same radius and centre B draw two more arcs. Draw a straight line through the points where the arcs cut. This is the locus of points equidistant from A and B (shown with a broken line).

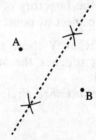

Exercise 1

1. Draw the locus of a point P which moves so that it is always 4 cm from a fixed point A.

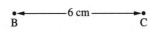

2. Draw points B and C 6 cm apart. Draw the locus of a point P which moves so that it is equidistant from B and C.

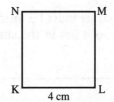

3. Draw the square KLMN. A tiny spider wanders around inside the square so that it is always nearer to corner K than to corner L. Shade the region to show the locus of the spider.

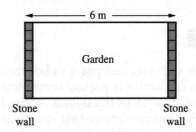

4. A newt crawls across a rectangular garden so that it is always at an equal distance from the two stone walls. Draw a sketch to show the locus of the newt.

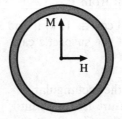

5. (a) Describe in words the locus of M, the tip of the minute hand, as the time changes from 3 o'clock to 4 o'clock.
   (b) Sketch the locus of H, the tip of the hour hand, as the time changes from 3 o'clock to 4 o'clock.

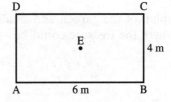

6. The diagram shows a rectangular room ABCD. Draw three diagrams with a scale of 1 cm to 1 m to illustrate the following loci:
   (a) Points in the room up to 3 m from A
   (b) Points in the room up to 2 m from E, the centre of the room.
   (c) Points in the room equidistant from A and B.

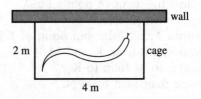

7. A snake's cage is built against a wall, as shown. The public are not allowed to be within one metre of the cage.
   Sketch the cage and show the locus of points where the public are not allowed.

A submarine is known to be within 26 km
of port P. The submarine is also known
to be within 15 km of port Q.
Show the region where the submarine
must be.

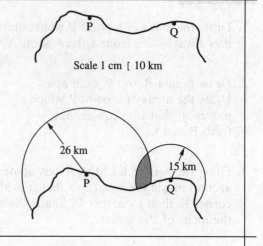

Scale 1 cm [10 km

(a) Draw an arc of radius 2·6 cm
    with centre P.
(b) Draw an arc of radius 1·5 cm
    with centre Q.
(c) The submarine must lie inside
    both arcs so it lies in the shaded
    region.

Exercise 2

1. Inspector Clouseau has put a radio transmitter on a
   suspect's car, which is parked somewhere in Paris.
   From the strength of the signals received at points
   R and P, Clouseau knows that the car is
   (a) not more than 40 km from R, and
   (b) not more than 20 km from P.

   Make a scale drawing [1 cm ≡ 10 km] and show
   the possible positions of the suspect's car.

2. A treasure is buried in the rectangular
   garden shown. The treasure is: (a) within
   4 m of A and (b) more than 3 m from the
   line AD.
   Draw a plan of the garden and shade the
   points where the treasure could be.

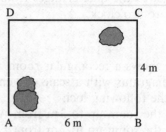

3. Draw four copies of square KLMN
   and show the locus of points *inside*
   the square which are:
   (a) within 3 cm of the mid point of KL,
   (b) equidistant from K and M,
   (c) nearer to M than to K,
   (d) more than 5 cm from N.

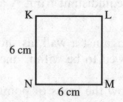

4. A goat is tied to one corner on the outside of a barn.
The diagram shows a plan view.
Sketch a plan view of the barn and show the locus of points where the goat can graze if the rope is 4 m long.

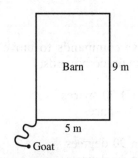

5. The diagram shows the plan view of a tall building (shaded), a flag F and two observers A and B.
(a) Can observer A see the flag?
(b) Can observer B see the flag?
(c) Copy the diagram and show the locus of points from which F cannot be seen.

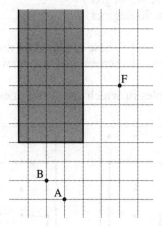

6.* A rectangular paving slab is rotated 90° about corner A as shown.
(a) Copy the diagram and use a pair of compasses to draw the locus of X during the first rotation.
(b) The slab is then rotated a further 90° clockwise, this time about the corner B. Draw the new position of the slab. Use compasses to draw the path of X during this second rotation.

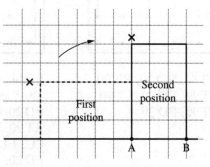

7.* Draw two points A and B 10 cm apart.

Place the corner of a piece of paper (or a set square) so that the edges of the paper pass through A and B.
Mark the position of corner C.
Slide the paper around so the edge still passes through A and B and mark the new position of C. Repeat several times and describe the locus of the point C which moves so that angle ACB is always 90°.

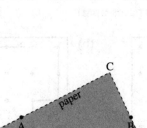

LOGO

LOGO is used to give commands to move a turtle on a computer.
Here is a list of the main commands.

FD 20   Go ForwarD 20 spaces
BK 30   Go BacK 30 spaces

RT 90   Right Turn 90 degrees
RT 45   Right Turn 45 degrees
LT 90   Left Turn 90 degrees

PU   Pen Up   } These are used to move across the
PD   Pen Down   } screen without drawing a line.

Here are two examples in which the turtle goes from A to B.

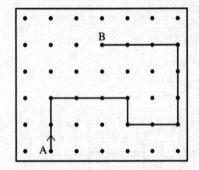   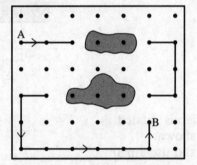

FD 20, RT 90, FD 30, RT 90,   In this one the turtle has to
FD 10, LT 90, FD 20, LT 90,   'fly over' the obstacles shown.
FD 30, LT 90, FD 30   FD 20, PU, FD 30, PD, FD 10,
                                     RT 90, FD 20, RT 90, FD 10,
                                     PU, FD 40, PD, FD 10, LT 90,
                                     FD 20, LT 90, FD 50, LT 90,
                                     FD 10

Exercise 3

1. Write down the commands that would move the turtle from A
   to B. The dots are 10 spaces apart

(a) 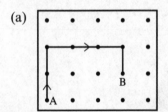   (b)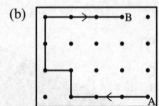

2. Write the commands that would move the turtle from A to B. In this question the turtle has to 'jump over' the obstacles shown by shaded areas.

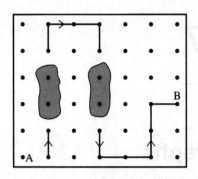

3. Write the commands that would move the turtle along the route given.
(a) A → E → D → C → F → A
(b) A → B → D → H → G → I → J → A
(c) A → B → A → F → C

4. Leslie Smith wants to write her initials. Write down the LOGO commands.

   [Start at the top of the 'L'.]

5. Write down the LOGO commands for *your* own initials.

6. Draw the patterns given by the commands below.
(a) FD 50, RT 90, FD 50, RT 90, FD 40, RT 90, FD 40, RT 90, FD 30, RT 90, FD 30, RT 90, FD 20, RT 90, FD 20, RT 90, FD 10, RT 90, FD 10.
(b) FD 40, RT 90, FD 20, RT 90, FD 20, RT 90, FD 20, LT 90, FD 20, LT 90, PU, FD 30, PD, FD 20, LT 90, FD 20, LT 90, FD 20, BK 20, RT 90, FD 20, LT 90, FD 20.

7. Design your own pattern and write down the LOGO commands for it. Ask a friend to test your commands.

8. Investigate the patterns you can obtain using the 'Repeat' command.

Part 7

7.1 Drawing graphs

- The points P, Q, R and S have coordinates (4, 4), (4, 3), (4, 2) and (4, 1) and they all lie on a straight line. Since the x-coordinate of all the points is 4, we say the *equation* of the line is $x = 4$.

- The points A, B, C and D have coordinates (1, 3), (2, 3), (3, 3) and (4, 3) and they all lie on a straight line. Since the y-coordinate of all the points is 3, we say the *equation* of the line is $y = 3$.

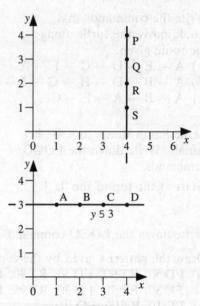

Exercise 1

1. Copy the graph and then write down the coordinates for each point.

A (2, 1)	H (,)
B (,)	I (,)
C (,)	J (,)
D (,)	K (,)
E (,)	L (,)
F (,)	M (,)
G (,)	N (,)

2. L lies on the line $x = 10$.
   Which other letter lies on $x = 10$?

3. Which letter lies on $x = 6$?

4. Which letters lie on $x = 4$?

5. G lies on the line $y = 8$.
   Which letter lies on $y = 10$?

6. Which letters lie on $y = 2$?

7. Which letters lie on $y = 5$?

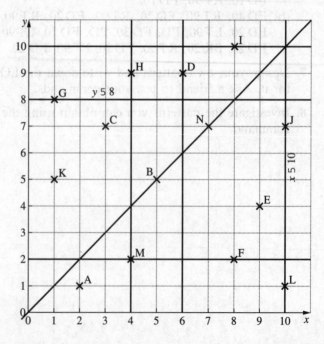

8. Which letters lie on $y = 7$?

9. Which letter lies on $x = 9$?

10. The x coordinate of B is the same as the y coordinate. We say that B lies on the line $y = x$ (or $x = y$).
    Which other letter lies on $y = x$?

11. Point M lies on $x = 4$ *and* $y = 2$. What point lies on $x = 8$ and $y = 2$?

12. What point lies on $x = 2$ and $y = 1$?

13. What point lies on $x = 10$ and $y = 7$?

14. What point lies on $x = 8$ and $y = 10$?

15. Name two lines which pass through C.

16. Name two lines which pass through G.

17. (Harder). Name *three* lines which pass through B.

Exercise 2

Draw axes for x and y from -6 to $+6$.
Draw and label these lines:

1. $x = 3$	**2.** $x = -2$	**3.** $y = 6$	**4.** $x = -5$
5. $y = -2$	**6.** $x = 0$	**7.** $y = 2$	**8.** $y = x$

In Questions **9** and **10** there is a line of dots A, a line of crosses B and a line of circles C.

Write down the equations of the lines in each question.

9.

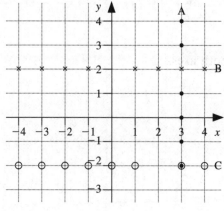

10.

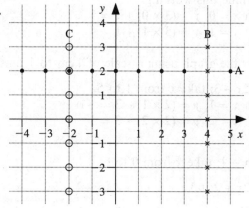

11. On squared paper
    (a) Draw the lines $y = 2$ and $x = 3$. Where do they meet?
    (b) Draw the lines $y = 5$ and $x = -1$. Where do they meet?
    (c) Draw the lines $x = 7$ and $y = -3$. Where do they meet?

Straight line graphs

In this section we work directly from the equation of the graph to
find the coordinates of the points.

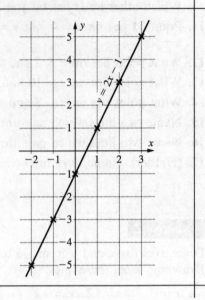

To draw the line $y = 2x - 1$, we begin
by working out the y values for different
values of x. In this case we take x from -2 to $+3$.

when $x = -2$, $y = 2 \times (-2) - 1 = -5$
$\quad x = -1$, $y = 2 \times (-1) - 1 = -3$
$\quad x = 0$, $\quad y = 2 \times (0) - 1 \quad = -1$
$\quad x = 1$, $\quad y = 2 \times (1) - 1 \quad = 1$
$\quad x = 2$, $\quad y = 2 \times (2) - 1 \quad = 3$
$\quad x = 3$, $\quad y = 2 \times (3) - 1 \quad = 5$

The points $(-2, -5)$, $(-1, -3)$...$(3, 5)$ are
plotted and a line is drawn through them.

Exercise 3

For each question, work out the y values for the range of x values
given. Draw the graph, using a scale of 1 cm to 1 unit on both axes.

1. $y = 3x + 1$; take x from 0 to 4.
   Continue this working:
   when $x = 0$, $y = (3 \times 0) + 1 = 1$
   $\quad x = 1$, $y = (3 \times 1) + 1 = 4$
   $\quad \vdots$

   Draw the graph using a scale of 1 cm to 1 unit on both axes.

2. $y = 2x - 3$; take x from 1 to 5.
   when $x = 1$, $y = (2 \times 1) - 3 = -1$
   $\quad x = 2$, $y = (2 \times 2) - 3 = 1$
   $\quad \vdots$

3. $y = x - 1$; take x from 0 to 6.

4. $y = 2x + 2$; take x from -2 to $+4$.

5. $y = 3x - 2$; take x from -2 to $+3$.

6. $y = x + 5$; take x from -3 to $+3$.

7. $y = 4x - 1$; take x from -2 to $+3$. Use scales of 1 cm to 1 unit
   on the x axis and 1 cm to 2 units on the y axis.

8. $y = 3x + 2$; take x from -3 to $+3$. Use the scales given in question 7.

9. $x + y = 10$; take x from 0 to 10.
   This equation looks different to those above but the method is similar. Ask yourself: 'If $x = 2$, what is y?; If $x = 5$, what is y?'...

10. $x + y = 6$; take x from 0 to 6.

11. $2x + y = 10$; take x from 0 to 6.

12. $3x + 2y = 18$; take x from 0 to 5.

13. Using the same axes, draw the graphs of $y = x + 1$ and $x + y = 7$. Take values of x from 0 to 6.
    Write down the coordinates of the point where the lines meet.

14.* On the same graph, draw the lines $y = 2x - 3$,
    $$y = \tfrac{1}{2}x,$$
    $$x + y = 9.$$
    Take values of x from 0 to 8.
    Write down the coordinates of the three vertices of the triangle formed.

15.* On the same graph, draw the lines $x + y = 8$,
    $$y = 2x + 2,$$
    $$y = 2.$$
    Take values of x from 0 to 8.
    Find the area of the triangle formed.

Curved graphs

Draw the graph of $y = x^2 - 3$ for values of x from -3 to $+3$.

$x = -3$, $y = (-3)^2 - 3$
$\qquad = 9 - 3$
$\qquad = 6$

$x = -2$, $y = (-2)^2 - 3$
$\qquad = 4 - 3$
$\qquad = 1$

$x = -1$, $y = (-1)^2 - 3 = -2$

$x = 0$, $y = 0^2 - 3 = -3$

$x = 1$, $y = 1^2 - 3 = -2$

$x = 2$, $y = 2^2 - 3 = 1$

$x = 3$, $y = 3^2 - 3 = 6$

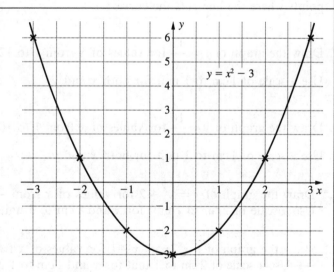

Draw a *smooth* curve through the points.
It helps to turn the page upside down so that your hand can be 'inside' the curve. Try not to look at the tip of your pencil. Instead look at next point through which you are drawing the curve.

Exercise 4

Draw the graph, using a scale of 2 cm to 1 unit on the x axis and 1 cm to 1 unit on the y axis (as in the above example).

1. $y = x^2$; take x from -3 to $+3$.

2. $y = x^2 + 2$; take x from -3 to $+3$.

3. $y = (x + 1)^2$; take x from -3 to $+3$.

4. $y = (x - 2)^2$; take x from -1 to $+5$.

5. $y = x^2 + x$; take x from -3 to $+3$.

6. $y = x^2 + x + 2$; take x from -3 to $+3$.

7. Draw the graph of $y = x^2 - 3x$ for values of x from -3 to $+3$.
   (a) What is the lowest value of y?
   (b) For what value of x does the lowest value occur?

8. Using the same axes, draw the graphs of $y = x^2 - 6x + 16$ and $y = 12$ for values of x from 0 to 6.
   Write down the x coordinates, correct to 1 d.p., of the two points where the line cuts the curve.

9. Draw the graph of $y = \dfrac{12}{x}$ for values of x from 1 to 12.
   Use a scale of 1 cm to 1 unit for both x and y.

10. Draw the graph of $y = \dfrac{16}{x}$ for values of x from 1 to 10.
    Use a scale of 1 cm to 1 unit for both x and y.

11.* Draw the graph of $y = x^3 + 2$ for values of x from -3 to $+3$.
    Use a scale of 2 cm to 1 unit for x and 1 cm to 5 units for y.

12.* Draw the graph of $y = 2x^2 + x - 1$ for values of x from -3 to $+3$. Use a scale of 2 cm to 1 unit for x and 1 cm to 1 unit for y.
    [Remember $2x^2 = 2(x^2)$. Work out x^2 and then multiply by 2.]

13.* Draw the graphs of $y = 2x^2 + x - 6$ and $y = 2x + 3$ for values of x from -3 to $+3$. Write down the x coordinates, correct to 1 d.p., of the two points where the line cuts the curve.

7.2 Gradient

- If we know the coordinates of two points on a line, we can use the formula

$$\text{Gradient} = \frac{\text{Difference between } y \text{ coordinates}}{\text{Difference between } x \text{ coordinates}}$$

The gradient of a line tells us how steep it is.
- Consider the line which passes through (1, 2) and (3, 6).

$$\text{Gradient} = \frac{6-2}{3-1} = \frac{4}{2} = 2$$

Notice that:

- a line sloping upwards to the right has a positive gradient;
- a line sloping downwards to the right has a negative gradient.

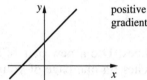 positive gradient

 negative gradient

[Some people think of a capital 'N' for negative.]

Exercise 1

1. Find the gradient of the line joining
   (a) (1, 3) and (2, 6)   (b) (1, 3) and (3, 7)
   (c) (2, 5) and (6, 7)   (d) (3, 9) and (9, 11)
   (e) (1, 4) and (3, 2)   (f) (2, 5) and (5, −1)
   (g) (6, 2) and (2, 10)   (h) (3, −2) and (−3, 2)
   (i) (−2, −4) and (−1, 2)   (j) (2, −3) and (−2, 6).

2. Find the gradient of the line joining:
   (a) A and B
   (b) B and C
   (c) C and D
   (d) D and A.

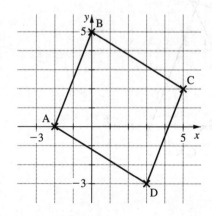

Gradient and intercept

A straight line can be described in terms of

(a) its gradient

(b) where it crosses the y-axis (the y-intercept).

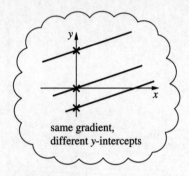

same gradient,
different y-intercepts

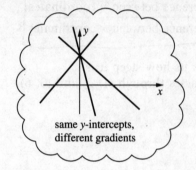

same y-intercepts,
different gradients

Exercise 2

Sketch the following straight lines. Use a new pair of axes for each
question. Draw about six sketches on one page of your book.

1. Gradient 2, y-intercept 3.   **2.** Gradient 1, y-intercept -3.

3. Gradient 2, y-intercept 0.   **4.** Gradient -1, y-intercept 4.

5. Gradient -3, y-intercept 0.   **6.** Gradient -2, y-intercept -2.

7. Give the gradient and y-intercept of each line.

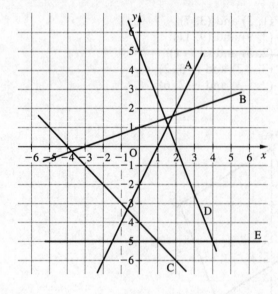

The line $y = mx + c$

$y = mx + c$ is the equation of a straight line with

- gradient m, and
- intercept c. [Hereafter the word 'intercept' is taken to be the y-intercept.]

Sketch the line with equation $y = 3x - 1$.

Gradient $= 3$.
Intercept $= -1$.

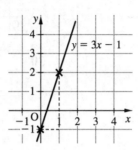

Exercise 3

Write down the gradient and intercept of each of the following lines:

1. $y = 2x - 3$ **2.** $y = 3x + 2$

3. $y = -x - 4$ **4.** $y = \frac{1}{2}x + 3$ Careful!

5. $y = -\frac{2}{3}x - 4$ **6.** $y = 2 - 3x$

7. $y = 4 - 7x$ **8.** $y = 2x - 1$

9. $y = 3 - \frac{1}{2}x$ **10.** $y = 7 - 2x$

In Questions **11** to **16** make y the subject and write down the gradient and intercept of the corresponding line:

11. $2x + y - 6 = 0$ **12.** $y - 3x + 7 = 0$

13. $y - 2x = 8$ **14.** $3x + 6y - 10 = 0$

15. $2x - 5y + 12 = 0$ **16.** $3y - 9x + 2 = 0$

Sketch each of the following lines:

17. $y = x + 2$ **18.** $y = 2x - 4$

19. $y = 3 - 2x$ **20.** $y = \frac{3}{4}x - 1$

21. $y = 2 - \frac{1}{3}x$ **22.** $y - 2x + 2 = 0$

23. $2x + 4y + 1 = 0$ **24.** $3y - 9x - 1 = 0$

In Questions **25** to **30** match each sketch with the correct equation from the list below.

25. 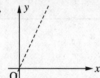   **26.**   **27.**

28.   **29.** 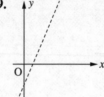   **30.**

(a) $y = -x - 4$ (b) $y = 2x - 1$ (c) $y = 2x + 3$
(d) $y = 3x$ (e) $y = 3 - x$ (f) $y = 5$

Parallel and perpendicular lines

Parallel lines have the same gradient.
For perpendicular lines the product of the gradients is -1.

Exercise 4

1. Write down the equation of any line which is parallel to
   (a) $y = 2x - 1$ (b) $y = 7x + 3$

2. Write down the gradient of a line which is perpendicular to a
   line of gradient
   (a) 3   (b) -1 (c) $\frac{1}{4}$.

3. Here are the equations of several straight lines.

   A $\boxed{y = 3x - 1}$ B $\boxed{y = x - 3}$ C $\boxed{y = \frac{1}{2}x + 1}$ D $\boxed{y = 3x + 5}$

   E $\boxed{y = -2x}$ F $\boxed{y = -x + 7}$ G $\boxed{y = 1 + 4x}$ H $\boxed{y = 4x}$

   (a) Find two pairs of lines which are parallel.
   (b) Find two pairs of lines which are perpendicular.

7.3 Interpreting graphs

Travel graphs

- The graph shows the journey of a car from
  Amble to Cabley via Boldon. The vertical axis
  shows the distance of the car from Amble
  between 1400 and 1700.
  (a) At 1530 the car is 60 km from Amble.
  (b) The car stopped at Boldon for 45
      minutes. The graph is horizontal from
      1430 until 1515 which shows that the car
      does not move.
  (c) The car takes $\frac{1}{2}$ hour to travel 50 km from
      Amble to Boldon. Thus the speed of the
      car is 100 km/h.
  (d) The speed of the car from Boldon to
      Cabley is 40 km/h.

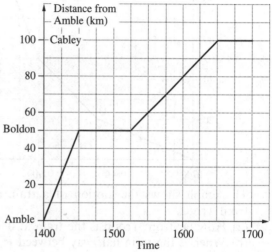

- This graph shows the details of a cycle ride
  that Jim took starting from his home.
  (a) In the first hour Jim went 30 km so
      his speed was 30 km/h.
  (b) He stopped for $\frac{1}{2}$ hour at a place
      30 km from his home.
  (c) From 0930 until 1100 he cycled back
      home. We know that he cycled back
      home because the distance from his
      home at 1100 is 0 km.
  (d) The speed at which he cycled home was
      20 km/h.

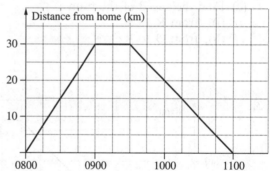

Exercise 1

1. The graph shows a car journey from
   A to C via B.
   (a) How far is it from A to C?
   (b) For how long does the car stop
       at B?
   (c) When is the car half way
       between B and C?
   (d) What is the speed of the car
       (i)   between A and B?
       (ii) between B and C?

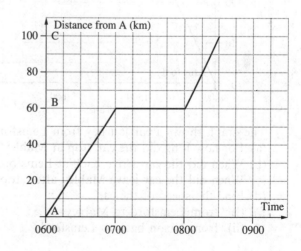

2.

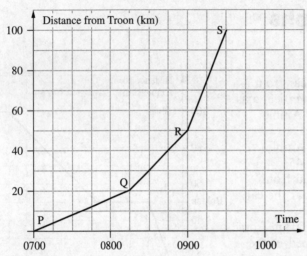

The graph shows the motion of a train as it accelerates away
from Troon.
(a) How far from Troon is the train at 0845?
(b) When is the train half way between R and S?
(c) Find the speed of the train
   (i)   from R to S
   (ii) from Q to R

3.

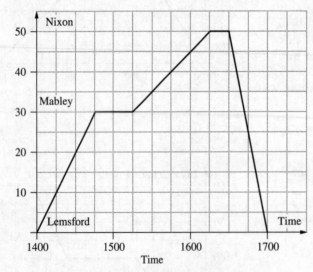

The graph shows a car journey from Lemsford.
(a) For how long did the car stop at Mabley?
(b) When did the car arrive back at Lemsford?
(c) When did the car leave Mabley after stopping?
(d) Find the speed of the car
   (i)   from Lemsford to Mabley
   (ii) from Nixon back to Lemsford.

4. This graph shows a car journey from London to Stevenage and back.

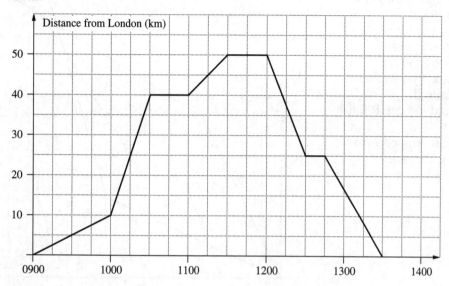

(a) For how long in the whole journey was the car at rest?
(b) At what time was the car half way to Stevenage on the outward journey?
(c) Between which two times was the car travelling at its highest speed?

5. The graph shows the journey of a coach and a lorry along the same road between Newcastle and Carlisle.

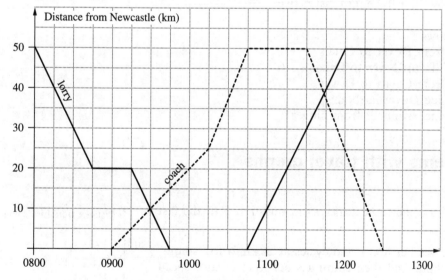

(a) How far apart were the two vehicles at 0915?
(b) At what time did the vehicles meet for the first time?
(c) At what speed did the coach return to Newcastle?
(d) What was the highest speed of the lorry during its journey?

6. The graph shows the motion of three cars A, B and C during a race of length 140 km.

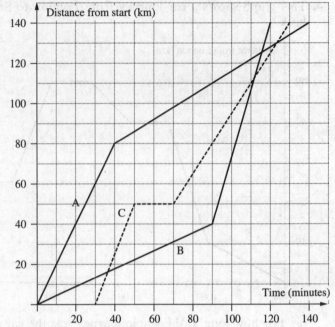

  (a) What was the order of the cars after 40 minutes?
  (b) Which car won the race?
  (c) At approximately what time did C overtake B?
  (d) At what speed did car B finish the race?
  (e) Describe what happened to car C during the race.

7. Explain why the two graphs below cannot be travel graphs.

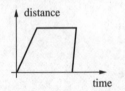
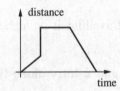

8. The diagram shows the travel graphs of five objects.
  Which graph shows:
  (a) A car ferry from Dover to Calais
  (b) A hovercraft from Dover to Calais
  (c) A car ferry from Calais to Dover
  (d) A buoy outside Dover harbour
  (e) A cross channel swimmer from Dover?

Solving problems with travel graphs

Exercise 2

In Questions **1** to **6** use the same scales as in question **5** of the last exercise.

1. At 1700 Lisa leaves her home and cycles at 20 km/h for 1 hour. She stops for $\frac{1}{4}$ hour and then continues her journey at a speed of 40 km/h for the next $\frac{1}{2}$ hour. She then stops for $\frac{3}{4}$ hour. Finally she returns home at a speed of 40 km/h.

Draw a travel graph to show Lisa's journey.
When did she arrive home?

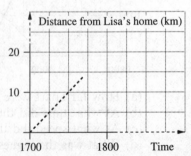

2. Suzy leaves home at 1300 on her horse and rides at a speed of 20 km/h for one hour.
Suzy and her horse then rest for 45 minutes and afterwards continue their journey at a speed of 15 km/h for another one hour.
At what time do they finish the journey?

3. As Mrs Sadler leaves home in her car at 1300 she encounters heavy traffic and travels at only 20 km/h for the first $\frac{1}{2}$ hour. In the second half hour she increases her speed to 30 km/h and after that she travels along the main road at 40 km/h for $\frac{3}{4}$ h. She stops at her destination for $\frac{1}{2}$ hour and then returns home at a steady speed of 40 km/h.

Draw a graph to find when she returns home.

4. At 12 00 Mr Dean leaves home and drives at a speed of 30 km/h. At 12 30 he increases his speed to 50 km/h and continues to his destination which is 65 km from home. He stops for $\frac{1}{2}$ hour and then returns home at a speed of 65 km/h.

Use a graph to find the time at which he arrives home.

5. At 08 00 Chew Ling leaves home and cycles towards a railway station which is 65 km away. She cycles at a speed of 30 km/h until 09 30 at which time she stops to rest for $\frac{1}{2}$ hour. She then completes the journey at a speed of 20 km/h.
At 09 45 Chew Ling's father leaves their home in his car and drives towards the station at 60 km/h.
(a) At what time does Chew Ling arrive at the station?
(b) When is Chew Ling overtaken by her father?

6. Kate lives 80 km from Kevin. One day at 1200 Kate cycles towards Kevin's home at 25 km/h. At the same time Kevin cycles at 30 km/h towards Kate's home

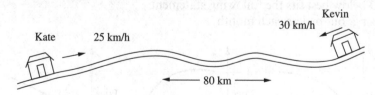

Draw a travel graph with 'Distance from Kate's home' on the vertical axis.
Approximately when and where do they meet?

Mixed questions

Exercise 3

1. The step graph shows the cost of travelling on a bus. [Note that an open dot, o, means the overlap point is not included.]
   Find the cost of travelling
   (a) 7 miles
   (b) 22 miles
   (c) 10 miles

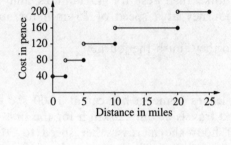

2. The graph below shows the depth of water at the centre of a puddle one summer day.

   Describe what might be happening at each stage A–B, B–C, etc.

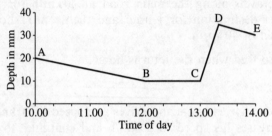

3. The line graph shows how the weight of an earthworm varies over the first 60 days of its life. Describe the main features of the graph and speculate about the possible causes of the main events.

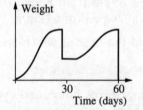

4. The graph shows the water level in a bath. Use the letters A, B, C etc to describe when the events below occurred.
   [For example: A → B '.....................']

   • John got out of bath
   • Water drained from bath
   • John got into bath
   • Both taps on
   • Hot tap on alone
   • More hot water added when John was in bath
   • John lies in bath, solving equations in his head.

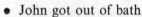

5. Which of the graphs A to D below best fits the following statement:
   'The price of paint is still rising, but by less each month.'

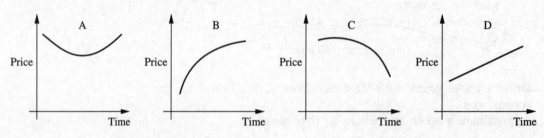

6. The graph converts pounds into French francs.
   (a) convert into francs
       (i) £2   (ii) £3·50
   (b) convert into pounds
       (i) 20F   (ii) 12F.
   (c) A mars bar costs 75p. Find the equivalent price in France.
   (d) A few years ago, the exchange rate was about 10 francs to the pound. Is it cheaper or more expensive nowadays as a British tourist in France?

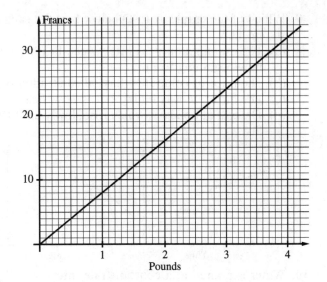

7. Most countries nowadays measure temperature in °C (Celsius), but some still prefer °F (Fahrenheit). This country used °F as the standard until about 20 years ago. Your grandparents will know that 75°F is 'hot' but may have no idea what 25°C means.
   (a) Draw axes, as shown, with a scale of 1 cm to 5°. Two equivalent temperatures are 32°F = 0°C and 86°F = 30°C.
   (b) Draw a line through the points above and use your graph to convert:
       (i)   20°C into °F
       (ii) −10°C into °F
       (iii) 50°F into °C
   (c) The normal body temperature of a healthy person is 98°F. Susie's temperature is 39°C. Should she stay at home today, or go to school as usual?

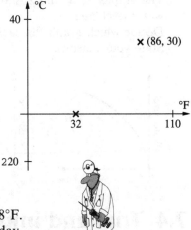

8. In the U.K., petrol consumption for cars is usually quoted in 'miles per gallon'. In other countries the metric equivalent is 'km per litre'.
   (a) Convert 20 m.p.g. into km per litre.
   (b) Convert 5 km per litre into m.p.g.
   (c) At a steady speed of 50 m.p.h., a Jaguar Sovereign travels 9 km on one litre of petrol. Convert this consumption into miles per gallon and hence work out how many gallons of petrol the car will use, if it is driven at 50 m.p.h. for 2 hours.

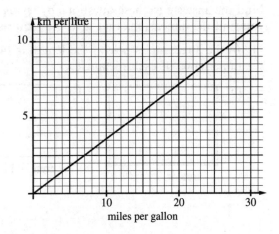

9. Which of the graphs A to D below best fits each of the following
   statements:
   (a) The examination pass rate, which has been rising steadily, is
       now beginning to fall.
   (b) The price of computers has fallen steadily over the last year.
   (c) The birthrate was falling but is now steady.
   (d) The cost of holidays, which rose slowly until 1998, is now rising
       fast.

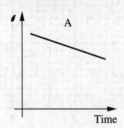 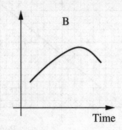 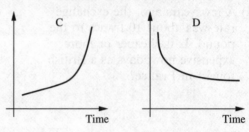

10. Water is poured at a constant rate into
    each of the containers A, B and C.
    The graphs X, Y and Z shows how the
    water level rises.
    Decide which graph fits each container.
    State your reasons.

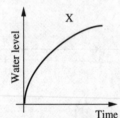 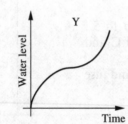 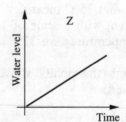

7.4 Trial and improvement

Exercise 1

Find the answers to these questions by trying different numbers until
you find the dimensions that give the required area.

1. In the 3 rectangles below, the length is *twice* the width. Find the
   dimensions of each rectangle.

(a)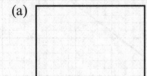
   area = 98 cm²

(b)
   area = 12.5 cm²

(c)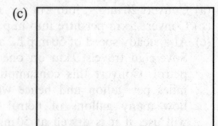
   area = 9.68 cm²

2. In these rectangles, the length is *three* times the width. Find the dimensions of each rectangle.

(a)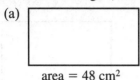

area = 48 cm²

(b)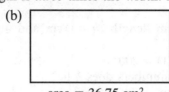

area = 36.75 cm²

(c)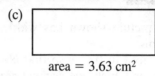

area = 3.63 cm²

3. In the rectangle below, the length is *1 cm greater* than the width. Find the dimensions of each rectangle.

(a)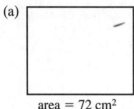

area = 72 cm²

(b)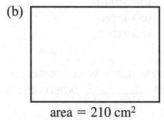

area = 210 cm²

(c)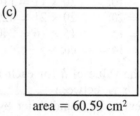

area = 60.59 cm²

4. The volume of the box is given by the formula $n(n-1)(n+1)$.
The box has a volume of $10\,626\,cm^3$.
Find the dimensions of the box.

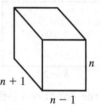

In the questions in the last exercise, we could always find dimensions which gave the *exact* answer required. In many problems this is not the case and we have to give the answer as an approximate value. This is not a major drawback because the solution can generally be found correct to as many decimal places as are required.

The rectangle shown has width h cm, length $(h+5)$ cm and area $525\,cm^2$. Find the value of h, giving your answer in the form:

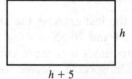

'h is between _____ and _____'.

The two numbers to be found differ by 0.01 [e.g. 3·61 and 3·62].

The equation to be solved is $h(h+5) = 525$.

Try $h = 15$: $15 \times 20 = 300$, $h = 15$ is too small.
Try $h = 25$: $25 \times 30 = 750$, $h = 25$ is too large.
Try $h = 20$: $20 \times 25 = 500$, $h = 20$ is too small.
Try $h = 21$: $21 \times 26 = 546$, $h = 21$ is too large.
Try $h = 20·5$: $20·5 \times 25·5 = 522·75$, $h = 20·5$ is too small.
Try $h = 20·6$: $20·6 \times 25·6 = 527·36$, $h = 20·6$ is too large.
Try $h = 20·55$: $20·55 \times 25·55 = 525·0525$, $h = 20·55$ is too large.
Try $h = 20·54$: $20·54 \times 25·54 = 524·5916$, $h = 20·54$ is too small.

When $h = 20·55$, the area of the rectangle is greater than $525\,cm^2$ and when $h = 20·54$, the area of the rectangle is less than $525\,cm^2$.

Answer: The value of h is between 20·54 and 20·55

Exercise 2

1. The picture shown has width h cm, length $(h+1)$ cm and area $200\,\text{cm}^2$.

   You need to find h so that $h(h+1) = 200$.

   Between which *one decimal place* numbers does h lie?

   Write your answer as 'h is between _____ and _____'.

   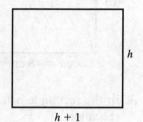

   Here is the start of the solution:

Try $h = 10$:	$10 \times 11 = 110$	too small
Try $h = 20$:	$20 \times 21 = 420$	too large
Try $h = 15$:	$15 \times 16 = 240$	too large
Try $h = 14$:	etc	

2. Find the value of h for each rectangle. Give your answer in the form: 'h is between _____ and _____', where the two numbers to be found differ by 0·1.

   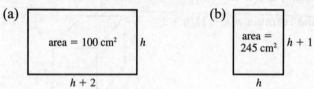

   (a) area = 100 cm² h $h+2$

   (b) area = 245 cm² $h+1$ h

3. Solve the equations below. Give your answers in the form 'x is between _____ and _____', where the two numbers to be found differ by 0·1.

   (a) $x(x+10) = 210$ (b) $x^2 + x = 300$ (c) $x(x-1) = 100$

Accuracy

In the last exercise the answers were given in the form 'h is between 20·54 and 20·55'.

Sometimes it is more convenient to give a solution which is correct to a specific degree of accuracy, like 2 decimal places or 3 significant figures.

In the example below, the answer is found correct to 2 decimal places.

Solve the equation $z(z-2) = 50$, giving the answer correct to 2 decimal places.

(a) Try different values for z.

$z = 10$:	$10(10-2) = 80$	Too large
$z = 8$:	$8(8-2) = 48$	Too small
$z = 8\cdot1$:	$8\cdot1(8\cdot1-2) = 49\cdot41$	Too small
$z = 8\cdot2$:	$8\cdot2 \times 6\cdot2 = 50\cdot84$	Too large
$z = 8\cdot13$:	$8\cdot13 \times 6\cdot13 = 49\cdot83$	Too small
$z = 8\cdot14$:	$8\cdot14 \times 6\cdot14 = 49\cdot996$	Too small
$z = 8\cdot15$:	$8\cdot15 \times 6\cdot15 = 50\cdot1225$	Too large

(b) At this stage we know that the answer is between 8·14 and 8·15. We also note that the value of $z = 8·14$ gave the value closest to 50. [i.e. 49·996]

(c) We can take the solution to be $x = 8·14$, correct to 2 decimal places.

(d) Notes: (i) We have tried values of x just above and just below 8·14 [namely 8·15 and 8·13].

            (ii) Strictly speaking, to ensure that our answer *is* correct to 2 decimal places, we should try $x = 8·145$. This degree of complexity is unnecessary at this stage.

Solve the equation $x^3 + 10x = 100$, giving the answer correct to one decimal place.

Try $x = 3$:	$3^3 + (10 \times 3) = 57$	$x = 3$ is too small.
Try $x = 4$:	$4^3 + (10 \times 4) = 104$	$x = 4$ is too large.
Try $x = 3·9$:	$3·9^3 + (10 \times 3·9) = 98·318$	$x = 3·9$ is too small.

Now 98·318 is closer to 100 than 104.

∴   The solution is $x = 3·9$, correct to 1 decimal place.

Exercise 3

1. Find the value of h, correct to 1 decimal place.

(a)

area = 738 cm² h

$h + 10$

(b)

area = 200 cm² h

$h + 5$

2. Solve the equations, correct to 1 decimal place.

(a) $x^2 + x = 13$ (b) $x^2 - x = 80$ (c) $x^3 - x = 70$

3. Use trial and improvement to find the cube root of 60, correct to 2 decimal places.
The cube root of 60 is written $\sqrt[3]{60}$.
Here is the start of the method:

Try 3: $3 \times 3 \times 3 = 27$ too small
Try 4: $4 \times 4 \times 4 = 64$ too big
Try 3·5:   etc

4. Use trial and improvement to find these roots, correct to 2 d.p.

(a) $\sqrt[3]{150}$ (b) $\sqrt[3]{58}$ (c) $\sqrt[3]{84}$ (d) $\sqrt{90}$ $\begin{bmatrix} \text{square root} \\ \text{not cube root} \end{bmatrix}$

5. A cuboid has a square base of side x cm, height $(x + 1)$ cm and volume 2000 cm^3.
Find the value of x, correct to 2 d.p.

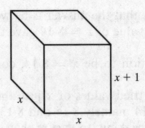

6. Find a solution to the equation $4x + 1 = x^2$. Try values of x between $x = 1$ and $x = 6$.
Give your answer correct to 2 d.p.

7. In this question we require much greater accuracy. The area of the picture is 40 cm^2.
Find the value of h correct to *five* decimal places.

Questions **8**, **9**, **10** are more difficult.

8.* The 'L' shaped card shown has an area of 45 cm^2. Find the value of x, correct to 2 decimal places.

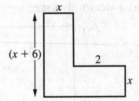

9.* So far, you have solved equations involving powers of x like x^2 or x^3. Solve the equations below where numbers are raised to the power x. Give your answers correct to 1 decimal place.

(a) $3^x = 10$ (b) $12^x = 100$ (c) $7^x = 0.1$

(d) This time a number x is raised to the power x.
Solve the equation $x^x = 150$.

10.* A rectangle has length $(x + 2)$ cm, perimeter $(4x + 6)$ cm and area 52 cm^2.

(a) Using the perimeter, find an expression for the width of the rectangle.

(b) Form an equation and solve it to find the value of x, correct to 3 significant figures.

Using a spreadsheet on a PC

This section is written for use with Microsoft Excel. Other spreadsheet programs work in a similar way. A spreadsheet can be used to solve an equation by trial and improvement.

Select Microsoft Excel from the desk top.

A spreadsheet appears on your screen as a grid with rows numbered 1, 2, 3, 4,...... and the columns lettered A, B, C, D, ...
The result should be a window like the one below.

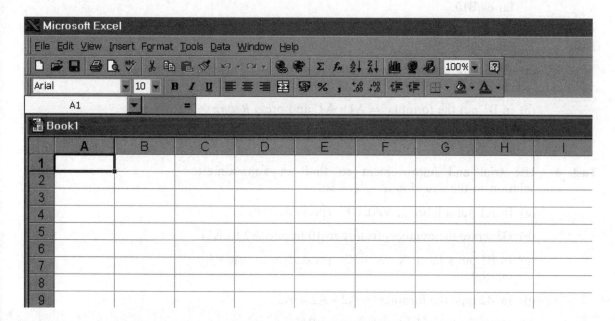

| Cell | The spaces on the spreadsheet are called cells. Individual cells are referred to as A1, B3, F9, like grid references. Cells may contain *labels, values* or *formulas*. The current cell has a black boarder. |

Cell   The spaces on the spreadsheet are called cells. Individual cells are referred to as A1, B3, F9, like grid references. Cells may contain *labels, values* or *formulas*. The current cell has a black boarder.

Label   Any words, headings or messages used to help the layout and organisation of the spreadsheet.

Value   A number placed in a cell. It may be used as input to a calculation.

Task 1.   To generate the whole numbers from 1 to 10 in column A.

    (a) In cell A1 type '1' and press *Return*. This will automatically take you to the cell below. (NOTE that you must use the *Return* button and not the arrow keys to move down the column.)

    (b) In cell A2 type the formula '= A1 + 1' and press *Return*. [NOTE that the = sign is needed before any formula.]

(c) We now want to copy the formula in A2 down column A as far as A10. Click on A2 again and put the arrow in the bottom right corner of cell A2 (a + sign will appear) and drag down to A10.

Task 2. To generate the odd numbers in column B.

(a) In B1 type '1' (press *Return*).

(b) In B2 type the formula '= B1 + 2' (press *Return*).

(c) Click in B2 and copy the formula down column B as far as B10.

Task 3. To generate the first 15 square numbers.

(a) As before generate the numbers from 1 to 15 in cells A1 to A15.

(b) in B1 put the formula '= A1 * A1' and press *Return*.

(c) Click in B1 and copy the formula down as far as B15.

Task 4. Use trial and improvement to find an approximate solution to the equation $x^2 + x = 50$.

(a) In A1 put a label 'X VALUE'. (press *Return*).

(b) Generate the numbers from 1 to 10 in cells A2 to A11.

(c) In B1 put a label 'X * X + X'. (press *Return*) (use * for multiply).

(d) In B2 type the formula '= A2 * A2 + A2'.

(e) Copy the formula down as far as B11.

We are looking for the number nearest to 50 in the B column.
We see that B7 = 42 and B8 = 56.
We need to get a more accurate solution.
We are going to get the numbers 6·1, 6·2, 6·3, ... 6·9 in column A as follows

(f) Highlight cells A8 to B16 (9 rows).

(g) Click on 'Insert' on the tool bar and then 'Rows'.

(h) In A8 type the formula '= A7 + 0·1'.

(i) Copy the formula down as far as A16.

(j) Copy from B7 down to B16.

The value closest to 50 is 50·16. So the approximate solution to the equation $x^2 + x = 50$ is $x = 6·6$ correct to 1 decimal place.

For even greater accuracy you can repeat steps (f) to (j) starting now at A13.

Highlight cells A13 to B21 (9 rows).

Click on 'Insert' and then 'Rows'.

In A13 type 'A12 + 0·01'.

Copy the formula down to A21.

Copy from B12 down to B21.

7.5 Inequalities

$x < y$ means 'x is less than y' [or 'y is greater than x']

$p \leqslant q$ means 'p is less than or equal to q' [or 'q is greater than or equal to p'].

$a > b$ means 'a is greater than b' [or 'b is less than a']

$n \geqslant t$ means 'n is greater than or equal to t'.

Notice that the inequality signs can be read from left to right or from right to left.

Inequalities occur frequently in everyday life.

- 'Each plant in the greenhouse produced more than 7 flowers.'

  We can write $f > 7$, where f is the number of flowers.

- 'Applicants for training as prison officers in Switzerland must be at least 1·70 m tall.'

  We can write $h \geqslant 1·70$ m, where h is the height of applicants.

- 'The percentage required for a grade B was between 49 and 62 inclusive.'

  We can write $49 \leqslant p \leqslant 62$, where p is the percentage mark.

- 'The speed limit along Valley Road is 40 m.p.h.'

  We can write $s \leqslant 40$, where s is the speed of cars in m.p.h.

Illustrate on a number line the range of values of x for which the following inequalities are true:

(a) $x > 1$ The circle at the left hand end of the range is open. This means that 1 is not included.

(b) $x \leqslant -2$ The circle at -2 is filled in to indicate that -2 is included.

(c) $-1 \leqslant x < 3$

[-1 included]   [3 not included]

Exercise 1

[The answers to Questions **1** and **2** can be written down or discussed in class.]

1. Write an inequality for each statement.
   (a) The maximum number of passengers, n, in the school minibus is 16.
   (b) For best results the temperature of the oven, T, has to be between 180 °C and 215 °C.
   (c) The minimum mark, m, for a pass in the Highway Code test is 80%.

2. Here is an advertisement for a job. Write the information given in the form of inequalities. Make up your own symbols for the relevant quantities.

> **Driver/Bodyguard Wanted**
>
> Age 20 to 50. Must have at least 5 years clean driving license.
>
> Applicants must have more than 2 GCSEs and weigh between 10 and 15 stones. Salary in excess of £300 per week.
>
> Phone 0182 996 13274.

3. Write down the inequalities displayed. Use x for the variable.

(a)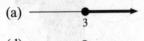

(b)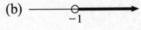

(c)

(d)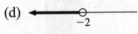

(e)

(f)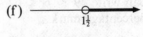

(g)

(h)

(i)

(j)

(k)

(l)

4. Draw a number line to display the following inequalities.
(a) $x > -1$ (b) $x \leqslant 4$ (c) $a > -2$
(d) $n \leqslant 0$ (e) $-5 < p < 5$ (f) $-1 \leqslant y$
(g) $0 \leqslant x \leqslant 10$ (h) $-2 < t \leqslant 7$ (i) $-3 \leqslant s < -1$

5. Answer true or false:
(a) $7 \cdot 1 > 7 \cdot 01$ (b) $-3 < 1$ (c) $3\frac{1}{2} < 3 \cdot 25$ (d) $-6 < -10$
(e) 1 metre $>$ 1 yard   (f) 1 kg $>$ 1 pound   (g) 1 inch < 2 cm   (h) $2^3 < 3^2$

6. If $\Box > 520$, write a possible number for $\Box$.

7. If $\Box < 6400$, write a possible number for $\Box$.

8. Write a possible number for $\Box$ in each of the following:
(a) $\Box < 2450$ (b) $650 < \Box$ (c) $200 < \Box$
(d) $1500 > \Box$ (e) $25\,000 < \Box$ (f) $\Box > 265$

9. Write a possible number for $\Box$ in each of the following:
(a) $1000 < \Box < 2000$ (b) $2540 < \Box < 2550$ (c) $-3 < \Box < 2$
(d) $-5 < \Box < -2$ (e) $16\,436 < \Box\; 16\,438$ (f) $9842 < \Box < 9843$

Solving inequalities

When we solve an equation, like $3x - 1 = x + 9$, we find one value of x which satisfies the equation.

When we solve an inequality, like $2x + 3 < 10$, we find the *range of values* of x which satisfy the inequality.
For example, the solution of the inequality $x - 3 < 11$ is $x < 14$. The variable x can be any value less than 14.

When solving inequalities we can:

- Add the same thing to both sides.
- Subtract the same thing from both sides.
- Multiply or divide both sides by the same *positive* number.

If we multiply or divide by a *negative* number the inequality sign must be *reversed*.
(a) Consider the inequality $4 > -2.$
     Now multiply both sides by (-1) $-4 < 2.$
                                        $\uparrow$
                       sign is reversed.

(b) Consider the inequality $-3 < 6$
     Divide both sides by (-3) $1 > -2$
     Again the inequality sign is reversed.

Solve the inequalities.

(a) $x - 3 < 4$

    Add 3 to both sides.

    $x < 7$

(b) $x + 5 > -2$

    Subtract 5 from both sides.

    $x > -2 - 5$

    $x > -7$

(c) $5x \geqslant 350$

    Divide both sides by 5.

    $x \geqslant 70$

(d) $\dfrac{x}{3} \leqslant -2$

    Multiply both sides by 3.

    $x \leqslant -6$

Exercise 2

Solve the inequalities.

1. $x - 10 \geqslant 2$
2. $x + 6 < 11$
3. $y - 6 > -3$
4. $7 + y < 11$
5. $3 + x \geqslant 9$
6. $x + 1 < 0$
7. $3n \geqslant 48$
8. $5y < 1$
9. $10x < 1000$
10. $x - 3 < -2$
11. $y + 7 > -7$
12. $5 + n \geqslant 4$

Find the range of values of x which satisfy each of the following inequalities and show the answer on a number line.

13. $\dfrac{x}{2} < 3$
14. $\dfrac{x}{5} > \dfrac{1}{2}$
15. $\dfrac{x}{3} \leqslant -1$
16. $-12 \geqslant 3x$
17. $\dfrac{1}{4} > \dfrac{x}{2}$
18. $\dfrac{3x}{2} > 6$
19. $x - 4 > 0$
20. $7 < x + 10$
21. $8 + x \leqslant 0$

In Questions 22 to 26 list the solutions which satisfy the given conditions.

22. $3n < 30$; n is a positive integer (whole number).

23. $0 < a < 12$; a is an even number.

24. $\dfrac{3x}{5} < 7$; x is a positive integer.

25. $0 < 2y < 9$; y is an integer.

26. $\dfrac{p}{3} < 8$; p is a prime number.

27. State the smallest integer for which $5y > 21$.

28. Write down any value of x such that $2^3 < x < 3^2$.

29.* Given that $1 \leqslant x \leqslant 5$ and $-3 \leqslant y \leqslant -1$, find
    (a) the greatest possible value of $x - y$.
    (b) the least possible value of $x^2 + y^2$.

30.* Given that $1 \leqslant a \leqslant 10$ and $-5 \leqslant b \leqslant 6$, find

    (a) the greatest possible value of $\dfrac{b}{a}$.

    (b) the greatest possible value of $b^2 - a$.
    (c) the greatest possible value of $a - b$

31.* (a) Given that $5x > 1$ and that $x - 2 < 3$, list all the possible whole number values of x.
    (b) If $3^x > 1000$, what is the smallest whole number value of x?

7.6 Simultaneous equations

Up to now the equations you have solved have had just one unknown. For example $3x - 1 = 1 - 4x$,

$$5(1 - x) = 2(3x + 1),$$

$$x(x + 1) = 100.$$

The equation $3x + y = 8$ involves two variables x and y. There are many pairs of values of x and y which satisfy the equation.
For example, if $x = 1$ and $y = 5$, $(3 \times 1) + 5 = 8$
    or, if $x = 4$ and $y = -4$, $(3 \times 4) + (-4) = 8$.

There is in fact an infinite number of pairs of solutions. Similarly the equation $2x + 5y = 1$ is satisfied by an infinite number of pairs of solutions.

When we solve a *pair* of *simultaneous* equations we find the one pair of values of x and y which satisfy *both* equations simultaneously.
Confirm that the equations $3x + y = 8$ and $2x + 5y = 1$ are both satisfied by $x = 3$ and $y = -1$.
These are the solutions of the simultaneous equations.

Graphical solution of simultaneous equations

The equations $x + y = 7$ and
              $2x - y = -1$

can be represented by straight lines as shown.

Since both lines pass through the point $(2, 5)$, the solutions of the simultaneous equations

    $x + y = 7$

    $2x - y = -1$

are $x = 2$, $y = 5$.

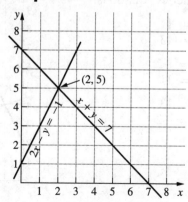

Solve the simultaneous equations

$$2x + y = 6$$
$$x - 2y = -2.$$

(a) Draw the line $2x + y = 6$.
   When $x = 0$, $y = 6$
   When $y = 0$, $x = 3$
   When $x = 1$, $y = 4$

(b) Draw the line $x - 2y = -2$.
   When $x = 0$, $y = 1$
   When $y = 0$, $x = -2$
   When $x = 6$, $y = 4$

(c) The lines intersect at $(2, 2)$ so
   the solutions are $x = 2$, $y = 2$.

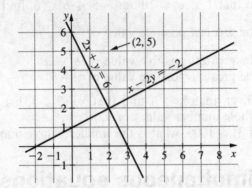

Exercise 1

1. Use the graph to solve the
   simultaneous equations.

   (a) $2x + y = 8$
      $x + y = 5$

   (b) $x - y = -5$
      $x + y = 5$

   (c) $2x + y = 8$
      $x - y = -5$

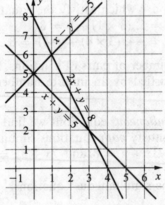

2. Use the graph to solve
   the simultaneous equations.

   (a) $x + y = 11$
      $x + 3y = 13$

   (b) $2x - y = -2$
      $x + y = 11$

   (c) $x + 3y = 13$
      $2x - y = -2$

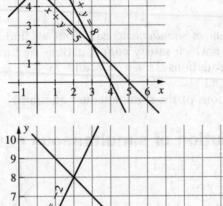

In Questions **3** to **8** solve the simultaneous equations by drawing graphs.

3. $x + y = 6$
   $\quad y = x + 3$

   Draw axes with x and y from 0 to 6.

4. $x + 2y = 11$
   $2x + y = 13$

   Draw axes with x and y from 0 to 13.

5. $3x + 4y = 24$
   $3x + 2y = 18$

   Draw axes with x and y from 0 to 9.

6. $x + y = 5$
   $\quad y = x + 2$

   Draw axes with x and y from 0 to 5.

7. $\quad y = 3x + 6$
   $x + y = 4$

   Draw axes with x and y from −2 to 6.

8. $2x + 5y = 17$
   $2x - 3y = -3$

   Draw axes with x and y from 0 to 6.
   [Give your answers correct to 1 d.p.]

9. Use the graph to solve the equations below. Give your answers correct to 1 d.p. where necessary.

(a) $x + y = 9$
   $\quad y = 2x - 3$

(b) $x + 3y = 5$
   $\quad x + y = 9$

(c) $x + 3y = 5$
   $\quad y = 2x - 3$

(d) $\quad y = 2x - 3$
   $5y = 4x + 18$

(e) $5y = 4x + 18$
   $\quad x + 3y = 5$

(f) $x + y = 9$
   $5y = 4x + 18$

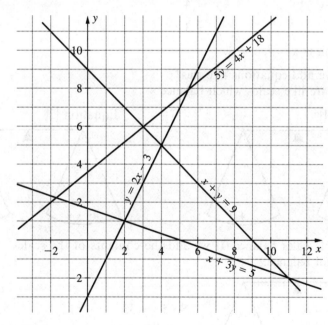

10. The simultaneous equations $x + 2y = 10$ and $x + 2y = 15$ have no solutions. What can you say about their graphs?

Algebraic solution of simultaneous equations

(a) Consider the simultaneous equations $5x + y = 21$ [1]

$$3x + y = 13 \qquad [2]$$

If we subtract equation [2] from equation [1] we eliminate the y terms.

We obtain $2x = 8$

$$x = 4$$

Now substitute $x = 4$ into equation [1] (or equation [2]).

$$(5 \times 4) + y = 21$$

$$y = 1$$

The solution is $x = 4$, $y = 1$

(b) Consider the simultaneous equations $x - y = 4$ [1]

$$4x + y = 31 \qquad [2]$$

If we *add* equation [1] to equation [2] we eliminate the y terms.

We obtain $5x = 35$

$$x = 7$$

Now substitute $x = 7$ into equation [1] (or equation [2]).

$$7 - y = 4$$

$$y = 3$$

The solution is $x = 7$, $y = 3$.

(c) Why can we add equations like this?
Equations are like scales which balance.

Equation [1]   Equation [2]

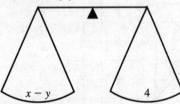 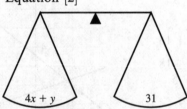

Both sets of scales balance. If we add the contents of the scales they will still balance.

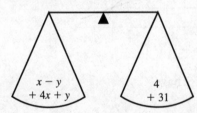

So $5x = 35$
$x = 7$

Solve the simultaneous equations

(a) $x + 2y = 7$ [1]

    $x - y = 4$ [2]

Label the equations [1] and [2]

[1] $-$ [2] gives $2y - (-y) = 3$

$$3y = 3$$
$$y = 1$$

Substitute $y = 1$ in [1]

$$x + (2 \times 1) = 7$$
$$x = 5$$

The solution is $x = 5$, $y = 1$.

(b) $3x + 2y = 10$ [1]

    $5x - 2y = 14$ [2]

In this case to eliminate the y terms we *add* the equations.

[1] $+$ [2] gives $8x = 24$

$$x = 3$$

Substitute $x = 3$ in [1]

$$9 + 2y = 10$$
$$2y = 1$$
$$y = \tfrac{1}{2}$$

The solution is $x = 3$, $y = \tfrac{1}{2}$.

Remember: 'If the signs in front of the letter to be eliminated are the *same* we *subtract*, but if the signs are different we add.'

Be careful with negative numbers when using this method. Look carefully at the following examples:

$$2 - (-2) = 2 + 2$$
$$= 4$$

$$3y - (+8y) = -5y$$

$$3y + (-3y) = 3y - 3y$$
$$= 0$$

$$-2x - (-2x) = -2x + 2x$$
$$= 0$$

$$-11 - (-3) = -11 + 3$$
$$= -8$$

$$-4y + (-4y) = -4y - 4y$$
$$= -8y$$

Exercise 2

1. Simplify

(a) $-3 + (-4)$ (b) $-3 - (-2)$ (c) $x + (-3x)$

(d) $2y - (-2y)$ (e) $-8x - (-8x)$ (f) $5 + (-6)$

(g) $-3x - (-7x)$ (h) $a + (-a)$ (i) $8n - (-2n)$

(j) $4y + (-8y)$ (k) $-5p - (-p)$ (l) $3p - (5p)$

Solve the simultaneous equations.

2. $5x + y = 22$
$2x + y = 10$

3. $6x + y = 31$
$3x + y = 16$

4. $5x + 2y = 16$
$x + 2y = 4$

5. $7x + 4y = 17$
$3x + 4y = 5$

6. $x + 3y = 11$
$x + 2y = 9$

7. $3x + 5y = 21$
$3x - y = 3$

8. $4x + 5y = 9$
$4x - 2y = 2$

9. $x - 2y = 8$
$x - 5y = 17$

10. $4x + 3y = -5$
$7x + 3y = -11$

In Questions **11** to **16** add the equations to eliminate the y terms.

11. $3x + y = 14$
$\quad\ 2x - y = 6$

12. $5x + 2y = 16$
$\quad\ 3x - 2y = 8$

13. $7x - 3y = 24$
$\quad\ 2x + 3y = 3$

14. $5x - y = -7$
$\quad\ x + y = -5$

15. $6x - y = -26$
$\quad\ 5x + y = -18$

16. $\ x + 3y = -4$
$\quad\ 2x - 3y = -11$

In Questions **17** to **28** either add or subtract to eliminate terms.

17. $3x + 2y = -1$
$\quad\ 3x - y = 5$

18. $\ a + b = 3$
$\quad\ 3a - b = 17$

19. $2a - b = 6$
$\quad\ 3a + b = 14$

20. $5a - 2b = 4$
$\quad\ 3a + 2b = 12$

21. $\ 5x + y = -7$
$\quad\ 5x - 2y = -16$

22. $3x + y = 14$
$\quad\ 3x - y = 10$

23. $\ m - 2n = 0$
$\quad\ 9m + 2n = 30$

24. $3x - y = 16$
$\quad\ 6x - y = 31$

25. $3x - 2y = 11$
$\quad\ 7x - 2y = 27$

26. $4x - 5y = -17$
$\quad\ 2x - 5y = -16$

27. $3x = y + 10$
$\quad\ 3x - 2y = 4$

28. $x = 3y + 15$
$\quad\ 5x + 3y = 3$

Sometimes we cannot eliminate either x or y terms unless we multiply one equation or both equations by a suitable number or numbers. Examples (a) and (b) illustrate the method.

(a) $3x + y = 14$ $\qquad\qquad$ [1]

$\quad\ x + 2y = 3$ $\qquad\qquad$ [2]

Multiply equation [1] by 2.

[1] $\times$ 2: $\ \ 6x + 2y = 28$ $\qquad$ [3]

[3] $-$ [2]: $\qquad\ \ 5x = 25$

$\qquad\qquad\qquad\quad x = 5$

Substitute $x = 5$ in [1] (or [2])

$(3 \times 5) + y = 14$

$\qquad\qquad\ y = -1$

The solution is $x = 5,\ y = -1$

(b) $5x + 2y = 23$ $\qquad\qquad$ [1]

$\quad\ 2x + 3y = 18$ $\qquad\qquad$ [2]

Multiply both equations.

[1] $\times$ 3: $\ \ 15x + 6y = 69$ $\qquad$ [3]

[2] $\times$ 2: $\ \ \ \ 4x + 6y = 36$ $\qquad$ [4]

[3] $-$ [4]: $\qquad\ \ 11x = 33$

$\qquad\qquad\qquad\quad x = 3$

Substitute $x = 3$ in [1] (or [2])

$(5 \times 3) + 2y = 23$

$\qquad\qquad\ y = 4$

The solution is $x = 3,\ y = 4$

Exercise 3

Solve the simultaneous equations.

1. $\ 4x + y = 14$
$\quad\ 5x + 2y = 19$

2. $\ 2x + y = 5$
$\quad\ 5x + 3y = 12$

3. $4x + 3y = 25$
$\quad\ x + 5y = 19$

4. $7a + 2b = 22$
$\quad\ 3a + 4b = 11$

5. $5m + 3n = 11$
$\quad\ 4m + 6n = 16$

6. $2x + 3y = 20$
$\quad\ x + 5y = 31$

In Questions **7** to **9** alter one of the equations and then add to eliminate the y terms.

7. $3x + 2y = 19$
$\quad 4x - y = 29$

8. $5x - y = 8$
$\quad 7x + 4y = 22$

9. $8x - 3y = 30$
$\quad 3x + y = 7$

In the remaining questions alter either one or both equations before eliminating the x or y terms.

10. $2x + 3y = 12$
$\quad 5x + 4y = 23$

11. $3x + 2y = 14$
$\quad 2x + 7y = 15$

12. $9a + 5b = 15$
$\quad 3a - 2b = -6$

13. $2x + 5y = 5$
$\quad 4x + 3y = 3$

14. $3x - 2y = 21$
$\quad 4x + 3y = 11$

15. $6x + 5y = 20$
$\quad 5x + 2y = 21$

16. $7x + 5y = 32$
$\quad 3x + 4y = 23$

17. $x - y = -1$
$\quad 2x - y = 0$

18. $y - x = -1$
$\quad 3x - y = 5$

19. $5x - 7y = 27$
$\quad 3x - 4y = 16$

20. $3x + 2y = 7$
$\quad 2x - 3y = -4$

21. $4x + 5y = -19$
$\quad 6x - 3y = 24$

22. $2x + 3y = 5$
$\quad 5x - 2y = -16$

23. $7a - 5b = 10$
$\quad 9a + 11b = -22$

24. $10x + 5y = 2\frac{1}{2}$
$\quad 7x - 2y = \frac{1}{10}$

Solving problems with simultaneous equations

Exercise 4

Solve the problems by forming a pair of simultaneous equations.
In Questions **1** to **4** there are two numbers to be found.

1. Find two numbers whose sum is 9 and which have a difference of 6. [Let the numbers be x and y.]

2. Twice one number plus the other number adds up to 13. The sum of the numbers is 10.

3. Double the larger number plus three times the smaller number makes 19. The difference between the numbers is 2.

4. The mean of the two numbers is 11. The larger number is one more than twice the smaller number.

5. Angle A is 12° greater than angle C. Find the angles of the triangle.

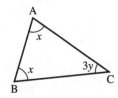

6. In the squares shown the sum of the numbers in each row and each column is given. Find the value of P and the value of Q in each case.

(a)

P	Q	P	Q	76
P	Q	P	P	92
Q	P	Q	Q	60
P	P	Q	Q	76
92	76	76	60	

(b)

P	Q	P	Q	P	25
P	P	P	Q	P	30
Q	P	Q	P	Q	20
P	P	P	P	Q	30
P	Q	P	Q	Q	20
30	25	30	20	20	

7. In this square there are three letters to be found. [Hint: Find A and B first.]

A	B	A	17
B	A	A	17
C	B	B	15
13	19	17	

8. 76 football fans need to be transported to an away match. A minibus can take 12 people and a car can take 5 people. How many of each are needed if 11 vehicles are taken?
[Let the number of minibuses be m and let the number of cars be c].

9. A theatre sold 470 tickets at two different prices. A total of £5770 was made when x seats were sold at £15 and y seats were sold at £11. Find the values of x and y.

10. Stephen bought 4 cassettes and 2 CD's which came to a total of £69 while Amanda bought 3 cassettes and 3 CD's for a total of £66. Assuming that all cassettes are the same price and all CD's are the same price find the cost of each.

7.7 Mixed problems

Exercise 1

1. Copy and complete the following bill.

$5\frac{1}{2}$ kg of carrots at 64p per kg = £ ☐

2 kg of meat at ☐ per kg = £9·70

☐ jars of marmalade at 85p per jar = £5·95

Total = £ ☐

2. A ship's voyage started at 20.30
on Monday and finished at 07.00
on the following Wednesday.
How long was the journey in
hours and minutes?

3. Twenty articles cost £50. How
many of these articles could be
bought for £7·50?

4. How many apples at 16p each
would be a fair exchange for 48
oranges costing 11p each?

5. Work out, without using a calculator
   (a) 0·4 − 0·04   (b) 0·03 × 1000   (c) 0·31 ÷ 10
   (d) 8·7 − 4   (e) 3% of £500   (f) $\sqrt{(11·38 + 13·62)}$

6. Write correct to the nearest pound:
   (a) £57·80   (b) £62·45   (c) £124·85
   (d) £6·781   (e) £11·382   (f) £567·60

7. (a) Increase £60 by 10%.
   (b) Decrease £900 by 20%.
   (c) Increase £2000 by 2%.

8. A man starts work each day at 07.30 and works until 16.00. He
stops working for one hour at lunchtime. How many hours
does he work in a 5-day week?

9. Copy each pattern and write down the next line
   (a) $2^2 = 1^2 + 3$ (b) $1 + 9 \times 0 = 1$
        $3^2 = 2^2 + 5$ $2 + 9 \times 1 = 11$
        $4^2 = 3^2 + 7$ $3 + 9 \times 12 = 111$
        $5^2 = 4^2 + 9$ $4 + 9 \times 123 = 1111$

Exercise 2

1. Use a calculator to work out, correct to 3 significant figures

(a) $19.6 - 6.2 \times 2.13$ (b) $\dfrac{18.7}{5.6 - 2.91}$ (c) $\left(\dfrac{8.2 + 1.173}{7.59}\right)^2$

2. Here is a number machine

Fill in the spaces to find the numbers which come out of each box.

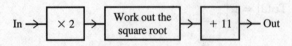

(a) $2 \rightarrow 4 \rightarrow \quad \rightarrow$
(b) $4\frac{1}{2} \rightarrow \quad \rightarrow \quad \rightarrow$
(c) $32 \rightarrow \quad \rightarrow \quad \rightarrow$

3. Steve is putting tennis balls into boxes. Six balls go in each box and he has 76 balls.
How many full boxes will he have and how many balls will be left over?

4. (a) Sarita puts a 2 digit whole number into her calculator. She multiplies the number by 10.
Fill in one other digit which you know must be showing on the calculator.

(b) Sarita starts again with the same 2 digit number and this time she multiplies it by 100. Fill in all four digits on the calculator this time.

5. Find the number indicated by the arrow on the scales below.

(a)

(b)

(c)

6. Work out
(a) $-4 \times (-2)$ (b) $8 - 15$ (c) $-3 - 4$
(d) $12 \div (-3)$ (e) $-10 + 2$ (f) $6 \times (-10)$

7. Use a calculator to work out 11^2, 111^2 and 1111^2. Use your answers to predict the values of $11\,111^2$ and $111\,111^2$.

8. At a party there are 116 people and there are 6 more boys than girls.
How many boys are there?

9. Mark uses 14 screws in each of the model aircraft which he makes.
How many *complete* aircraft can he make using a box of 350 screws?

10. Here are some number cards $\boxed{0}$ $\boxed{1}$ $\boxed{2}$ $\boxed{3}$ $\boxed{4}$ $\boxed{5}$ $\boxed{\cdot}$

(a) Jody picked the cards $\boxed{1}$, $\boxed{2}$ and $\boxed{4}$ to make the number 412. What extra card could she take to make a number ten times as big as 412?

(b) Sam chose 3 cards to make the number 3·2.
   (i) What cards could he take to make a number ten times as big as 3·2?
   (ii) What cards could he take to make a number 100 times as big as 3·2?

Exercise 3

1. A greengrocer sells 9 kg of carrots for £2·79.
Find:
(a) the cost of 1 kg,
(b) how many kg can be bought for £1·86.

2. Arrange the following numbers in order, smallest first:
$\frac{1}{2}$, 0·6, $\frac{1}{3}$, 0·06

3. It costs 10p per minute to operate a machine. How much will it cost to operate the machine from 12 50 to 14 15?

4. A garden 9 m by 12 m is to be treated with fertilizer. One cup of fertilizer covers an area of 3 m² and one bag of fertilizer is sufficient for 18 cups.
(a) Find the area of the garden.
(b) Find the number of bags of fertilizer needed.

5. Write down *two* possible answers for the missing digits. Ask a friend to check your solutions.

    3 0 × ☐ ☐ ÷ ☐ = 60

6. (a) Use a calculator to work out (i) 350 ÷ 99
                                    (ii) 350 ÷ 999
                                    (iii) 350 ÷ 9999
   (b) Use your answers to *predict* the answer to 350 ÷ 99 999, correct to 9 decimal places.
   (c) Predict the answer to 350 ÷ 999 999, correct to 11 decimal places.

7. The numbers 1 to 12 are arranged on the star so that the sum of the numbers along each line is the same.

   Copy and complete the star.

   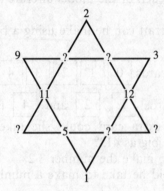

8. A jar with 8 chocolates in it weighs 160 g. The same jar with 20 chocolates in it weighs 304 g. How much does the jar weigh on its own?

9. Use the clues to find the mystery number
   • the sum of the digits is 8
   • the number reads the same forwards as backwards
   • the number is less than 2000
   • the number has four digits

10. Every year the Government spends about £8·8 billion paying teachers (who deserve every penny they get). A wad of a hundred £10 notes is about 1 cm thick. As a publicity stunt, the Minister of Education decides to make a single pile of £10 notes of total value £8·8 billion. How high would the pile be? (1 billion = 1000 million)

Exercise 4

1. If $x = 3$, $y = -4$ and $z = -5$, work out
   (a) $x + z$ (b) $3y + x$ (c) $yz + x$

2. Use a calculator to evaluate the following, correct to 3 s.f.
   (a) $\dfrac{(3 \cdot 2^2 - 7)}{7(6 \cdot 5^2 + 1)}$ (b) $\dfrac{8 \cdot 2 + 5 \cdot 9}{\sqrt{(7 \cdot 1 - 1 \cdot 3^2)}}$ (c) $\dfrac{7 \cdot 3}{1 \cdot 5} - \dfrac{3 \cdot 6}{1 \cdot 31^2}$

3. Small cubes of side 1 cm are stuck together to form a large cube of side 4 cm. Opposite faces of the large cube are painted the same colour, but adjacent faces are different colours. The three colours used are red, black and green.
   (a) How many small cubes have just one red and one green face?
   (b) How many small cubes are painted on one face only?
   (c) How many small cubes have one red, one green and one black face?
   (d) How many small cubes have no faces painted?

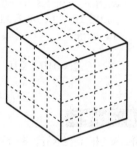

4. A sales manager reports an increase of 20% in sales this year compared to last year.
   The increase was £70 800.
   What were the sales last year?

5. The diagram shows a rectangle. Work out x and then find the area of the rectangle.

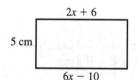

6. That's the way the money goes: used banknotes, chopped up and compressed, are dumped for the Bank of England at a landfill site near Tilbury. The bank has to dispose of seven tonnes a day. To avoid pollution they are no longer burned, but selling them as novelty firelighters is among proposals being investigated.

   Estimate the value of the banknotes which are dumped each day.
   Make the following assumptions:
   (a) All the notes dumped are £10 notes.
   (b) each note weighs 0·87 grams,
   [1 tonne = 1000 kg]

7. How many points inside and outside the square are the same distance from B and C and are also 5 cm from A?

8. A sewing machine cost £220 *after* a price
   increase of 10%. Find the price before the increase.

9. To get the next number in a sequence you
   double the previous number and subtract two.
   The third number in the sequence is 50.
   Find the first number.

10. A code uses 1 for A, 2 for B, 3 for C and so on
    up to 26 for Z. Coded words are written
    without spaces to confuse the enemy, so 18
    could be AH or R. Decode the following
    message.

      208919   919   1   2251825   199121225   31545

Exercise 5

Show all necessary working

1. *Car Hire*

   | £13 per day plus |
   | 14p per km |

   Mr. Hasam hired a car
   for 6 days and travelled
   550 km. How much did it
   cost?

   A   £177
   B   £155
   C   £77·13
   D   £771·30

2. A pile of 250 cards is 1 m
   deep. How thick is each
   card?

   A   0·4 cm
   B   0·4 m
   C   2·5 cm
   D   0·25 cm

3. A ship sails south-west.
   On what bearing does it
   sail?

   A   045°
   B   225°
   C   135°
   D   315°

4. Which of the
   statements
   is(are) true?

   A   1 only
   B   1 and 2
   C   1 and 3
   D   1, 2 and 3

   1. $a = b$
   2. $c = a$
   3. $c = d$

   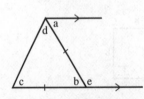

5. Simplify

   $$\frac{a + a + a + a + a}{a}$$

   A $4a$
   B a^4
   C   5
   D   can't be done

6. A piece of wire 48 cm
   long is bent to form a
   rectangle in which the
   length is twice the width.
   Find the area of the
   rectangle.

   A 48 cm^2
   B 128 cm^2
   C 256 cm^2
   D 512 cm^2

7. The maximum number
   of obtuse angles in a
   quadrilateral is

   A   0
   B   1
   C   2
   D   3

8. Which is the largest
   number?

   A $0 \cdot \dot{2}$
   B $0 \cdot \dot{2} \dot{1}$
   C   22%
   D $\frac{21}{100}$

9. Which point does not lie
   on the line $y = -x$?

   A $(-3, -3)$
   B $(2, -2)$
   C $(0, 0)$
   D $(-4, 4)$

10. Two dice are rolled and the scores are added to give a total. How many different totals can you get?

A 6
B 11
C 12
D 36

11. How many wine glasses of capacity 30 ml can be filled from a barrel containing 240 litres?

A 3
B 125
C 800
D 8000

Use the graph below for questions **12** to **15**.

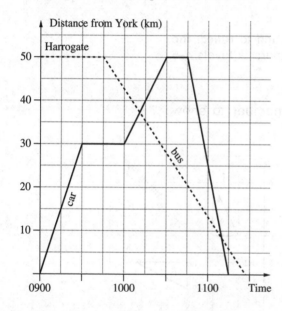

12. When does the car arrive in Harrogate?

A 0900
B 0930
C 1030
D 1115

13. When does the bus leave Harrogate?

A 0900
B 0945
C 1000
D 1126

14. At what speed does the car travel on the return journey to York?

A 30 km/h
B 40 km/h
C 50 km/h
D 100 km/h

15. How far apart are the car and the bus at 1015?

A 2·5 km
B 5 km
C 10 km
D 22·5 km

16. The area of one face of a cube is $9\,\text{cm}^2$. The total length, in cm, of all the edges of the cube is

A 36
B 48
C 54
D none of the above

17. How many of the statements below are true?

A 1
B 2
C 3
D 4

$\frac{1}{3} > \frac{1}{4}, \ \frac{1}{2} + \frac{1}{3} = \frac{2}{5},$

$\frac{1}{3} \div \frac{1}{4} = 1\frac{1}{3}, \ \frac{2}{3} \text{ of } \frac{1}{5} = \frac{2}{15}$

18. When £306 is divided between three people in the ratio $2:3:4$, the largest share is

A £136
B £102
C £34
D £68

19. Which is the odd one out?

A b
B d
C f
D g

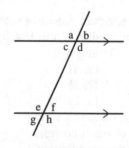

20. Find which of the five numbers below is the mean of the other four. 23, 17, 22, 24, 34

A 17
B 22
C 23
D 24

21. A length of one inch is approximately

A 1 cm
B 2·5 cm
C 4 cm
D 30 cm

22. Find the ratio (shaded area) : (unshaded area)

A $3:4$
B $4:1$
C $3:1$
D $3\frac{1}{2}:1\frac{1}{2}$

Part 8

8.1 KS3 Practice papers

The questions in these practice papers are written to reflect the style and content of questions in recent KS3 papers at levels 4–6 and 5–7.

Paper 1. You may use a calculator but remember to show your working.

1. Triangle A was reflected onto triangle B.
   Here are the coordinates of the triangles:

Triangle A	Triangle B
(1, 3)	(3, 1)
(2, 3)	(3, 2)
(2, 5)	(5, 2)

   (a) Describe what happens to the co-ordinates of each corner.

   (b) Triangle C with co-ordinates (6, 2), (8, 5), (9, 4) is reflected in the same line onto triangle D. Write down the co-ordinates of the corners of triangle D.

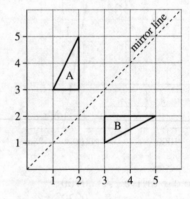

2. Carine wants to buy 9 drinks at 29p each but she has only £3 to spend. *Without* using a calculator, show how you can tell that she will have enough money *without* working out the exact answer.

3. Here are four expressions involving an unknown number n

A	B	C	D
$2n + 1$	$n - 5$	$2n + 3$	$3n + 1$

   (a) Find the value of n if the expressions A and B are equal.
   (b) Find the value of n if the expressions C and D are equal.
   (c) Which two expressions could never be equal for *any* value of n?

4. Here are some number cards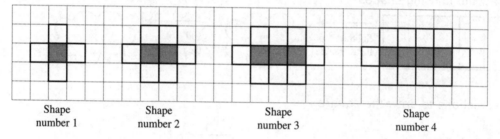

(a) Ian picks the cards | 2 | 3 | and | 5 | to make the number

325. What extra card could he take to make a number ten times as big as 325?

(b) Neha chose 3 cards to make the number 41
   (i)   What cards could she take to make a number ten times as big as 41?
   (ii) What cards could she take to make a number 100 times as big as 41?

5. This is a series of shapes with black and white tiles.

      Shape   Shape   Shape   Shape
   number 1   number 2   number 3   number 4

(a) How many black tiles and how many white tiles are there in shape number 10?
(b) How many black tiles and how many white tiles are there in shape number 150?

6. Andy, Brian, Chris and Don are in a diving competition. The order in which they dive is decided by drawing cards with their names on from a bag. The names are taken out one at a time without looking.

(a) Write down all the possible orders of diving with Chris going first.
(b) In the main competition there are 12 divers.
   The probability that Chris dives first is $\frac{1}{12}$.
   Work out the probability that Chris does *not* dive first.

7. Look at these diagrams

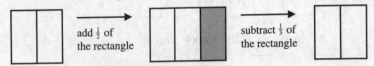

Draw the diagrams below and fill in the missing fractions

(a)
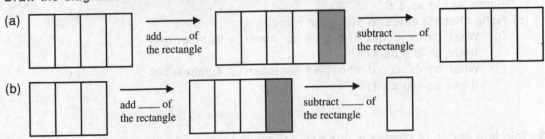

(b)

(c) Draw the missing shapes

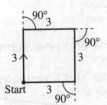

8. The instructions to draw the square are

FORWARD 3, RT 90, FORWARD 3, RT 90,
FORWARD 3, RT 90, FORWARD 3.

Write instructions to draw each of these shapes. For each
shape the first instruction is 'FORWARD 4'.

(a) 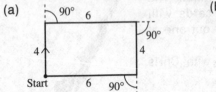   (b)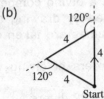

9. A sports shop had a closing down sale.
The sale started on Wednesday.
For each day of the sale, prices were
reduced by 20% of the prices on the day
before.

A tennis racket had a price of £30 on
Tuesday.
What was the price of the racket on
Thursday?

10. The diagram shows a flag in the shape of a triangle.
   (a) Find the area of the triangle.

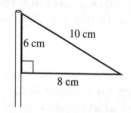

   (b) The flag has a red circle of
       diameter 3 cm. Work out the
       area of this circle.
   (c) A rule for advertising states that
       the area of the circle must be
       less than 30% of the area of the flag.
       Is the area of this circle within the
       rule?

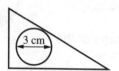

11.

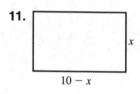

Lisa draws a rectangle with sides x cm
and $(10 - x)$ cm
   (a) Work out the perimeter of the
       rectangle.
   (b) The *area* of the rectangle is 20 cm².
       She wants to find x so that
       $x(10 - x) = 20$.

       Between which *one decimal place*
       numbers does x lie?
       Write your answer as 'x is
       between _____ and _____'.

12. Nicola puts 3 white balls and 1 black ball
   in a bag. She then takes out one ball
   without looking.

   (a) Nicola asks her parents about the
       probability of getting a black ball.
       Her mum says   Her dad says
       'It is $\frac{1}{3}$ because there   'It is $\frac{1}{4}$ because there
       are 3 whites and 1 black.'   are 4 balls and only 1 black.'

   Which of her parents is correct?

   (b) Daniel has another bag containing red and white balls.
       The probability of picking a red ball from the bag is $\frac{3}{8}$.
       What is the probability of picking a white ball from Daniel's
       bag?
   (c) How many balls of each colour *could* be in Daniel's bag?
   (d) Write down another possibility for the number of balls of
       each colour that could be in Daniel's bag.

13. A river divides a farm into two halves
of equal area: the west half and the east half.

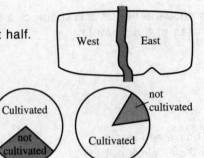

The pie charts show the area of each
part of the farm which is cultivated.
(a) About what percentage of the
    west half of the farm is
    cultivated?
(b) About what percentage of the
    east half of the farm is
    cultivated?
(c) Sketch a pie chart to show the whole farm and draw a sector
    to show approximately what percentage is cultivated.

14. (level 7) A vet does a survey in
which he records the number of
kittens born in each litter. Here
are the results for 20 litters.
(a) Work out the mean number
    of kittens born in each litter.
(b) From the table, the mode is 4
    and the median is 5.
    Every year 400 female cats
    have kittens.
    Work out how many kittens
    you would expect to be born.
    Explain your method.
(c) About how many litters would
    you expect to have 7 kittens?

Number of kittens	Number of litters
2	1
3	2
4	6
5	5
6	5
7	1

15. (level 7) Chocolates are sold in the boxes shown.
(a) The area of the lid is 165 cm².
    Work out the volume of the box.

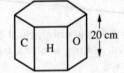

(b)
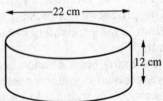
length
| C | H | O | C | S | ! | 20 cm

The label that goes round the tin has an area of 960 cm².
Work out the distance around the tin.
(c) A Super deluxe Xmas Special Offer tin
of chocolates comes in the shape of a cylinder.
Work out the volume of one of these tins.

Paper 2. You may use a calculator but remember to show your working.

1. Copy and complete this shopping bill, filling in the missing amounts

Baking potatoes	15 kg at 30p a kg	?
Tomatoes	05 kg at 50p a kg	?
Carrots	075 kg at 32p a kg	?
Broccoli	065 kg at £130 a kg	?
Flowers		3.99 +
	Total	?

2. 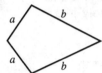 The perimeter of this shape is $2a + 2b$.
We write $p = 2a + 2b$.

Write an expression for the perimeters of each of these shapes.

   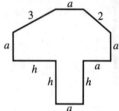

3. Here is information about the sales of snacks. This question is about estimating the total income from sales.

(a) In your estimate what number will you use instead of 18 973?

(b) What price will you use for the cost of one snack?

(c) Work out an estimate for the total income, in pounds, from the sales of the snacks.

> Two sorts of snacks are sold: Twix for 20p and Aero for 40p.
>
> About the same number of Twix and Aero are sold.
>
> Altogether 18 973 snacks were sold.

4. (a) A square tile has sides of length l cm.
Write an expression for the perimeter of the tile.
Write the answer as a number multiplied by l.

(b) A cross is made from five tiles.
Write an expression for the perimeter of the cross.

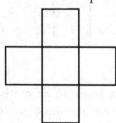

(c) The perimeter of the cross is 60 cm.
Use your answer to part (b) to form an equation involving l.
Solve your equation to find the value of l.

5. Sarita is designing a sticker to go on parcels
   Here is a rough sketch of the sticker, which
   consists of a semicircle and a triangle.
   She needs to know the total height of the
   shape.
   Make an accurate full size drawing of the
   shape and measure its height.

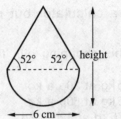

6. Here are some of the ingredients
   for a cake using imperial measures.

   Copy this table where the amounts
   are converted approximately into
   metric units.

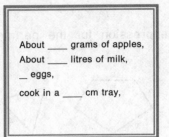

7. The charts show the rainfall recorded in a village over two
   months.

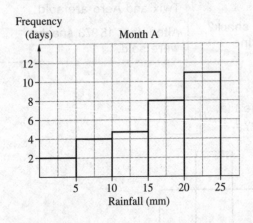

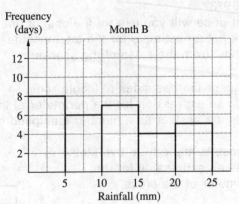

(a) How many days were there in month B?

(b) Katy said 'For month A it rained more at the end of the
    month'. Explain whether Katy is right or wrong.

(c) For how many days was there 10 mm or more of rain in
    month B?

8. A car dealer sells five makes of car. Here are the records of sales for 1968 and 1998.

(a) In 1968 what percentage of the total sales were Ford cars?

(b) In 1968, for every Nissan sold, how many Rovers were sold?

(c) For every Renault sold in 1968, how many were sold in 1998?

(d) Mel thinks that from 1968 to 1998 the sales of VW cars went up by 4%.

Is Mel correct? Explain your answer.

Make of car	Sales 1968	Sales 1998
Ford	315	520
Nissan	23	475
Renault	120	240
Rover	655	450
VW	307	311
Total	1420	1996

9. Here are 2 spinners.

If I spin the arrow on both of the spinners I could get a 4 followed by a 2 (as shown). I write this as (4, 2).

Write a list of all the combinations of numbers you could get with both spinners, including (4, 2).

10. Houses can be made using matches

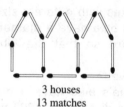

| 1 house | 2 houses | 3 houses |
| 5 matches | 9 matches | 13 matches |

The rule for finding the number of matches is

(multiply the number of houses by 4 and then add 1)

(a) Sam made a pattern with 10 houses. How many matches did he use?

(b) m = number of matches
h = number of houses
Use symbols to write down the rule connecting m and h.

(c) Jack makes a pattern using 37 matches.
How many houses did he make?

11. (a) What is the probability of getting a 6 with this spinner?

(b) Draw a spinner like this with 8 equal sectors. Shade some sectors so that the chance of getting a shaded sector is three times the chance of getting a white sector.

(c) This spinner has some 1s, 2s and 3s written in the sectors. The chance of getting a 2 is twice the chance of getting a 3. The chance of getting a 1 is three times the chance of getting a 3.

Draw the spinner and replace the question marks with the correct number of 1s, 2s and 3s.

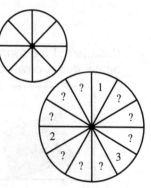

12. (a) Iglis did a survey in which he counted the number of hours for which the television was watched by his family. He kept records for 48 hours of viewing.

Copy the pie chart shown and add sectors to show that 8 hours were spent watching news and 4 hours were spent watching sports.

(b) Joanna conducted a similar survey in her home but she did the survey over 36 hours.
Joanna recorded 12 hours of comedy and $4\frac{1}{2}$ hours of news.
For how many hours were the programmes
   (i)   sports
   (ii) films?

13. Max and Sophie have bikes with different size wheels.
   (a) The wheels on Max's bike have a diameter of 55 cm. Max rolls the bike forward so that the wheels turn round exactly once.
   How far has Max moved?
   (b) The wheels on Sophie's bike have a diameter of 62 cm. Sophie rolls forward a distance of 1200 cm.
   Calculate how many times the wheels go around *completely*.

14. (level 7). You have to find the answer to this calculation:

$$\frac{53 \times 16 - 18^2}{22 \times 8}$$

   (a) Show which keys you press on a calculator.
   (b) The numbers 53 and 18 are lengths which have been rounded to the nearest whole centimetre.
   (i)   Write down the longest length 53 cm could have been.
   (ii) Write down the shortest length 18 cm could have been.

15. (level 7) A room has a bed in this position.
   [All the diagrams are views looking down on the room.]

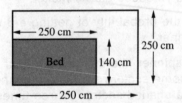

Calculate if the room is wide enough to turn the bed as shown below into a new position.

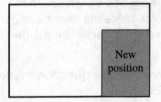

New position

Paper 3. No calculators allowed.

1. Here is a number machine

In $\rightarrow$ [÷ 2] $\rightarrow$ [Work out the square root] $\rightarrow$ [+ 7] $\rightarrow$ Out

Fill in the spaces to find the numbers which come out.

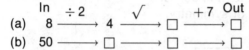

(a) 8 $\xrightarrow{÷2}$ 4 $\xrightarrow{\sqrt{\ }}$ □ $\xrightarrow{+7}$ □

(b) 50 $\longrightarrow$ □ $\longrightarrow$ □ $\longrightarrow$ □

(c) 288 $\longrightarrow$ □ $\longrightarrow$ □ $\longrightarrow$ □

2. Emma's photo measures $4\,cm \times 6\,cm$.

(a) She wants to enlarge the photo so that it just fits a frame $12\,cm \times 18\,cm$.
By what scale factor should she multiply the original photo?

(b) Emma also wants a small photo to stick into an identity card.
The small photo is $24\,cm$ by $36\,cm$.
By what scale factor should she multiply the original photo?

6 cm

4 cm

3. David has four packets of sweets and 5 sweets left over.
Each packet contains n sweets

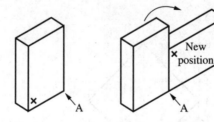

(a) Which of these expressions gives the correct total number of sweets?

  A $9n$ **B** $(4+5)n$ **C** $4n+5$

(b) There are 73 sweets altogether.
Form an equation involving n and solve it to find the number of sweets in one packet.

4. The first diagram shows a rectangular block. The second diagram shows the new position after the block is rotated about the corner A.

New position

B

A   A

On isometric paper draw the position of the block after it is rotated again, this time about corner B. Draw the X on the diagram.

Part 8

5. This is shape A.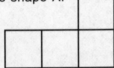

By adding one more square the new shape has the dashed line as a line of symmetry

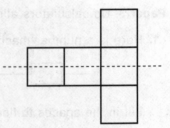

Copy each of the diagrams below and add the number of squares stated so that the dashed line is a line of symmetry.

(a)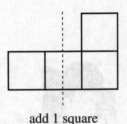

add 1 square

(b)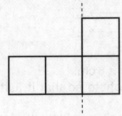

add 2 squares

(c)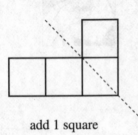

add 1 square

(d)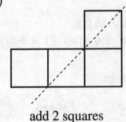

add 2 squares

6. (a) A lorry is loaded with 240 parcels each weighing 37 kg.
Work out the total weight of the parcels.
(b) The maximum load allowed on the lorry is 9 tonnes.
How many more parcels could go on the lorry?
(c) All the parcels have a height of 22 cm.
The height inside the lorry is 190 m.
How many layers of parcels can be put into the lorry?

 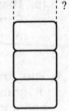

7. The square shown has four lines of symmetry. One line of symmetry is shown by the broken line.
(a) Copy and complete this sentence with the correct equation.
'The broken line has equation
[, $y = -x$; $x + y = 6$; $y = x + 6$].
(b) Write down the equation for each of the other lines of symmetry.

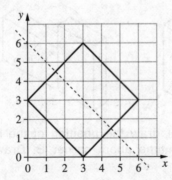

8. Here is a number chain 5 → 8 → 11 → 14 → 17 →
The rule is 'add on 3 each time'.

Here is the start of another number chain 1 → 6 →
(a) Show *three* different ways to continue this number chain
(b) For each chain write down the *rule* you are using.

9. (a) Mel puts a 2 digit whole number
into her calculator. She multiplies
the number by 10.

Fill in *one* other digit which you know must now be on the
calculator.

(b) Mel starts again with the same
2 digit number and this time
she multiplies it by 1000.
Fill in all five digits on the
calculator this time.

10. This solid cube is made from
alternate black and white centimetre cubes.
(a) Find the volume of the black cubes.
(b) How many centimetre cubes are on
the outside of the cube?

11. The prices for coating a
metal plate with
preservative are:

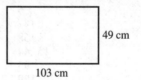

Up to 2000 cm²   £3
From 2000 cm² to 4000 cm²   £550
From 4000 cm² to 8000 cm²   £850.

The measurements of a plate are shown.
(a) *Estimate* its area. Show your working.
(b) Using your estimate, what price
would you pay for the coating?
(c) Without a calculator, work out the
exact area of the plate.

49 cm

103 cm

12. Mr Davis is buying things for his new shop. He buys
computers, televisions, videos and phones.
He buys *n* computers.
Your answers to the following questions will involve *n*.
(a) He buys twice as many televisions as computers. How
many televisions does he buy?
(b) He buys ten more videos than televisions. How many
videos does he buy?
(c) He buys twice as many phones as televisions. How many
phones does he buy?
(d) How many things does he buy altogether?

INDEX